Eog Odel Carlson
1961

# CYTOLOGY

# REINHOLD BOOKS IN THE BIOLOGICAL SCIENCES

*Consulting Editor:*
PROFESSOR PETER GRAY

*Department of Biological Sciences*
*University of Pittsburgh*
*Pittsburgh, Pennsylvania*

Cover photograph courtesy of Dr. Daniel Mazia, University of California, Berkeley. Phase-contrast Photomicrograph of Mitotic Apparatus Isolated from Eggs of the Sea Urchin. (See Figure 6-4 on page 145.)

# CONSULTING EDITOR'S STATEMENT

CONTEMPORARY CYTOLOGY is the meeting ground of molecular and cellular biology and is a correspondingly difficult subject for a book. Some authors bewilder the student with an array of thermodynamical formulas while others bore him with laborious accounts of what can be seen through the microscope. Professors Wilson and Morrison happily avoid both extremes without slighting either approach. No student who uses this book can fail to get a clear picture of the structure of the cell or is ever led to doubt that the cell is a living entity. These views are presented with great clarity in the first chapter on "The Cell Concept" and then exemplified by a discussion of the biochemistry of the cell, which leads naturally to consideration of the nature and interaction of the cytoplasmic organelles. There follows, as there must in a modern book, much on the structural and dynamic concepts of the role played by the nucleus, but this is never allowed to distort the student's view that he is learning about the cell as a functional entity. All this is done from the broadest possible point of view, so that neither the plant cell in general, nor the peculiar problems of the replication of genetic material in microorganisms, are neglected. The bibliography appended to each chapter refers the student both to classic accounts and to contemporary research, and there is a special annotated reading list at the end of the book for those who wish to go even more deeply into the subject. Finally, there is a chapter explaining the techniques of both optical and electron microscopy. I welcome this addition to the REINHOLD BOOKS IN THE BIOLOGICAL SCIENCES both as a text for the student and as a reference for the teacher.

PETER GRAY

*Pittsburgh, Pennsylvania*
*September, 1961*

# CYTOLOGY

### G. B. Wilson

*Professor of Botany and Plant Pathology*
*Michigan State University*
*East Lansing, Michigan*

### John H. Morrison

*Associate Professor of Biology*
*Kent State University*
*Kent, Ohio*

*New York*
REINHOLD PUBLISHING CORPORATION
*Chapman & Hall, Ltd., London*

*In memory of*
CHARLES LEONARD HUSKINS
*1897-1953*

# *Preface*

THIS BOOK IS concerned with a discussion of the basic facts, concepts, and problems of cellular biology. The authors have provided a general picture of the field, the details of which may be filled in by reference to the many fine sources available. In our opinion a beginning course in cytology should be so designed as to encourage the student to make use of reference materials necessary to gain the requisite knowledge of his subject. This can be accomplished best, in the authors' experience, by providing a suitable map so that exploration may be carried out logically and without the student becoming hopelessly lost in a welter of detail. The basic purpose of writing this book has been to provide such a map. Another purpose the authors have had in mind is to provide the specialist in other biological and biologically related disciplines with a useful survey of the field of cytology. Finally, the book was so designed that component parts or even whole chapters may be selected by the teacher of general biology at either the secondary or college level as sources of essential information concerning cells.

As the authors are concerned primarily with presenting the student with a workable interpretation of the essentials of cytology, many of the references as to information sources have been confined purposely to articles, symposia, or supplemental volumes of journals in which a particular concept or technique is found reviewed in detail. The authors, however, have also made reference wherever possible in the text to original works in order that the student may appreciate the contributions of the past in the establishment of the basic concepts which form the foundations of modern cytology. Reference sources are placed at the end of each chapter in a bibliography which includes those sources referred to specifically in the chapter as well as others selected by the authors as useful sources of information concerning the various topics discussed in the chapter. At the end of the book, in place of the usual long list of papers, we have provided an annotated list of books, reviews, symposia, and some classical papers as a guide to the teacher and student.

The authors are indebted to Drs. N. G. Anderson, Wolfgang Beermann, H. G. Callan, C. deDuve, R. E. Duncan, A. Ficq, Helen Gay, Françoise Haguenau, Daniel Mazia, Barbara McClintock, R. G. E. Murray, B. R. Nebel, C. Pavan, C. M. Pomerat, Keith R. Porter, Fred Rapp, O. W. Richards, George G. Rose, Syôito Satô, Arnold H. Sparrow, T. N. Tahmisian, P. O. T'so, D. von Wettstein, W. Gordon Whaley, M. H. F. Wilkins, Philip S. Woods, and Ralph W. G. Wyckoff, and to Mr. P. G. Coleman, Mr. L. V. Leak, and Mrs. Lillie Wang who have so generously contributed photomicrographs from their own personal studies. The acknowledgement in figure captions is only a small expression of the authors' appreciation to writers and publishers from whom illustrations have been borrowed.

Special thanks are due Mrs. A. Engle, Librarian, Western Reserve University, for assistance in obtaining reference materials and Mr. Edward Pfister for preparation of many of the drawings in Chapter 11.

The authors express their appreciation to Miss Gabriele Mühling, Miss Carolyn Roth, Mrs. Sarah Au, Mrs. Jill Oakley, and Mrs. John H. Morrison for help in preparing the manuscript; to Dr. Jack Van't Hof and Mr. Paul Van Dreal for providing and checking information; and to Mr. P. G. Coleman for assistance with the illustrations.

The authors acknowledge the interest and helpful cooperation shown by members of the editorial staff of the Reinhold Publishing Corporation, especially Mr. James Ross, Managing Editor, and Mrs. Dorothy Donath, Copy Editor.

G. B. WILSON
JOHN H. MORRISON

*East Lansing, Michigan*
*Kent, Ohio*
*September, 1961*

# Contents

# CYTOLOGY

# 1

# The Cell Concept

CYTOLOGY MAY BE defined as that branch of Science which deals with the morphology and physiology of the cell. This definition raises the question, "What is a cell?" The answer normally given is purely descriptive, and a cell constructed according to this description would be difficult if not impossible to find in nature; indeed it is doubtful that such a cell could even exist. A cell defined by a cataloguing of its contents, valuable as such a definition may be from the point of view of classification, scarcely provides a fundamental concept. Further, such a definition, accepted uncritically, may simulate a degree of knowledge not consistent with the facts. A cell, whatever its morphological peculiarities may be, is an integrated and continuously changing system. When it ceases to have the power of change it also ceases to be a cell in the biological sense and becomes a mere mass of disintegrating matter.

Living organisms are made of protoplasm. How one may define protoplasm depends largely on one's point of view or that of one's favorite authority. Protoplasm, like the cell, must be considered to be a system. As such it cannot be defined adequately in terms of its chemical constituents. Assuming that we could run a precise quantitative chemical analysis of a portion of protoplasm, and it is possible to make a close approximation to this, we are still unable to put together the ingredients in the requisite quantities and thus produce living matter. No one has yet made a synthetic cell and it seems unlikely that anyone will ever do so, though amino acids and even low molecular weight proteins with a tendency to make microspheres superficially similar to micrococci have been reported (Fox, 1960).

Since we are highly ignorant of the system, a cell becomes very difficult to define in anything but descriptive terms. What we commonly think of as cells consist at least of a mass of protoplasm surrounded by a membrane and containing a nucleus. Specific types of cells may have, and in most cases apparently must have, other contents of obviously organized nature. Even this skeletal definition leads us into a certain amount of trouble. We must, for instance, assume either that coenocytic organisms and structures are single cells regardless of the number of nuclei or that a membrane is essential only where a cell is in contact with nonprotoplasmic material. As noted later, even some coenocytic cells appear to be compartmentalized by membranes visible only with the electron microscope. We may avoid this difficulty by defining a cell as a nucleus and that portion of the surrounding protoplasm upon which it exerts a major effect. This may seem to imply that the nucleus is the real essential of the cell, which of course is probably untrue, although in the case of viruses we may be approaching the situation where a nucleus or part thereof exists in the presence of a minimum or none of its own cytoplasm, for example, the bacteriophage. In general, however, it would seem that both parts of the system are essential and interactive. Nonetheless, most evidence indicates that the nucleus is essentially a control center or seat of organization. Enucleate protoplasts either fail to carry on life processes at all or do so only temporarily and then in an imperfect fashion. Decytoplasmated nuclei, however, are even more inadequate.

The historical development of the science of cytology is of considerable interest, and some knowledge of it is almost essential in order to appreciate its present problems and direction. In the introduction to the third edition (1925) of "The Cell," E. B. Wilson gives a brief but rather complete sketch. A more up-to-date interpretive discussion is found in Schrader (1953) and a general history of the science has been provided by Hughes (1959). Since there is little that can be added to these excellent accounts, only a very brief note of the more important developmental stages will be offered here.

Although M. J. Schleiden (1838) and Theodore Schwann (1839) are generally credited as the initiators of the cell theory, this is not altogether fair. It does seem to be true that they were the first to assemble convincing evidence that both plant and animal tissues are made up of aggregations of cellular units and they were perhaps also the first to attach a meaning to the term "cell" which is acceptable today. Schleiden, however, was wrong on many details, especially in regard to his notions concerning cellular replication. His main theory in this regard was, briefly, that new cells were formed inside of old ones from the nucleus which he consequently referred to as the cytoblast. This point of view seems to have been rather widely adopted and, despite some criticism, it was not until the late 1840's that overwhelming evidence against this concept and for the notion of cell formation by some form of replication was put forth, primarily by Hugo von Mohl and K. Nägeli.

Long before Schleiden and Schwann advanced their ideas and observations on cellular structure, many workers had described or illustrated cellular units. In 1665 Robert Hook introduced the term "cell" to describe the microscopic texture of cork, and in 1672 Nehemiah Grew provided a number of illustrations of plant material which indicate that he noticed the cellular structure. From 1674 over a considerable period of years Anton van Leeuwenhoek, who is best remembered as a master of the art of grinding short focal-length lenses, described many microorganisms, blood cells, and spermatozoa in amazing detail. That cellular organization is characteristic of tissues appears to have been recognized by a number of biologists including Wolff (1759), de Mirbel (1802), Oken (1805), and Lamark (1809). From 1824 to 1830, works of Dutrochet, Turpin, and Meyers among others not only confirmed the universality of cellular structure but also hinted at the concept of cellular autonomy in both the morphological and physiological sense. In 1831 Robert Brown described the nucleus; in 1832 Dumortier reported on cell division in algae, and from 1835 to 1839, von Mohl sketched many features of mitosis. These workers might be considered founders of the specialized aspect of cytology sometimes known as karyology which was to hold the center of the stage from the late 1800's to the late 1930's. This promising start, however, was slowed somewhat by the rather wide acceptance of Schleiden's erroneous views on cell replication. Between 1840 and 1860 the work of von Mohl, Nägeli, Remak, and Virchow provided strong evidence for the idea that every cell is derived from a pre-existing cell by some type of division. As this idea gradually became established it led rather directly to the notion of cell lineage and the tremendous work beginning in the late 1800's and continuing to this day on the mechanics of cell and nuclear replication. In 1882 Flemming described somatic division in considerable detail and applied the term "mitosis" to the process. His description, based on his own work together with that of many other observers including van Beneden and Strasburger, differs little from current views except for the erroneous notion that, during interphase, chromosomes were hooked together in end to end association as a continuous spireme. During the last two decades of the 19th century, two other developments of major importance occurred. Oscar Hertwig in a series of studies showed that fertilization involved the fusion of two nuclei, one of which was derived from the male and the other from the female parent. This finding was confirmed and extended in application to both plants and animals by a number of workers, including the great German botanist, Strasburger. This finding, more than anything else, pointed to the importance of the nucleus in heredity. The second development, generally credited to Edouard van Beneden, was the demonstration that gametic nuclei contained half the number of chromosomes of the zygote, from which it could be concluded that gametogenesis involved some type of reduction division in which maternal and paternal chromosomes segregated. The significance of these findings were realized by Weismann and led directly to development of the Chromosome Theory of Heredity which was further established by many workers including especially Boveri and Sutton. Elucidation of the process of meiosis, which was a necessary prelude to cytogenetics, proved a somewhat more difficult problem but by 1903 the main features had been described by Flemming, van Beneden, Boveri, Montgomery, and Sutton.

The extranuclear aspects of cytology lagged far behind nuclear studies and, indeed, have only recently received major attention. A number of workers in the late 1800's including Heitzmann, Klein, Flemming, and Bütschli described a vacuolar or reticular texture which may be considered as representing the modern submicroscopic reticulum even though the originally described network was probably a fixation artefact. Various inclusions such as plastids, mitochondria, and the Golgi complex were recognized and studied in some detail by a number of workers before 1900. Meyer, de Vries, and Meves discussed questions of origin and function of plastids; Benda used methods of differential staining to reveal mitochondria; Kingsbury (1912) was the first to suggest that the mitochondria function in cellular respiration though this activity was not clearly proven until 1934 when Bensley and Hoerr separated them from live tissue; the Golgi complex discovered by C. Golgi in 1898 in nerve cells was later found to be present in many kinds of animal cells but its significance is still somewhat obscure. Finer inclusions named "microsomes" by Hanstein in 1882 were studied in detail by Altmann over a period of years but there is considerable doubt that even the finer of Altmann's granules represent the microsomal portion of the modern biochemical cytologist.

Before a science is properly established as such, it must have (1) one or more basic concepts, (2) a body of observational and experimental data, and (3) a series of working hypotheses. By the turn of the century, cytology was well equipped with regard to these requirements. The basic concept, of course, was the notion that the cell represented the unit of structure, function, and reproduction.

In 1865, Gregor Mendel published a paper in which he described the results of certain crosses involving garden peas. He found that the contrasting characters with which he was concerned were distributed among the offspring according to a rather simple and precise mathematical formulation. For some thirty-five years few people were aware of this work, but in 1901 several outstanding biologists including Correns, deVries, and von Tschermak discovered and publicized Mendel's work. Thus the modern science of genetics became established with the basic concept that hereditary characters (more precisely potentialities) were determined by specific factors, later called genes, which were transmitted from parent to offspring through the gametes. The parallels between the deduced behavior of the genes and the observed behavior of the chromosomes made it inevitable that the geneticist would, in due course, accept the chromosome as the carrier of the genes—or, in other words, accept some version of Weismann's chromosome theory of heredity. The first half of the twentieth century has found the majority of trained cytologists concerned with the relationship between chromosome behavior and genetic effect. This has been to the distinct advantage of genetics, but probably at the cost of advance in fundamental knowledge of the cell. This overshadowing of cytology by genetics presumably accounts for our very considerable ignorance of many of the fundamental structures and functions of the cell.

Prior to the middle forties, the approach to cytology tended to be largely descriptive and qualitative and the term "cytologist" was generally restricted to those workers primarily concerned with the nucleus and even more specifically to those interested in questions of general structure and behavior of chromosomes. In recent years, however, the approach to cytological problems has been not only far more dynamic and quantitative but also more in terms of the whole cell. Such changes in attitude and outlook are evolutionary rather than revolutionary. The history of cytology begins with the cell as a unit; continues with a study of its parts; and ultimately returns to the cell as reflecting the integration of its parts. The considerable progress of the past few years in cytology seems to have resulted partly from refusion of the several branches of cellular biology and partly from the development of new techniques for examination of cellular structure and processes. In a later chapter several of the techniques and types of equipment, widely used in modern studies of the cell, are described. A few of those which have helped greatly in establishing the concept of the cell that we currently possess should be mentioned. In the first place, ability to fix and section biological material in such a way as to make it suitable for electronmicrographic studies has reached the level at which it is possible to study structures at the angstrom level with about the same degree of confidence that we can accord the light microscope at the micron level. In the second place, modern methods of tissue homogenization and differential centrifugation have made it possible to separate cellular components in sufficient amount and with sufficient purity to allow determination of physical and chemical potentialities. Finally, radioactive tracers and more or less specific colorimetric methods may be used to provide data on both the degree and site of synthesis of many important products of cellular metabolism. A combination of all three general methods of attack may go far, as it has for instance in the case of mitochondria, in determining the relationship between structure and function.

If the road ahead seems long and tortuous, we may derive consolation from the fact that we have traveled far since Schleiden and Schwann and much of this journey has been made in the past few decades. The sincere student will always recognize his debt to the past and will also realize that the "new fact" is often nothing more than confirmation of an old suspicion. Ideas are not accepted without travail. The late Prof. C. L. Huskins commented that there are commonly three stages: "(1) we don't believe it; (2) it's of little or no significance; (3) we knew it long ago." This process merely indicates a natural tendency to backdate knowledge once a suspicion is confirmed. The seeds of progress have often been planted in the past, frequently unconsciously, and history should be read not only for pleasure but for profit. History is a mine of ideas not a worked-out vein.

## BIBLIOGRAPHY

Bensley, R. R. and Hoerr, N. L., 1934. "Studies on Cell Structure by the Freezing-Drying Method. VI. The Preparation and Properties of Mitochondria," *Anat. Record,* **60**, 449-455.

Fox, S. W., 1960. "How Did Life Begin?", *Science,* **132**, 200-208.

Hughes, A., 1952. "Some Historical Features in Cell Biology," *Intern. Rev. Cytol.,* **1**, 1-7.

Hughes, A., 1959. "A History of Cytology," Abelard-Schumann, London.

Huskins, C. L., 1951. "Science, Cytology and Society," *in* "Symposium on Cytology," Michigan State University Press, E. Lansing, Mich., pp. 53-69.

Kingsbury, B. F., 1912. "Cytoplasmic Fixation," *Anat. Record,* **66**, 39-52.

Mendel, G., 1865. "Experiments in Plant Hybridization," translation *in* "Principles of Genetics," by E. W. Sinnott, L. C. Dunn, and T. Dobzhansky, Appendix, 5th ed., 1958. McGraw-Hill Book Co., New York, N.Y.

Schrader, F., 1948. "Three Quarter-Centuries of Cytology," *Science,* **107**, 155-159.

Schrader, F., 1953. "Mitosis," 2nd ed., Columbia University Press, New York, N.Y.

Wilson, E. B., 1925. "The Cell in Development and Heredity," 3rd ed., The Macmillan Co., New York, N.Y.

# 2

# *General Morphology and Chemistry of the Cell*

## CELLULAR ORGANIZATION

CELLS RANGE in size all the way from the very large egg cells of birds which may measure several inches in diameter down to the minute bacteria with dimensions as small as 0.0001 millimeter. In part this range is more apparent than real, since the major variant is often due to variation in amount of nonliving material contained such as stored food products, cellular excretions, etc. Nonetheless, cells from comparable tissues of different organisms show easily measurable and consistent differences in size. For example, the root tip cells of two different flowering plants may differ by a diameter factor of two or more. The relation between surface area and cell volume and the particular level of metabolic activity have long been recognized as important factors in determining cell size. The mechanisms which operate to control cell size are obviously complex and difficult to analyze by virtue of the constant state of change exhibited by the cell. Because most cells measure less than a millimeter in size, it is convenient to express their dimensions in *micron* units ($\mu$) which is one thousandth of a millimeter (0.001 mm). To determine the dimensions of most cell structures requires the use of even finer units of measurement such as the millimicron (m$\mu$) which corresponds to one thousandth of a micron (0.001$\mu$). Further subdivision of the millimicron into units of ten gives the *Angstrom* unit (Å). This unit corresponds to one tenth of a millimicron (0.1 m$\mu$) and is used to measure submicroscopic structures revealed with the electron microscope and to determine the wavelength of radiations. The dimensions of various molecules, particles, and cells, in microns, as compared with the wavelengths of different radiations measured in angstrom units are shown in Table 2-1.

TABLE 2-1. Comparison Between the Diameters of Molecules, Viruses, Bacteria, and Cells. The lower limits of resolution are shown for microscopes employing visible light, ultraviolet light, and electron beams.*

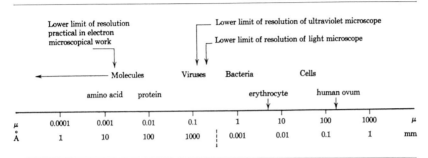

| | | | | | | | | | | | |
|---|---|---|---|---|---|---|---|---|---|---|---|
| $\mu$ | 0.0001 | 0.001 | 0.01 | 0.1 | 1 | 10 | 100 | 1000 | | | $\mu$ |
| Å | 1 | 10 | 100 | 1000 | | 0.001 | 0.01 | 0.1 | 1 | | mm |

* Data from Windle, W. F., 1960. "Textbook of Histology," 3rd ed., McGraw-Hill Book Co., New York, N. Y., Fig. 1-1, p. 2.

Shape, like size, is highly variable, ranging from spherical to columnar and including amorphous types which have no specific geometrical formula (Figure 2-1). Most of this variation can be assigned more or less adequately to extraneous factors such as mechanical pressure and surface tension. A naked protoplast left to itself tends to approach the spherical as an ideal rarely realized in nature except to a certain extent in the case of gamete mother cells and possibly certain blood cells. That there is a close correlation between shape and function is generally admitted, but again the question has received relatively little attention. A few such associations appear obvious, as, for example, the varying shape of an ameba with motility, the spindle shape of a smooth muscle cell with undirectional contraction and elongation, and the columnar shape of a vascular element in plants with transport of sap. How such shapes become established is, however, an unsolved problem bound up with the whole question of growth and differentiation. In his delightful book, "Growth and Form," D'Arcy Thompson discusses the problem of cell shape particularly in relation to equilibrium figures arising from surface tension phenomena. From this discussion it would appear likely that internal stresses, as well as external pressures, dictate shape.

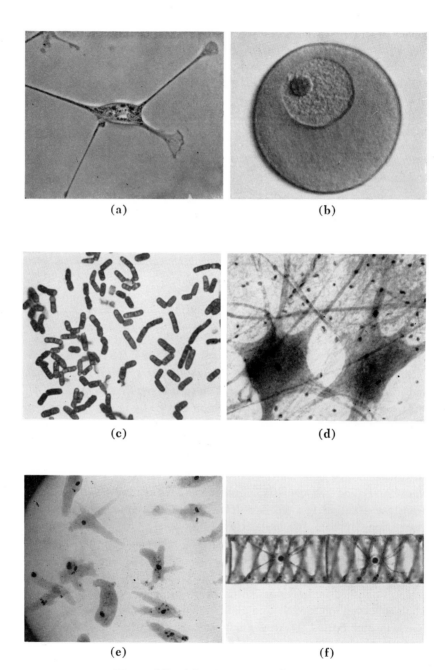

(a)

(b)

(c)

(d)

(e)

(f)

Figure 2-1. (*Contin.* on opposite page.)

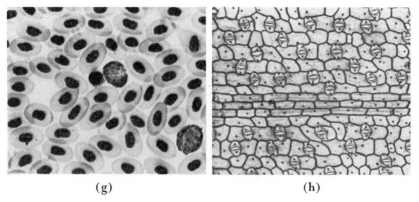

(g)                    (h)

Figure 2-1. Plant and Animal Cells Exhibiting Differences in Shape:
(a) oligodendrocyte from 5-day culture of rat brain tissue (corpus cal-
losum); (b) unfertilized animal egg cell of starfish; (c) bacterial cells
(*Azobacter* species); (d) giant multipolar motor nerve cells from ox spinal
cord; (e) unicellular animal organism (*Ameba* species); (f) grouping of
alga cells (*Spirogyra*); (g) nucleated erythrocytes of bird; (h) guard cells
associated with leaf stomata. (Fig. (a) from Lumsden, C. E. and Pomerat,
C. M., 1951. "Normal Oligodendrocytes in Tissue Culture," *Exptl. Cell Res.*,
2, Fig. 5, p. 109. Courtesy of Dr. C. M. Pomerat, Pasadena Foundation for
Medical Research. Figs. (b) through (h), courtesy of General Biological
Supply House, Inc., Chicago, Ill.)

In addition to the nucleus, the cytoplasm of the cell usually contains a
number of distinct bodies or structures that presumably carry out one or
more rather specific functions (Figure 2-2). These structures, which are
discussed in Chapters 3 and 4, are frequently classified according to
whether they are living (organelles) or dead (inclusions). Our lack of
knowledge concerning ontogeny and function of many of them makes
such a classification of dubious utility. For purposes of discussion, the
components of the cytoplasm may be broadly classified, on the basis of
light and electron microscope studies, as follows: (1) mitochondria,
(2) plastids, (3) lysosomes, (4) endoplasmic reticulum, (5) "microsomes," (6) cytoplasmic matrix, (7) Golgi complex, (8) cell membrane, (9) vacuoles, and (10) cytoplasmic inclusions.

Although attempts to apply the methods of chemical analysis to living
matter are almost as old as organic chemistry, it is only in recent years
that major advances have been made in this direction. Quite apart from
the innate complexity of protoplasm is the technical difficulty of obtaining analytic samples in "pure" form. The relative amounts of various

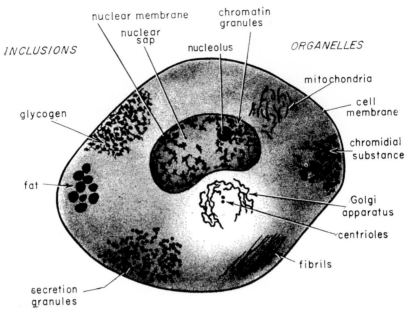

**Figure 2-2.** Diagrammatic Drawing of a Composite Cell, designed to show in a single cell the various components of nucleus and cytoplasm that can be demonstrated with the light microscope. Cytoplasmic organelles are shown on the right and cytoplasmic inclusions on the left. (From Ham, A. W., 1957. "Histology," 3rd ed., J. B. Lippincott Co., Philadelphia, Pa., Fig. 52, p. 74.)

protoplasmic constituents vary from cell to cell and from tissue to tissue with the age of the cell and the kind and degree of differentiation. Nonetheless, crude analysis has given us some idea of kinds of substances and their relative percentages which are characteristic of living matter generally (Table 2-2).

TABLE 2-2. Chemical Components of Protoplasm.

| Substance | Percentage | Kinds |
|-----------|-----------|-------|
| Water | 85 to 90 | Free and bound |
| Protein | 7 to 10 | Albumines, globulins, histones, protamines, and nucleoproteins |
| Fatty substances | 1 to 2 | Lipids |
| Other organics | 1 to 1.5 | Carbohydrates |
| Inorganics | 1 to 1.5 | Na, K, Ca, Mg, Cl, $SO_4$, $PO_4$ |

In principle, protoplasm may be considered to be primarily protein-aceous, and many of its properties are similar to those of colloidal dispersions of complex proteins. A colloid may be defined as the disper-sion of one substance in another, with chemical properties intermediate between those of true solutions and suspensions. Most of their reactions are surface rather than molecular and depend primarily on size, shape, and type of dispersion as well as electrical charge. The most important type of colloid in living cells is apparently the coacervate, which may be somewhat oversimply defined as a semiflocculated colloid in which the dispersed particles tend to occur in aggregates. Most biologically im-portant coacervates appear to be those which result from the interaction of two hydrophilic (water-loving) colloids of opposite charge, as, for example, histones and nucleic acids. It would be a mistake to assume, however, that the properties of protoplasm in general could be dupli-cated by any test-tube colloidal complex. While certain kinds of colloidal systems may be used as models to demonstrate different protoplasmic properties especially with respect to flow phenomena and sol-gel trans-formations, protoplasm as already noted has structural qualities and organization not matched by any of the known synthetic colloids.

TABLE 2-3. Relative Abundance of Water and Protein Molecules in Cultured Carrot Cells.*

| Per cent $H_2O$ | Mass of Cell in $\mu$gms per Cell | No. of $H_2O$ Molecules per Cell | No. of Protein Molecules per Cell | $H_2O$ Molecules per Protein Molecules |
|---|---|---|---|---|
| 90 | 0.10 − 0.15 | ca. $3 \times 10^{15}$ | ca. $10^9$ | ca. $10^6$ |

* The number of protein molecules per cell was determined from the total pro-tein nitrogen per cell. The molecular weight of protein was estimated to be 64,000. Courtesy of Dr. F. C. Steward, Cornell University.

Water is an absolutely essential constituent of living matter. Without it the cell could not function or even exist. It may exist "free," that is, as water of solution, or "bound," usually to ionized groups of proteins. The number of water molecules bound to protein in the cell may be appreciable, as can be seen from examination of Table 2-3. Free water is the major solvent of the cell and serves as a medium for a variety of metabolic reactions. Both free and bound water are intimately associated with maintenance of the colloidal state of protoplasm, though the precise details of the association are poorly understood (Frey-Wyssling, 1953).

# GENERAL CHEMISTRY

## Proteins

The organic basis of protoplasm is generally considered to be protein. In terms of elementary chemical composition, proteins contain carbon, hydrogen, oxygen, nitrogen, and sulfur. They are complex molecules with molecular weights varying from $10^3$ to $10^6$ and yield a mixture of amino acids when hydrolyzed by alkali, acid, or enzymes. Amino acids are chain carbon compounds containing carboxyl (—COOH) and amino (—$NH_2$) groupings. The structure of a typical amino acid is shown in Formula (2-1), where "R" represents a specific group which determines the particular kind of amino acid.

$$R-\overset{\overset{\displaystyle H}{|}}{\underset{\underset{\displaystyle COOH}{|}}{C}}-NH_2 \qquad \text{α-carbon} \tag{2-1}$$

In the protein molecule, the amino acids are linked together by bonds between the carboxyl group of one amino acid and the amino group of another (Formula (2-2)). The —CO—NH— linkage between the two

$$R-\overset{\overset{\displaystyle H}{|}}{\underset{\underset{\displaystyle NH_2}{|}}{C}}-CO-NH-\overset{\overset{\displaystyle H}{|}}{\underset{\underset{\displaystyle COOH}{|}}{C}}-R^1 \tag{2-2}$$

amino acids is called a *peptide* bond. When only two amino acids are involved, the resulting protein is called a *dipeptide*. The combination of an amino group and/or carboxyl group in the dipeptide with other amino acids makes possible a large variety of combinations which are spoken of as *polypeptides*. Because the component amino acids of a protein contain potential acidic (carboxyl) and basic (amino) groups, proteins may act either as acids or bases depending on the pH of the environment. Proteins, on this basis, are considered to be *amphoteric* substances. Using glycine as an example, the formula of an amino acid (protein) in its fully dissociated form may be illustrated in Formula (2-3). In this form, the amino acid carries both positive and negative

$$CH_2\overset{\displaystyle \diagup NH_3^+}{\diagdown COO^-} \tag{2-3}$$

charges and is called a *zwitterion*. Glycine may act either as an acid or base by liberating or combining with a proton (H+), as shown in Formula (2-4). The fact that proteins differ in the relative number of acid or base groups which they contain makes it possible by specific staining methods to distinguish between certain types, particularly those which are highly acidic or basic in character (see Chapter 11 for details).

$$CH_2 {\stackrel{\textstyle /NH_3^+}{\textstyle \backslash COOH}} \quad \xleftarrow{\;+H^+\;} \quad CH_2 {\stackrel{\textstyle /NH_3^+}{\textstyle \backslash COO^-}} \quad \xrightarrow{\;-H^+\;} \quad CH_2 {\stackrel{\textstyle /NH_2}{\textstyle \backslash COO^-}} \qquad (2\text{-}4)$$

POSITIVE             GLYCINE             NEGATIVE
CHARGE           (Zwitterion)           CHARGE

The character of a protein is determined, in part, by the sequence of amino acids in the molecule. Since there are some 20 amino acids which may occur in any order with various repetitions and almost any number in high polymers, the potential for different proteins on this basis alone is astronomical. As indicated above, proteins may be classified as acidic or basic depending on the balance of positive and negative charges prevailing in a given medium. They may also be classified in terms of the number and frequency of the amino acids yielded on hydrolysis. Finally, they may be characterized by their molecular structure such as straight chain, branched chain, or cyclic.

Proteins are usually combined with other substances; in this form they are known as conjugated proteins and provide the basis for the structural organization of the cell. The most common conjugated proteins are the nucleoproteins (nucleic acid + protein) and the lipoproteins (lipid + protein). Most known enzymes are also proteins. Some of these are "soluble" and appear not to be directly attached to any particular structural component of the cell, others are more "insoluble" and more difficult to separate from cell parts, such as the mitochondria and microsomes, to which they may be bound intimately. Enzymes may be considered as organic catalysts which determine the rate of specific biochemical reactions. In general, the evidence favors the view that enzymatic activity is closely associated with the molecular structure of the protein involved. This specificity of molecular structure determines the particular substrate with which the enzyme will combine or interact. The formation of substrate-enzyme complexes involves combination of specific groupings of the substrate, say **A** and **B**, with corresponding groups **A′** and **B′** which are present on the enzyme surface in a fixed position (Figure 2-3).

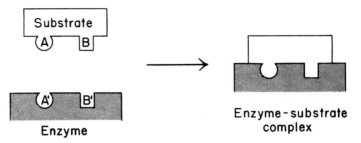

Enzyme

Enzyme-substrate
complex

**Figure 2-3.** Diagram Showing the Formation of Substrate - Enzyme Complex as the Result of Coupling Between Two Reactive Sites of the Substrate and Enzyme. (From Harrow, B. and Mazur, A., 1958. "Textbook of Biochemistry," 7th ed., W. B. Saunders Co., Philadelphia, Pa., p. 130.)

### Nucleic Acids

Although nucleic acids have long been known to be a constant constituent of living tissues, it is only during the past twenty years that any considerable attention has been paid to their distribution and role in the cell. Nucleic acids are organic polymers composed of repeating units called nucleotides, each of which consists of a pentose sugar, an organic nitrogenous base, and phosphoric acid bound together by sugar-phosphate linkages (Formula (2-5)). Two kinds of nucleic acids are recog-

$$\text{base} \qquad \qquad \text{base} \qquad \qquad \text{base}$$
$$C_{3'}-O-\overset{\overset{\textstyle O}{\|}}{\underset{\underset{\textstyle OH}{|}}{P}}-O-C_{3'}-O-\overset{\overset{\textstyle O}{\|}}{\underset{\underset{\textstyle OH}{|}}{P}}-O-C_{3'} \qquad (2\text{-}5)$$

nized on the basis of the pentose sugar component they contain and to some extent by the differences in bases making up the individual nucleotide units. The pentoses concerned are D-ribose characteristic of ribonucleic acid (RNA) and deoxyribose characteristic of deoxyribose nucleic acid (DNA). The structural difference between these two sugars involves carbon 2 as is shown in Formula (2-6). This difference appears to be rather small but it is quite sufficient to distinguish one sugar from the other by chemical means.

The nitrogenous bases consist of two types, namely, the pyrimidines and purines. The former are monocyclic, the latter dicyclic. The most commonly occurring pyrimidines are thymine, cytosine, and uracil while

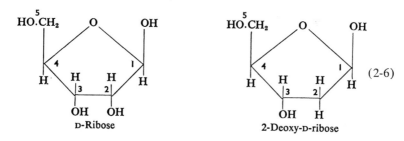

D-Ribose        2-Deoxy-D-ribose        (2-6)

the purines are adenine and guanine (Formula (2-7)). In so far as the bases are concerned, the only difference between the two kinds of nucleic acids is that thymine is found as a component only in DNA. Uracil appears to be confined exclusively to RNA. As to distribution in the cell, DNA appears to be specifically associated with the chromosomes while RNA is found in the nucleolus, chromosomes, and cytoplasm. Although

Thymine        Cytosine        Uracil

(2-7)

Adenine        Guanine

the role of nucleic acid in cell metabolism is not completely known, there are some general relationships which are now accepted rather widely. There apparently is a relatively clear-cut relationship between DNA and sites of "genetic information." The strongest direct evidence for this is the fact that in some strains of bacteria it has been clearly shown that highly purified DNA can transmit genetic material. RNA appears to be intimately associated with protein synthesis but exactly what this relationship is has yet to be determined (see Chapter 4 for details). In some viruses, for example the tobacco mosaic virus, RNA apparently also plays a major genetic role (Figure 2-4).

The molecular organization of nucleic acids, especially DNA, has received a good deal of attention in recent years. In view of the fact that DNA appears to represent the basis of organization of genetic information, the question of structure is vital. The classic notion, primarily that of P. A. Levene, was that the nucleic acid molecule is made up of

**Figure 2-4.** Electron Micrograph of Tobacco Mosaic Virus Protein Rods. Approximately 70,000✕. (From Wyckoff, R. W. G., 1958. "The World of the Electron Microscope," Yale University Press, New Haven, Conn., Fig. a, Plate X. Courtesy of Dr. R. W. G. Wyckoff, University of Arizona.)

repeating units of the four bases in equal amounts. This has been referred to as the tetranucleotide hypothesis. One expectation from this hypothesis would be that the four bases should show a 1:1:1:1 correspondence. Biochemical work over the past twenty years has shown quite clearly that this expectation is not realized (Davidson, 1957). Most analyses of DNA show that there is a 1:1 relationship between adenine and thymine and between guanine and cytosine but the sum of the last two may be greater or less than the sum of the first two. This fact alone suggests intimate association of specific pairs of bases. From the biochemical data and from X-ray diffraction studies, Watson and

Crick (1953) proposed a molecular model which is widely accepted as representing the natural state of the DNA molecule. Essentially, this consists of two pentose-phosphate chains in a double entwined helical arrangement bound together by base pairs presumably linked by hydro-

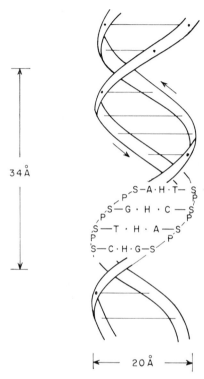

**Figure 2-5.** Schematic Representation of the Watson-Crick Model of the DNA Molecule. The molecule consists of two sugar-phosphate chains (-P-S-P-) entwined to form a helix which is held together by hydrogen bonds (·H·) between the companion bases of the two chains. A, adenine; T, thymine; G, guanine; C, cytosine. The horizontal solid lines represent complementary bases held together by hydrogen bonding in other parts of the helical molecule. (Redrawn from Watson, J. D., and Crick, F. H. C., 1953. "Genetical Implications of the Structure of Deoxyribonucleic Acid," *Nature*, 171, Fig. 2, p. 965.)

gen bonds (Figure 2-5). Each turn of the helix is about 34 Å and there are about 10 base pairs for every gyre. The diameter is about 20 Å, this dimension corresponding to the minimal space required to fit in the base pairs, which on the basis of these measurements would be adenine-thymine and guanine-cytosine. Since this molecule is quite stable and fairly rigid, the only way in which one can imagine it carrying genetic information is by virtue of the order of the base pairs. For example, the order may be something like A-T, T-A, T-A, G-C, C-G or any combination thereof. The question of replication of this molecule is a complex one. Presumably each of the two component strands replicates a complementary one to give a new double helix which is identical with the original but the mechanism involved is still in the realm of speculation.

## Lipids

Lipids are also important constituents of cell organelles, especially of the cell membrane, mitochondria, microsomes, chromosomes, and nucleolus, and possibly of the nuclear membrane. When involved in structure, they are normally conjugated with protein. Certain of the lipids appear to play essential roles in such processes as phosphorylation, methylation, and protein denaturation. The lipids are also directly involved in oxidative metabolism, such as the fatty acid derivative acetyl coA (acetyl coenzyme A) which forms a central point in the pathways of oxidation of carbohydrate and fatty acids (Figure 3-9). There are a number of lipid derivatives the better known of which are the vitamins D, E, and K, and the sex hormones corticosterone and 11-dehydrocorticosterone.

Lipids include the fats and oils of plant and animal origin, and related substances such as lecithin and cholesterol. The fats are mixtures of triglycerides, each of which contains a molecule of the glycerol associated with three molecules of fatty acids. Glycerol is a straight-chain carbon compound and is represented by the formula:

$$
\begin{array}{c}
\text{H} \\
| \\
\text{H--C--OH} \\
| \\
\text{H--C--OH} \\
| \\
\text{H--C--OH} \\
| \\
\text{H}
\end{array}
$$

The fatty acid molecule consists of a long backbone chain of carbon atoms, with one of the terminal carbons forming a carboxyl group such as in stearic acid

$$CH_3(CH_2)_{16}COOH$$

The formation of a simple triglyceride, such as the fat tristearin, involves the combination of one molecule of glycerol with three molecules of stearic acid by means of ester linkages and may be illustrated as follows:

$$
\begin{array}{l}
\underset{\text{H}}{\overset{\text{H}}{\text{H}-\text{C}-\text{OH}}} + \text{HO}-\overset{\text{O}}{\overset{\|}{\text{C}}}-(\text{CH}_2)_{16}\text{CH}_3 \qquad \underset{\text{H}}{\overset{\text{H}}{\text{H}-\text{C}-\text{O}}}-\overset{\text{O}}{\overset{\|}{\text{C}}}-(\text{CH}_2)_{16}\text{CH}_3 + \text{H}_2\text{O} \\[4pt]
\text{H}-\text{C}-\text{OH} + \text{HO}-\overset{\text{O}}{\overset{\|}{\text{C}}}-(\text{CH}_2)_{16}\text{CH}_3 \longrightarrow \text{H}-\text{C}-\text{O}-\overset{\text{O}}{\overset{\|}{\text{C}}}-(\text{CH}_2)_{16}\text{CH}_3 + \text{H}_2\text{O} \\[4pt]
\underset{\text{H}}{\text{H}-\text{C}-\text{OH}} + \text{HO}-\overset{\text{O}}{\overset{\|}{\text{C}}}-(\text{CH}_2)_{16}\text{CH}_3 \qquad \underset{\text{H}}{\text{H}-\text{C}-\text{O}}-\overset{\text{O}}{\overset{\|}{\text{C}}}-(\text{CH}_2)_{16}\text{CH}_3 + \text{H}_2\text{O}
\end{array}
$$

GLYCEROL      STEARIC ACID      TRISTEARIN      WATER
(one    (three molecules)    (one molecule)    (three
molecule)                                            molecules)

Most natural fats are mixed triglycerides in which different fatty acids are attached to the glycerol molecule. The general formula for a mixed triglyceride containing the three different fatty acids, $R_1$, $R_2$, and $R_3$, is

$$
\begin{array}{l}
\text{H}_2\text{C}-\text{O}-\overset{\text{O}}{\overset{\|}{\text{C}}}-\text{R}_1 \\[4pt]
\text{HC}-\text{O}-\overset{\text{O}}{\overset{\|}{\text{C}}}-\text{R}_2 \\[4pt]
\text{H}_2\text{C}-\text{O}-\overset{\text{O}}{\overset{\|}{\text{C}}}-\text{R}_3
\end{array}
$$

## Carbohydrates

Carbohydrates are chain carbon compounds, the simplest of which are the monosaccharides. Depending on the number of carbons in the chain, the monosaccharides are designated as trioses (glyceraldehyde), tetroses (erythrose), pentoses (ribose, deoxyribose), hexoses (glucose, fructose), and heptoses (sedoheptulose). The structural configurations of some of these sugars are shown in Formula (2-8). Low molecular

$$
\begin{array}{lllll}
\text{CHO} & \text{CHO} & \text{CHO} & \text{CHO} & \text{CH}_2\text{OH} \\
\text{H.C.OH} & \text{H.C.OH} & \text{H.C.OH} & \text{H.C.OH} & \text{C}=\text{O} \\
\text{CH}_2\text{OH} & \text{H.C.OH} & \text{H.C.OH} & \text{HO.C.H} & \text{HO.C.H} \\
\text{GLYCERALDEHYDE} & \text{CH}_2\text{OH} & \text{H.C.OH} & \text{H.C.OH} & \text{H.C.OH} \\
 & \text{ERYTHROSE} & \text{CH}_2\text{OH} & \text{H.C.OH} & \text{H.C.OH} \\
 & & \text{RIBOSE} & \text{CH}_2\text{OH} & \text{H.C.OH} \\
 & & & \text{GLUCOSE} & \text{H.C.OH} \\
 & & & & \text{CH}_2\text{OH} \\
 & & & & \text{SEDOHEPTULOSE}
\end{array}
$$

(2-8)

weight carbohydrates resulting from combinations of two or more mono-saccharides (disaccharides, trisaccharides) are called oligosaccharides. The individual sugar units making up an oligosaccharide are bound to-gether by glycosidic linkages (Formula (2-9)). Polysaccharides are high molecular weight carbohydrates composed of many monosaccharide re-peating units which are also linked to one another by means of glycosidic bonds. Many of the polysaccharides yield glucose as the end product following complete hydrolysis (e.g., cellulose, starch, glycogen).

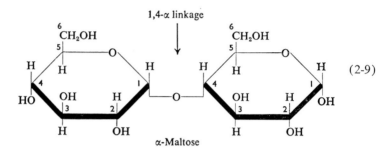

$$\text{(2-9)}$$

α-Maltose

Carbohydrate, which is synthesized in the presence of light through the intermediacy of chlorophyll in green plants (see Figure 3-17), is a universal constituent of all living cells. It is one of the primary sources of energy for maintenance of cellular activity (see Chapter 3, Figures 3-9 and 3-11). The relative efficiency of carbohydrates in promoting cell function is due to the cell's ability to phosphorylate available carbo-hydrate and to partially degrade this phosphorylated product before it is finally broken down to $CO_2$ and $H_2O$ by the oxidative mechanisms of the cell. In addition to its role as an energy source, carbohydrate in the polymerized form is an important constituent of certain cell structures. For example, cellulose is an integral component of plant cell walls, while chitin constitutes the major part of the exoskeleton of insects and crustaceans.

## Inorganic Constituents

Besides being complexed with organic molecules, many inorganic salts occur free and in the ionized state. The relationship between various in-organic salts and between the salts and organic constituents is extremely complex. In general, it is presumed that they provide the necessary ionic balance for a variety of physiological processes. Almost every element in the periodic table can be shown to play some relatively important role in the living organism. The divalent calcium ($Ca^{++}$) ion appears to be essential in maintaining the integrity of many cell structures. Magnesium ($Mg^{++}$) and manganese ($Mn^{++}$) are important as cofactors or "activators" in a number of enzymatically controlled reactions (Figure 2-6). Metals are also important constituents of chromoproteins, many of which are enzymes. Iron is an essential component of the enzymes catalase, peroxidase, and cytochrome c. This same metal also forms an integral part of the pyrrole ring of the hemoglobin protein molecule. In plants, the green pigment, chlorophyll, contains magnesium and is complexed with protein.

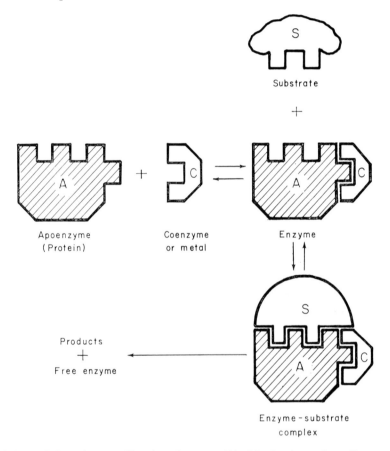

**Figure 2-6.** Diagram Showing One Possible Mechanism of an Enzyme-catalized Reaction Involving Combination of the Enzyme (Apoenzyme) with a Coenzyme or Metal. (From Harrow, B. and Mazur, A., 1958. "Textbook of Biochemistry," 7th ed., W. B. Saunders Co., Philadelphia, Pa., Fig. 33, p. 125; after McElroy, W. D., 1947. "The Mechanism of Inhibition of Cellular Activity by Narcotics," *Quart. Rev. Biol.*, **22**, Fig. 1, p. 26.)

# BIBLIOGRAPHY

Butler, J. A. V., 1959. "Inside the Living Cell," Basic Books, Inc., New York, N.Y.

Cantarow, A. and Schepartz, B., 1954. "Biochemistry," W. B. Saunders Co., Philadelphia, Pa.

Crick, F. H. C., 1957. "The Structure of DNA," *in* "Chemical Basis of Heredity," W. D. McElroy and B. Glass (Eds.), Johns Hopkins University Press, Baltimore, Md., pp. 532-539.

Davidson, J. N., 1957. "The Biochemistry of the Nucleic Acids," 3rd ed., John Wiley & Sons, Inc., New York, N.Y.

DeRobertis, E. D. P., Nowinski, W. W., and Saez, F. A., 1954. "General Cytology," 2nd ed., W. B. Saunders Co., Philadelphia, Pa.

Frey-Wyssling, A., 1953. "Submicroscopic Morphology of Protoplasm," Elsevier, Amsterdam.

Gerard, R. W., 1949. "Unresting Cells," Harper & Bros., New York, N.Y.

Ham, A. W., 1957. "Histology," 3rd ed., J. B. Lippincott Co., Philadelphia, Pa.

Harrow, B. and Mazur, A., 1958. "Textbook of Biochemistry," 7th ed., W. B. Saunders Co., Philadelphia, Pa.

Heilbrunn, L. V., 1956. "The Dynamics of Living Protoplasm," Academic Press, New York, N.Y.

Levene, P. A. and Simms, H. S., 1926. "Nucleic Acid Structure as Determined by Electrometric Titration," *J. Biol. Chem., 70,* 327-341.

Levene, P. A. and Bass, L. W., 1931. "Nucleic Acids," Chemical Catalog, New York, N.Y.

Maximow, A. A. and Bloom, W., 1957. "A Textbook of Histology," 7th ed. W. B. Saunders Co., Philadelphia, Pa.

Mitra, J. and Steward, F. C., 1961. "Growth Induction in Cultures of *Haplopappus gracilis*. II. Behavior of the Nucleus," *Amer. J. Botan.* (in press).

Seifriz, W., 1955. "Microscopic and Submicroscopic Structure of Cytoplasm," *Handbuch der Pflanzenphysiologie. 1,* 301-339.

Swanson, C. P., 1960. "The Cell," Prentice-Hall, Inc., Englewood Cliffs, N.J.

Szent-Györgyi, A., 1957. "Bioenergetics," Academic Press, New York, N.Y.

Thompson, D'Arcy W., 1942. "On Growth and Form," The Macmillan Co., New York, N.Y.

Watson, J. D. and Crick, F. H. C., 1953. "Molecular Structure of Nucleic Acids," *Nature, 171,* 737-738.

Watson, J. D. and Crick, F. H. C., 1953. "Genetical Implications of the Structure of Deoxyribonucleic Acid," *Nature, 171,* 964-967.

Watson, J. D. and Crick, F. H. C., 1953. "The Structure of DNA," *Cold Spring Harbor Symposia Quant. Biol., 18,* 123-131.

# 3

# Structure and Function of Cytoplasmic Organelles

As NOTED EARLIER, the cytoplasm of most cells contains a number of organelles. Until recently, knowledge of the origin, structure, and function of most of these has been something less than satisfactory. During the last decade the development of a number of techniques has made it possible to improve our knowledge by a considerable factor. Among the more important technical advances have been the following: (1) Improvement in methods of preparing cells and tissues for observation with the electron microscope has made it possible to describe the fine structure of the cytoplasm and the contained organelles at levels which are measured in angstroms rather than microns; (2) improvement in techniques of isolation and preparation of various cell components has allowed the biochemist to study many of the *in vitro* biochemical potentials of specific organelles and even fractions of them; and (3) development of techniques of autoradiography, the general use of tracer elements, and specific cytochemical tests have provided much useful information concerning the location of chemical compounds and their function and interrelationship in the cell.

When information from these and other techniques is assessed, it becomes possible to provide what appears to be a fairly reliable picture of the major subcellular particles (Figure 3-1). In the discussion to follow, the more generally accepted concepts of structure and function of the better-known cell components will be outlined.

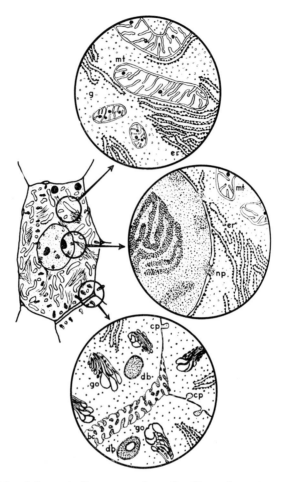

**Figure 3-1.** Schematic Representation of a Parenchymatous Cell of Rat Liver. The cell components whose submicroscopic structure is depicted are as follows: mitochondria (**mt**); basophilic material or endoplasmic reticulum (**er**); glycogen deposits (**g**); nuclear pores (**np**); Golgi complex (**go**); "dense bodies" or lysosomes (**db**); interlocking cell processes (**cp**); bile canaliculus (**bc**). (From Novikoff, A. B., 1956. "Electron Microscopy: Cytology of Cell Fractions," *Science,* **124,** Fig. 1, p. 970.)

## MITOCHONDRIA

The term "mitochondria" refers to a group of distinct cytoplasmic components which exhibit a variety of morphologic forms. In the phase-contrast microscope the mitochondria are variously seen as granules, rods, or threads which vary in size, number, and distribution from cell to cell (Figure 3-2 (a) and (b)). They are most readily identified in the living cell by their affinity for the vital dye, Janus green. In size, they range from elongate objects of several micra in length down to the limit of resolution of the light microscope. When sections through individual mitochondria are viewed with the electron microscope, a general pattern

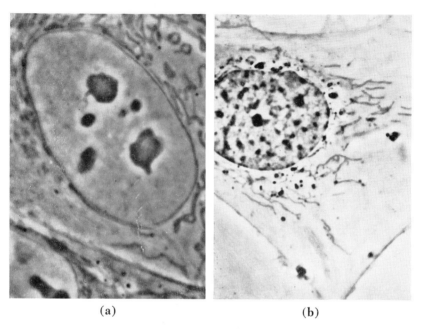

(a)                                            (b)

Figure 3-2. Phase-Contrast Photomicrographs of Mitochondria in Living Cells from Culture of (a) Fetus Kidney, and (b) Salamander Heart. (Fig. (a), courtesy of Mr. C. G. Lefeber, Pasadena Foundation for Medical Research. Fig. (b), from Maximow, A. A. and Bloom, W., 1957. "Textbook of Histology," 7th ed., W. B. Saunders Company, Philadelphia, Fig. 1-4A, p. 4. Courtesy of Mrs. L. Wang.)

of structure is revealed regardless of the type of cell in which they are found. Basically, the mitochondrion is bounded by a double osmiophilic membrane, each layer of which measures approximately 40 Å in thickness (Figure 3-3 (a) and (b)). The double membrane encloses an inner matrix of variable diameter which is less osmiophilic and electron-dense. The outer membrane is separated from the inner one by a space of some 70 Å in width. The interior is subdivided into a series of compartments by a system of double membranes, called the *cristae mito-*

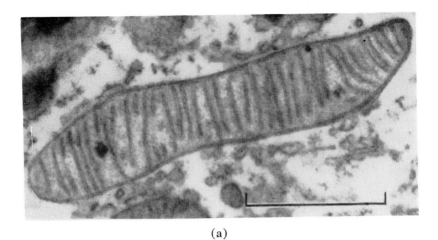

(a)

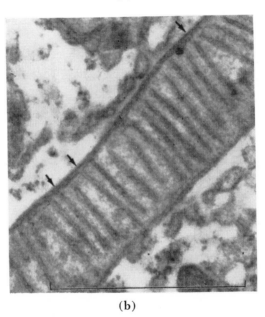

(b)

**Figure 3-3.** (a) Electron Micrograph of a Single Mitochondrion in a Cell from the Proximal Convoluted Tubule of Mouse Kidney, showing numerous regularly spaced cristae. Electron-dense granules are visible near opposite ends of the mitochondrion; (b) Enlargement of the Mid-portion of the Mitochondrion in (a), showing the continuity between the cristae and the inner of the two limiting membranes (arrows). (From Dalton, A. J. and Felix, M. D., 1957. "Electron Microscopy of Mitochondria and the Golgi Complex," *Symp. Soc. Expt'l. Biol.*, **10**, Figs. 4A and 4B, Plate 2.)

*chondriales,* which generally extend into the interior or matrix of the organelle perpendicular to its long axis (Figure 3-3). Whether the cristae are invaginations of the inner membrane or separate structures is still debatable. The matrix into which the cristae extend is a homogeneous, amorphous material. Electron-dense granules, the function of which is by no means clear, are sometimes encountered apparently embedded in the matrix. A number of three-dimensional models of the mitochondrion have been proposed. One such model is shown in Figure 3-4.

Mitochondria

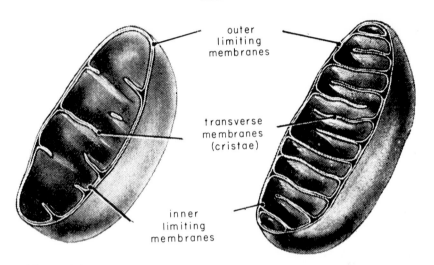

outer
limiting
membranes

transverse
membranes
(cristae)

inner
limiting
membranes

**Figure 3-4.** Diagrammatic Drawing to Illustrate the Three-dimensional Structure of the Mitochondrion. (From Ham, A. W., 1957. "Histology," 3rd ed., J. B. Lippincott Co., Philadelphia, Pa., Fig. 58, p. 79.)

While the structural organization described above is the most typical, many variations have been noted. The significance of these in terms of function is not known, but it seems highly probable that they ultimately will be shown to be associated with alterations in specific function. For example, in certain kinds of cells, both plant and animal, the cristae extend parallel to the long axis rather than perpendicular to it (Figure 3-5). In still other cases, as in the interstitial cells of the opossum testis, the cristae are irregular in both spacing and orientation (Figure 3-6). In secretory cells of the adrenal cortex, the cristae are frequently either filamentous or saccular in form. Cristae of similar morphology have also

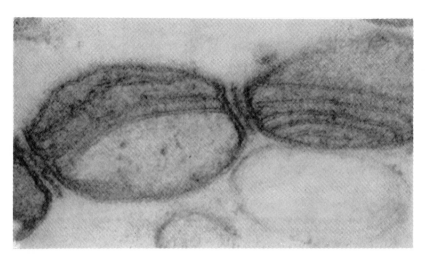

**Figure 3-5.** Electron Micrograph of Mitochondria in Human Spermatogonium, showing cristae arranged in parallel and completely transversing the organelle. (From Selby, C. C., 1959. "Electron Microscopy: Techniques and Applications in Cytology," *in* "Analytical Cytology," R. C. Mellors (Ed.), 2nd ed., McGraw-Hill Book Co., Inc., New York, N. Y., Fig. 4-10C, p. 300. Electron micrograph by Dr. D. W. Fawcett, Harvard Medical School.)

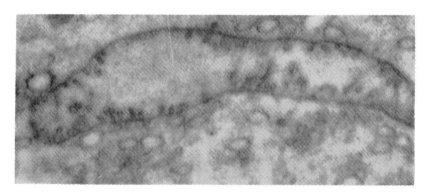

**Figure 3-6.** Electron Micrograph of Mitochondria in Interstitial Cell of the Opossum Testis. The cristae are short, irregularly oriented projections from the inner mitochondrial membrane. (From Selby, C. C., 1959. "Electron Microscopy: Techniques and Applications in Cytology," *in* "Analytical Cytology," R. C. Mellors (Ed.), 2nd ed., McGraw-Hill Book Co., Inc., New York, N. Y., Fig. 4-10B, p. 300. Electron micrograph by Dr. D. W. Fawcett, Harvard Medical School.)

been observed in mitochondria of the grasshopper kidney, in certain protozoa, and in hepatic cells (Figure 3-7). Even more complex arrangements have been described.

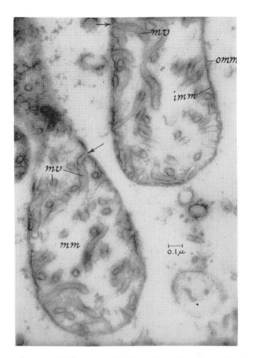

**Figure 3-7.** Electron Micrograph Showing Portion of Two Mitochondria in the Cortex of *Paramecium multimicronucleatum*. The envelope delimiting the mitochondrion is double, consisting of an outer (**omm**) and inner (**imm**) mitochondrial membrane. Structures corresponding to the cristae mitochondriales in mammalian somatic cells are present as extensive finger-like projections or microvilli (**mv**) protruding into the matrix of the organelle from the inner mitochondrial membrane. The lumen of a microvillus appears continuous with the space separating the inner and outer mitochondrial membranes at the points indicated by arrows. (From Sedar, A. W. and Porter, K. R., 1955. "The Fine Structure of Cortical Components of Paramecium Multimicronucleatum," *J. Biophys. Biochem. Cytol.*, 1, Fig. 14, Plate 157.)

Some of the reported changes in mitochondrial shape, distribution, and internal organization appear to be closely correlated with cell differentiation (Fawcett, 1959). In rat, guinea pig, and opossum spermatogonia the mitochondria are few in number, but otherwise quite typical. In the derived spermatocytes they are more nearly spherical, their cristae are irregularly oriented, and the average number per cell is greater. The mitochondria in spermatids appear empty owing to the fact that the cristae are folded over and flattened against the inner limiting membrane. In mature spermatids of the opossum, the large spherical mitochondria are filled with many layers of concentrically arranged cristae (Figure 3-8). During the same developmental sequence, not only does

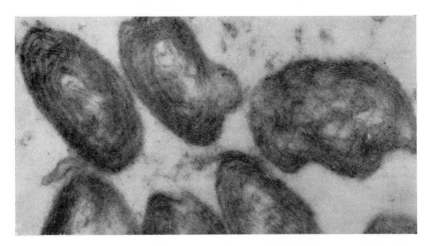

**Figure 3-8.** Electron Micrograph of Mitochondria from Opossum Spermatid, showing the concentric disposition of the cristae. The mitochondria in early germ cells of the opposum testis are typical in their structure, with cristae oriented perpendicular to the limiting membrane. These cytoplasmic organelles change in the course of spermatid differentiation to give rise to morphological types of the kind shown above. (From Selby, C. C., 1959. "Electron Microscopy: Techniques and Applications in Cytology," *in* "Analytical Cytology," R. C. Mellors (Ed.), 2nd ed., McGraw-Hill Book Co., Inc., New York, N. Y., Fig. 4-10A, p. 300. Electron micrograph by Dr. D. W. Fawcett, Harvard Medical School.)

the submicroscopic appearance of the mitochondria change, but also there are marked changes in their particular location in the cell. In the young spermatid, the mitochondria aggregate in large numbers adjacent to the cell membrane, but in later stages of differentiation they collect around the base of the flagellum where they elongate to form the mitochondrial sheath of the middle piece.

That the mitochondria play a major role in cell respiration has been known for some time. Biochemical studies over the past twenty years, especially on mitochondrial-rich fractions of the cell, have provided a rather detailed picture of how this respiratory function is carried out. In general, isolated mitochondria have been shown to possess the ability to catalyze the reactions of the Krebs citric acid cycle using pyruvate or acetate as fuel (Figure 3-9). As the result of operation of this cycle,

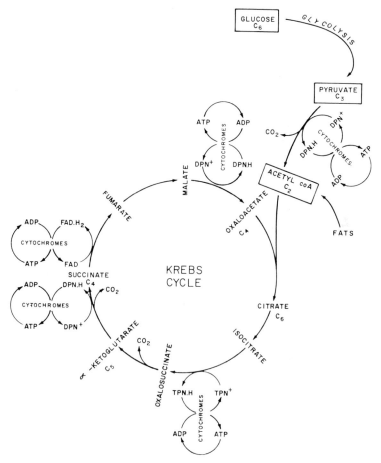

**Figure 3-9.** Schematic Diagram of the Kreb's, or Tricarboxylic Acid Cycle. The reactions of the cycle where synthesis of adenosine triphosphate (ATP) is coupled with the electron transport chain (oxidative phosphorylation) are shown.

pyruvate is completely oxidized to carbon dioxide and water with the concomitant release of energy. This oxidation involves, essentially, the removal of electrons from a substrate by appropriate electron acceptors (dehydrogenases), such as the di- and triphosphopyridine nucleotides

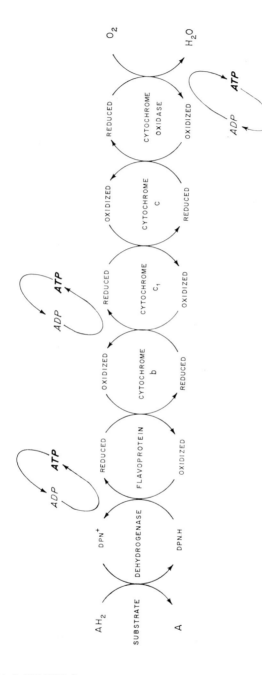

**Figure 3-10.** Schematic Representation of the Electron Transport Chain as It Is Considered to Occur in the Mitochondrion. The flow of electrons along the chain from substrate ($AH_2$) to molecular oxygen is indicated by arrows. The points in the chain are shown where oxidation and phosphorylation are linked. (Redrawn from Novikoff, A. B., 1959. "The Intracellular Localization of Chemical Constituents," *in* "Analytical Cytology," R. C. Mellors (Ed.), 2nd ed., McGraw-Hill Book Co., Inc., New York, N. Y., p. 90.)

(DPN and TPN, respectively). These electrons are then passed to molecular oxygen via a series of specialized enzymes known as the cytochromes, which are also associated with the mitochondria. The energy released by this electron transfer is conserved, in part at least, by coupling oxidation with the phosphorylation of adenosine diphosphate (ADP) to form adenosine triphosphate (ATP). This process is called *oxidative phosphorylation* (Figure 3-10) and the energy thus produced can be utilized by the cell through cleavage of the terminal phosphate of ATP to give ADP plus energy. In addition to their role in the oxidation of carbohydrate, isolated mitochondria have also been shown to be capable of oxidizing long-chain fatty acids to carbon dioxide and water, but there is little or no evidence that they can synthesize fatty acids (Figure 3-11). *In vitro* experiments have indicated that the mitochondria can account for practically all of the oxygen uptake of the intact cell and the generation of as much as 90 per cent of the ATP formed (Lehninger, 1959).

The mitochondria need not be intact in order to carry out oxidation reactions, since isolated fragments have been shown to contain respiratory enzyme assemblies which exhibit oxidative activity and contain the enzymes necessary for the coupling of phosphorylation with electron transport (Watson and Siekevitz, 1956; Green, 1959). It has been found that these assemblies (electron transport particles) of respiratory chain enzymes are distributed throughout the membranes of the mitochondrion, particularly the cristae. On this basis, the mitochondrion may be visualized as a polymer made up of a series of repeating units of these respiratory assemblies (Green, 1959). Presumably the number of assemblies in a single mitochondrion may vary and each may possibly correspond to the unit of mitochondrial growth. One important aspect of mitochondrial structure so far as function is concerned is the retention of a double membrane. This is borne out by the fact that loss of the double membrane structure results in inability of the respiratory unit or electron transport particle to carry out oxidative phosphorylation. Likewise, the capacity of mitochondria to carry out the reactions of the Krebs citric acid cycle also appears to depend on the existence of a double membrane structure. Most of the enzymes concerned with the substrate reactions of the citric acid cycle and fatty acid oxidation are easily extracted in soluble form following disruption of the mitochondrion and hence are considered to be located in the inner soluble matrix of this organelle (Lehninger, 1959).

The problem of change in number of mitochondria in a cell, particu-

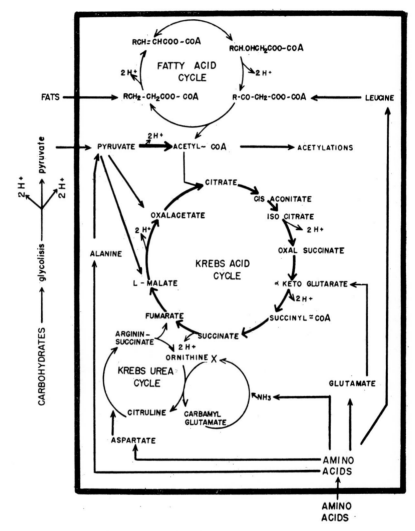

**Figure 3-11.** Diagram Showing the Interrelationship of the Pathways for the Oxidation of Carbohydrates, Fats, and Amino Acids in the Mitochondrion. (From Junqueira, L. C. V. and Hirsch, G. C., 1956. "Cell Secretion: A Study of Pancreas and Salivary Glands," *Intern. Rev. Cytol.,* **5**, Fig. 6, p. 337.)

larly in division, has never been solved satisfactorily. One view is that they arise *de novo;* another that they replicate by some form of fission. Certainly the number does increase or decrease in specialized cells and, as a general rule, it must be assumed that replication occurs at cell divi-

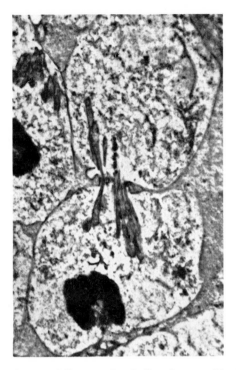

Figure 3-12. Electron Micrograph of Grasshopper Testis Cell in Telophase of Meiosis. The elongated mitochondria are shown being pinched in half at the constricting cleavage furrow, with the result that they are distributed in approximately equal numbers to each daughter cell. Approximately 5000×. (From Tahmisian, T. N., Powers, E. L., and Devine, R. L., 1956. "Light and Electron Microscope Studies of Morphological Changes of Mitochondria During Spermatogenesis in the Grasshopper," *J. Biophys. Biochem. Cytol., Suppl.,* **2,** Fig. 23, Plate 105. Courtesy of Dr. T. N. Tahmisian, Argonne National Laboratory.)

sion since each daughter cell receives roughly half the number of mitochondria present in the mother cell (Figure 3-12).

Accumulated facts concerning both the structure and function of the mitochondrion serve to illustrate the complexity of metabolic interaction which may be associated with any particular subcellular organelle.

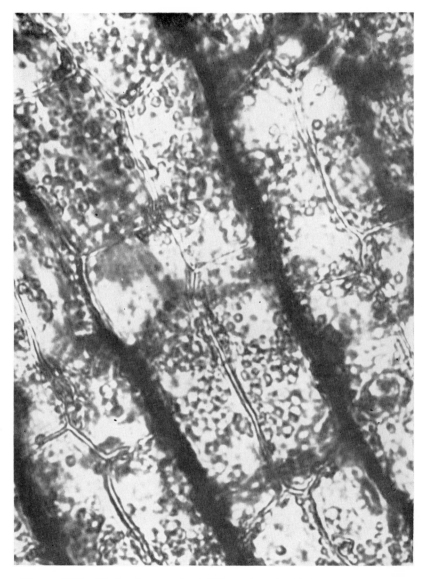

**Figure 3-13.** Photomicrograph of Chloroplasts in Living Cells of *Elodea* Leaf.

# PLASTIDS

With the possible exception of the very lowest groups of plants, plastids are found in the cells of most tissues of members of the plant kingdom. Plastids vary in size, number, shape, and chemical organization with the tissue and organism concerned. "Mature" plastids can be shown to arise from more or less undifferentiated plastid primordia which occur

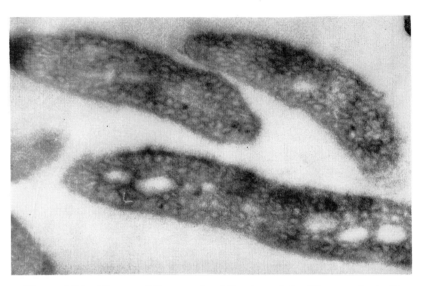

**Figure 3-14.** Electron Micrograph of Section of the Photosynthetic Bacterium, *Rhodospirillum rubrum.* Note the discrete photosynthetic particles (chromatophores) which pack the entire cytoplasm of the cell when it is exposed to light during growth. (From Murray, R. G. E., 1960. "The Internal Structure of the Cell," *in* "The Bacteria," I. C. Gunsalus and R. Y. Stanier (Eds.), Vol. I, Academic Press, New York, N. Y., Fig. 10, p. 49. Courtesy of Dr. R. G. E. Murray, University of Western Ontario.)

in meristematic cells, or those of the developing embryo. Such primordia range in size down to the virtually invisible, so that it is difficult, indeed, to determine their origin. In general, plastids appear to be centers of carbohydrate synthesis and metabolism. They are generally classified on the basis of color, though such a classification is not necessarily related to function. Noncolored plastids are usually referred to as leucoplasts, while colored ones are called chromoplasts. Since leucoplasts may give rise to various types of chromoplasts, such classification is of only superficial value. Leucoplasts often may function as storage organelles by

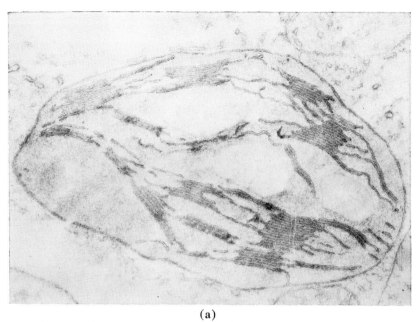

(a)

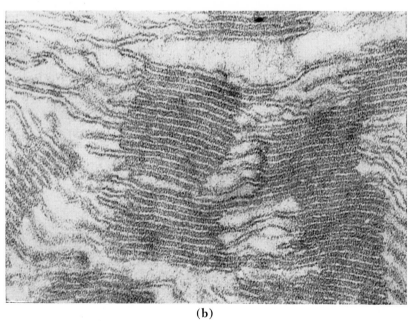

(b)

Figure 3-15. (Caption on opposite page.)

accumulating large amounts of starch (amyloplasts), oil (elaioplasts), or protein (aleurone-plasts) within their interior. The most important of the chromoplasts, so far as present knowledge is concerned, appears to be the chloroplast, which is concerned with the elaboration of chlorophyll and carbohydrate photosynthesis. The photosynthetically active chromoplasts (i.e., chloroplasts) contain both chlorophyll and carotenoid pigments, while chromoplasts exhibiting no photosynthetic activity generally contain carotenoids but are lacking in chlorophyll.

Chloroplasts are present in all green plants and are particularly abundant in cells actively engaged in photosynthesis (Figure 3-13). Not all organisms capable of photosynthesizing carbohydrate contain organized chloroplasts, for example, blue-green algae and certain bacteria which photosynthesize in the infrared. In these cases the photosensitive pigments appear as minute granules or vacuoles, called *chromatophores,* dispersed in the cytoplasm (Figure 3-14). The typical chloroplast is a more or less ovoid structure bounded by a double-layered membrane and containing a relatively homogeneous matrix called the *stroma* in which are embedded granules or lamellae referred to as the *grana.* As viewed with the electron microscope, the grana appear to have a layered structure consisting of a series of membranes stacked one on top of the other (Figure 3-15 (a) and (b)). The grana, which are more or less centrally placed in the body of the chloroplast, are connected with each other by paired membranes which also extend out into the stroma (*stroma lamellae*). Spherical, highly electron-dense bodies called *globuli* are often found freely dispersed in the more internal parts of the organelle. In higher plants, the dimensions of the grana appear to be in the order of 0.5 microns, while the number of membranes or lamellae making up the individual grana vary considerably. The membranes of the grana measure about 40 to 60 Å in thickness and appear to be double-layered structures. The stroma lamellae are apparently also paired membranes and are somewhat thinner, measuring about 20 to 30 Å (Figure 3-16 (a) and (b)). The lamellae of the chloroplast are considered to be protein structures and to carry one or more layers of chlorophyll intermixed with other components of the photosynthetic system such as the carotenoids and pyri-

---

**Figure 3-15.** (a) Electron Micrograph of Chloroplast from Tobacco Leaf showing the grana, starch grains (large, clear spherical areas), and double-layered enveloping membrane. Approximately 60,000×. (b) Highly Magnified Section of a Barley Leaf Chloroplast showing the lamellar arrangement of the grana. Approximately 190,000×. (Courtesy of Dr. D. von Wettstein, Forest Research Institute, Stockholm, Sweden.)

dine nucleotides. The stroma is composed of unpigmented lipoproteins which are probably the location of enzymes involved in secondary reactions of photosynthesis (e.g., carbon dioxide fixation and phosphate transfer).

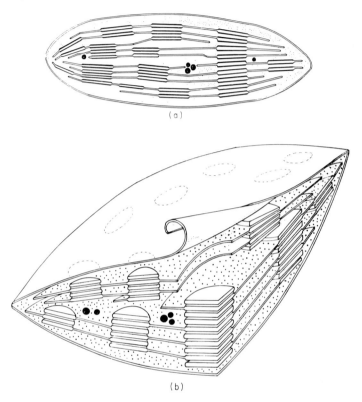

(a)

(b)

Figure 3-16. (a) Schematic Diagram of the Submicroscopic Structure of the Plant Chloroplast as Seen in Cross-section. (b) Schematic Diagram of the Three-dimensional Structure of the Chloroplast in the Higher Plant. (Fig. (a) from von Wettstein, D., 1959. "Developmental Changes in Chloroplasts and their Genetic Control," *in* "Developmental Cytology," D. Rudnick (Ed.), Ronald Press, New York, N. Y., Fig. 23, p. 129. Courtesy of Dr. D. von Wettstein, Forest Research Institute, Stockholm, Sweden. Fig. (b), courtesy of Dr. D. von Wettstein.)

Photosynthesis, or the light-activated synthesis of carbohydrate from carbon dioxide and water by green plants, is absolutely essential for maintenance of cells, particularly animal cells, which are dependent on the oxidation of exogenous carbohydrate as a means of carrying out reduction reactions. The over-all reaction of photosynthesis may be represented as follows:

$$6 \, CO_2 + 12 \, H_2O \longrightarrow C_6H_{12}O_6 + 6 \, O_2 + 6 \, H_2O$$

The light energy absorbed by the chloroplast is converted to chemical energy by this same organelle and is used to bring about the photolysis or breakdown of water in the photosynthetic process (Figure 3-17).

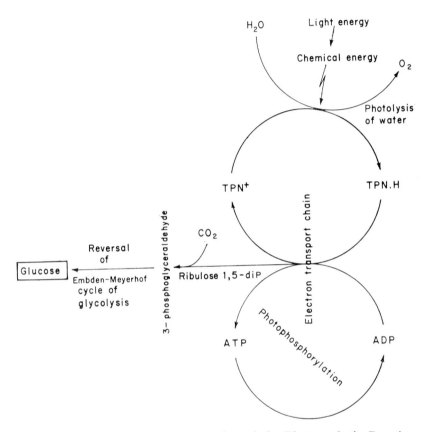

**Figure 3-17.** Schematic Representation of the Photosynthetic Reaction.

The electron released during photolysis reduces triphosphopyridine nucleotide (TPN) with the concomitant release of molecular oxygen. The reduced pyridine nucleotide (TPN.H) is oxidized by an electron transport system consisting of flavins, ascorbic acid, and possibly vitamin K and a cytochrome. The energy derived from this oxidation is utilized to phosphorylate ADP to ATP and is called *photophosphorylation*. The fixation or incorporation of carbon dioxide into ribulose 1,5-diphosphate leads to the production of 3-phosphoglyceric acid. The latter is subsequently reduced to 3-phosphoglyceraldehyde by TPN and ATP generated in the photophosphorylation reaction. Reversible operation of the Embden-Meyerhof cycle of glycolysis starting with 3-phosphoglyceraldehyde proceeds through a series of enzymatic steps, all of which are exergonic, to produce glucose (Figure 3-17).

Recent biochemical studies have demonstrated that both intact and fragmented chloroplasts and grana are all capable of carrying out photophosphorylation. These observations, particularly those pertaining to the grana, recall the previous comments concerning the respiratory enzyme assemblies isolated from mitochondria which were found to exhibit oxidative phosphorylation.

As in the case of mitochondria, it is not known whether plastids are produced *de novo* in the cell or by some form of replication. Indirect evidence favors the latter view. For example, plastids which for one reason or another have lost their capacity to produce chlorophyll apparently give rise to similarly deficient plastids. It is interesting to note that chloroplasts and mitochondria somewhat resemble each other in that both: (1) increase in number in the cell, (2) segregate at cell division, (3) contain respiratory pigments, (4) consist largely of lipoprotein, and (5) possess a double-layered limiting membrane and an internal lamellar organization. In spite of the apparent similarities in structure and behavior of these two organelles, there is no real evidence to indicate that one can be converted into the other.

The development of chloroplasts in green plants has been studied with the aid of the electron microscope. According to von Wettstein (1959), the steps involved (Figure 3-18) are the following: (1) synthesis of vesicles within the plastid primordia, (2) aggregation of these vesicles to form single chains of interconnected vesicles, (3) rearrangement and fusion of the chains to form parallel double membranes or lamellae, (4) multiplication of the lamellae, and (5) the growth and differentiation of the lamellae into grana and stroma lamellae. This developmental sequence is obviously under the control of many genes, and mutations would be expected to block development at numerous points. In most cases the phenotypic endpoint would be the same, namely, a functionless chloroplast. Comparison of the development of chloroplasts in known mutants may often serve to show the location of the block, at least with respect to the structural deficiency. For example, in the white or albina-20 mutant of barley, electron microscopy studies have shown that the plastids increase in size but do not develop grana. These plastids can synthesize chlorophyll in the presence of light but it is broken down as fast as it is formed. In the barley mutant, xantha-3, the plastids differentiate to the extent of developing some internal layered structures, but no true lamellae are ever found and large numbers of globuli accumulate within the plastid. Some chlorophyll and carotenoid pigments are synthesized and localized in the globuli, but since there is no extensive lamellar

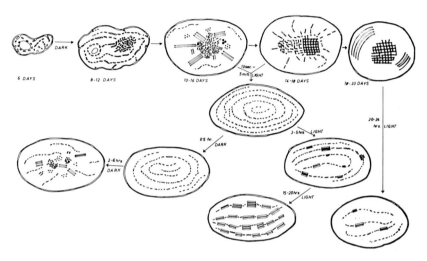

**Figure 3-18.** Schematic Diagram Depicting the Sequence of Changes in Plastid Structure of Etiolated Primary Leaf of *Phaseolus vulgaris* L. Grown in the Dark and Light. It can be seen from the diagram that exposure of 10- to 16-day dark-grown leaves to light results in rapid reorganization of plastid structures and formation of the grana. (Courtesy of Dr. D. von Wettstein, Forest Research Institute, Stockholm, Sweden.)

structure formed these cannot be properly distributed as in the normal plastid. In the xantha-10 mutant, lamellae are developed, but rather than being arranged in the more typical parallel fashion, are concentrically orientated. The structural organization of plastids in this mutant is similar to that found in plastids of etiolated plants grown in the dark (Figure 3-19). Biochemical studies indicate that this concentric arrangement of lamellae is correlated with a deficiency in the synthesis of chlorophyll precursors in the xantha-10 mutant. The fact that plastids in this particular mutant develop a lamellar structure in spite of the apparent block in chlorophyll synthesis, suggests that development of lamellae may be independent of the synthesis of chlorophyll.

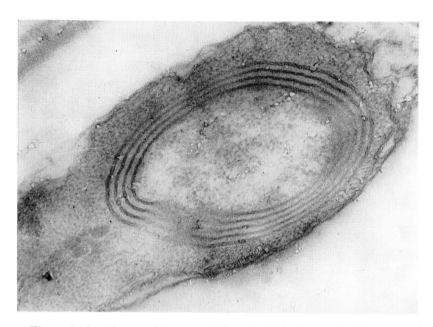

**Figure 3-19.** Electron Micrograph Showing Submicroscopic Structure of Plastid in a Three-Week-Old Etiolated Barley Leaf. Note concentric arrangement of the grana lamellae. Approximately 37,000×. (From von Wettstein, D., 1959. "Developmental Changes in Chloroplasts and Their Genetic Control," *in* "Developmental Cytology," D. Rudnick (Ed.), Ronald Press, New York, N. Y., Fig. 1, p. 150. Courtesy of Dr. D. von Wettstein, Forest Research Institute, Stockholm, Sweden.)

## LYSOSOMES

The term "lysosomes" was originated by deDuve and group (1955) to designate a class of subcellular particles which, on the basis of centrifugation studies, were deduced to be the cell sites of specific hydrolytic enzymes. These enzymes (so-called "lysosomal hydrolases") included acid phosphatase, ribonuclease, deoxyribonuclease, cathepsin, and $\beta$-glucuronidase. Uricase, and possibly catalase and D-amino oxidase, was also considered by these workers as attached either to the lysosomes or to particles of similar nature (deDuve, 1959). Electron microscope examination of isolated liver fractions rich in the above-mentioned hydrolases by Novikoff, Beaufay, and deDuve (1956) revealed the presence of a group of particles which were morphologically distinct from the mitochondria and the microsomes. These particles, termed "dense bodies," exhibited a variety of shapes, and ranged in size from $0.25\mu$ to $0.50\mu$. Many of the particles possessed numerous electron-dense granules, a distinct internal cavity, and were bounded by an external limiting membrane. Electron micrographs of liver sections showed the dense bodies to be mostly localized along the bile canaliculi of the parenchymatous cells. This intracellular distribution corresponds to that of acid phosphatase, which previously had been demonstrated by Holt (1954) to be essentially localized along the bile canaliculi in association with specific granules. On the basis of these observations, it would appear that the pericanicular dense bodies correspond to the acid phosphatase-containing granules associated with the bile canaliculi and represent the lysosomes, at least in terms of this particular enzyme (deDuve, 1959, 1960).

Polymorphic bodies corresponding morphologically with the dense bodies and located adjacent to the bile canaliculi have been observed by Rouiller (1954) and Palade and Siekevitz (1956) in electron micrographs of parenchymatous cells of mammalian liver. Also the so-called "microbodies" described by Rouiller and Bernhard (1956) in regenerating liver cells, and suggested by these workers as possible precursors of the mitochondria, may be identifiable with the dense bodies described by Novikoff and group (deDuve, 1959). Recently, Beaufay and coworkers (1959) have achieved fractionation of the lysosome-rich fraction into two biochemical components: one containing the typical lysosomal hydrolases (acid phosphatase, ribonuclease, $\beta$-glucuronidase, etc.); the other containing uricase, catalase, and D-amino acid oxidase. This differential separation of two distinct groups of hydrolases suggests that each enzyme group probably operates as a unit and is associated with a specific type of particle (Beaufay, et al., 1959). Electron microscopy studies of Beaufay (unpublished) on purified preparations of lysosomes from rat liver have demonstrated the existence of two distinct types of particles associated with this fraction (Figure 3-20 (a) and (b)). One morphological component is represented by the pericanicular dense bodies or true lysosomes. The other component, the so-called "microbodies," differs from the pericanicular dense bodies by the presence of a lamellar or crystalloid core. Whether or not the microbodies represent the subcellular particles with which the hydrolases—uricase, catalase, and D-amino acid oxidase—are associated, remains to be determined (deDuve, 1960).

Available evidence suggests that the lysosomes may be involved in intracellular digestive activities such as phagocytosis and pinocytosis. It has also been suggested that a relationship may possibly exist between

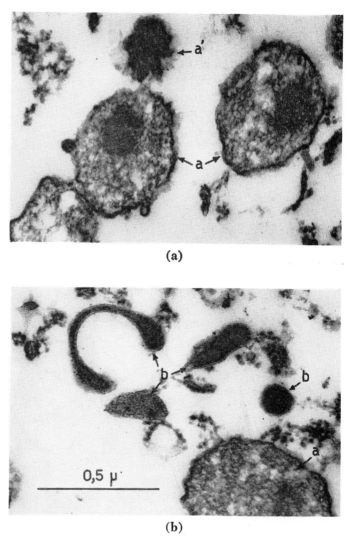

(a)

(b)

**Figure 3-20.** Electron Micrographs Showing the Two Distinct Types of Subcellular Particles Present in Lysosome-rich Fractions Isolated from Rat Liver. The particles in Fig. (a), marked "a," are the so-called microbodies, and are characterized by a lamellar or cystalloid core. One such isolated core is shown as a'. The particles in Fig. (b), marked "b," are the pericanicular dense bodies or true lysosomes. It is not known whether the microbodies, a, represent a separate biochemical entity or a second form of lysosome. (Courtesy of Dr. C. deDuve, Université de Louvain.)

the lysosomes and the mitochondria; however, their precise morphological identification remains to be determined.

## ENDOPLASMIC RETICULUM

The first electron micrographs of cells were published in 1945 by Porter, Claude, and Fullam, who noted the presence of a network or reticulum of strands and associated vesicle-like bodies in the cytoplasm of thinly spread tissue culture cells. Further electron microscopy observations of Porter and Thompson (1947) on the same kind of material indicated that the strands were actually vesicular bodies interconnected to form a complex network which was confined, in most instances, to the inner or endoplasmic portion of the cytoplasm. This network, on the basis of its reticular form and endoplasmic location, was termed the *endoplasmic reticulum*. Some five years later, electron microscopy studies of thin sections of cells generally confirmed the observations of Porter and his colleagues. Since that time improvements in fixation, embedding, and sectioning have led not only to further confirmation, but also to a generally accepted concept of a structural organization of the cytoplasm (Palade, 1956; Porter, 1957). Recently, Fawcett and Ito (1958) and Rose and Pomerat (1960) have studied the form and distribution of the endoplasmic reticulum in living tissue culture cells by phase-contrast microscopy (Figure 3-21).

Despite variations in patterns and differences in opinion concerning details, the following description of the endoplasmic reticulum appears to be reasonably valid. In almost all cells, the cytoplasm is traversed by a three-dimensional network of cavities bounded by a system of membranes, these cavities occurring either as vesicles or tubules. This is more extensive than Porter's original observations suggested. This membrane system is interconnected to produce a more or less continuous network which separates two distinct phases in the cytoplasm. One phase is represented by the material inside the cavities of the network, the other by the cytoplasmic matrix surrounding the elements of the reticulum. In many types of cells, especially those concerned with protein synthesis, small, electron-dense granules are found associated with the outer (matrix) surface of the membranes bounding the cavities of the endoplasmic reticulum. Because these granules were first described in detail by Palade (1955) they are frequently referred to as the "small granules of Palade," though a more common term now is "ribosome." In size, these granules measure about 100 Å, occasionally occur freely dispersed in the cytoplasm, and are reported to have a high content of ribonucleoprotein. Those ele-

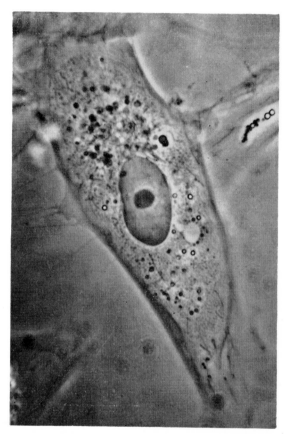

Figure 3-21. Phase-contrast Micrograph of Living Cell from Culture of Human Cystic Adenocarcinoma. The endoplasmic reticulum fills the greater part of the cytoplasm of the cell. It exhibits a multiplicity of forms with erratic bends or curves, of varying lengths, and often in equally spaced parallel array. The larger, more dense elongated forms are the mitochondria. A Golgi complex is visible adjacent to the nucleus in the upper part of the cell. (From Rose, G. G. and Pomerat, C. M., 1960. "Phase Contrast Observations of the Endoplasmic Reticulum in Living Tissue Cultures," *J. Biophys. Biochem. Cytol.,* 8, Fig. 3, p. 425. Courtesy of Dr. George G. Rose, Hermann Hospital, Houston, Texas.)

ments of the reticulum which bear the small granules are termed "rough-surfaced" to distinguish them from the smooth-surfaced ones which are not associated with granules. The smooth-surfaced elements predominate in the cytoplasm of such cells as the mature leucocyte and spermatocyte

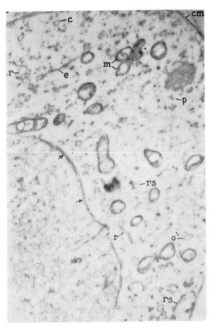

**Figure 3-22.** Electron Micrograph of Portion of Rat Spermatocyte. The nucleus is seen in the lower left corner of the figure, surrounded by a double-layered nuclear envelope containing numerous pores (arrows). The endoplasmic reticulum is predominantly of the smooth-surfaced variety, made up of numerous circular (c) and oval (o) profiles, isolated or in rows (r), and a few elongated membrane elements (e). Profiles with dense particles attached to the outer membrane surface are relatively rare (rs). Mitochondria (m) and clusters of small, electron-dense particles (p) are present in the cytoplasm. The cell membrane is visible at cm. (From Palade, G. E., 1956. "The Endoplasmic Reticulum," *J. Biophys. Biochem. Cytol.*, 2, Suppl., Fig. 1, Plate 31.)

(Figure 3-22), while the rough-surfaced elements are characteristic of exocrine cells of the pancreas and plasma cells (Figure 3-23).

In protein-synthesizing cells in general both types of membranes are represented (Figure 3-24). The smooth elements appear as tightly packed vesicles which form a randomly disposed network usually at the periphery of the cell. The rough-surfaced elements are elongate and arranged more or less parallel to one another. These parallel arrays are interpreted as flattened vesicles of irregular outline and have been termed

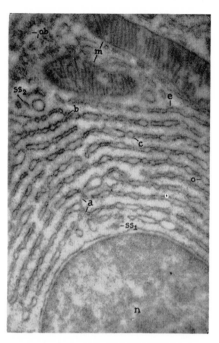

**Figure 3-23.** Electron Micrograph of Basal Portion of Exocrine (acinar) Cell of Guinea Pig Pancreas. The endoplasmic reticulum consists of parallel rows of vesicles bounded by rough-surfaced membranes and arranged concentric with the nucleus. Branching of the rows (**b**) and anastomoses between adjacent rows (**a**) is shown. Elongated profiles (**e**) predominate; however, circular (**c**) and oval (**o**) profiles are also present in many of the rows. Profiles of the rough-surfaced variety are seen in oblique section (**ob**) in the upper left corner of the figure. Smooth-surfaced membrane elements ($ss_1$ $ss_2$) are rare in this type of cell and, when present, often occur in small clusters ($ss_1$). The nucleus appears at **n** and two mitochondria at **m**. (From Palade, G. E., 1956. "The Endoplasmic Reticulum," *J. Biophys. Biochem. Cytol.*, 2, Suppl., Fig. 4, Plate 34.)

*cisternae* by Porter and coworkers (Figure 3-25). The cisternae, together with their associated granules, apparently coincide with the basophilic regions of the cytoplasm and on this basis would correspond to the chromidial substance or *ergastoplasm* of gland cells first described by Garnier in 1899 (Porter, 1957).

The electron microscope studies published to date on the submicro-scopic structure of the cytoplasm are more or less in general agreement concerning the reality of the endoplasmic reticulum, but considerable

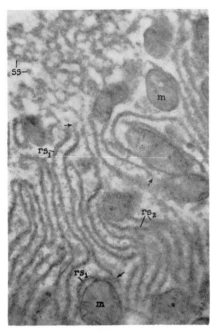

**Figure 3-24.** Electron Micrograph of Portion of Cytoplasm of Rat Parenchymal Liver Cell. Note local differentiation of membrane elements of the endoplasmic reticulum into smooth- and rough-surfaced types. The smooth-surfaced elements (ss) appear as vesicles and tubules disposed in discontinuous groups mostly at the periphery of the cell. The rough-surfaced elements ($rs_1$ $rs_2$) are arranged more or less parallel to one another in large arrays. Profiles of rough-surfaced elements sectioned normal to their surface are marked as $rs_1$, and oblique to their surface as $rs_2$. Points of continuity between the smooth- and rough-surfaced elements are indicated by arrows. Numerous mitochondria (m) are seen in the field. (From Palade, G. E., 1956. "The Endoplasmic Reticulum," *J. Biophys. Biochem. Cytol.*, 2, Suppl., Fig. 3, Plate 33.)

confusion still exists regarding terminology and interpretation of indi-vidual components of the system. For example, the cisternae are inter-preted by Porter and Palade as pairs of membranes arranged in parallel and connected at their ends. Sjöstrand (1956), on the other hand, suggests that the cisternae actually represent a discontinuous series of double membranes separated from each other by an organized layer of lipid. This lipid layer constitutes a third membrane, thus giving a three-layered element. Sjöstrand also classifies the different membranes as follows: (1) α cyto-membranes, which are those elements delimiting the

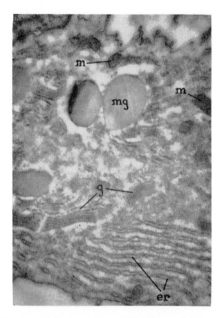

**Figure 3-25.** Electron Micrograph of Portion of Mucus-secreting Cell in Olfactory Epithelium of the Frog. The basal surface of the cell is at the bottom of the figure, the free surface at the top. Mucin granules (**mg**) and mitochondria (**m**) are visible in the cytoplasm. The parallel arrays of rough-surfaced profiles (**er**) located in the basal region of the cell represent vertical sections through flattened vesicles or cisternae (500 to 1200 Å thick) and are characteristic of the endoplasmic reticulum in this and other protein-secreting cells. The arrays of parallel profiles designated as g represent part of the Golgi complex in these cells. (From Porter, K. R., 1957. "The Submicroscopic Morphology of the Protoplasm," Harvey Lectures 1955-56, Academic Press, Inc., New York, N. Y., Fig. 7, Page 184.)

cisternae; (2) β cyto-membranes, which are unfoldings of the cell membrane into the interior of the cell; and (3) γ cyto-membranes, which are smooth-surfaced and generally arranged in parallel as in the Golgi complex.

Some European workers, including Sjöstrand, have suggested replacing the term, "endoplasmic reticulum" by the term, "ergastoplasm."

In our opinion, the present state of knowledge does not justify setting up any very sophisticated terminology for purposes of classification.

The endoplasmic reticulum tends to show a characteristic morphological pattern depending on the kind of cell in which it is found. Likewise, variations in structural complexity and disposition of the endoplasmic reticulum during cell differentiation have been noted (Fawcett, 1959). In the developing guinea pig spermatogonia, the endoplasmic reticulum consists of only a few tubular and vesicular elements. In the spermatocytes, it is a centrally disposed network of extensive cisternae which are peripherally arranged in layers parallel to each other and to the cell surface. Most of the granules are distributed throughout the cytoplasm rather than being extensively associated with the membrane system. During development of spermatids, cisternae disappear, leaving a reticulum consisting of a sparse network of tubular elements. By the end of development, there is virtually no trace of the reticulum and the Palade granules are randomly disposed in the cytoplasm.

The functional significance of the membrane system in general is not known. The cisternae with their associated granules seem to be involved in protein synthesis, but whether this is a function of the membrane system *per se* or of the granules alone is, so far, not clear. Porter has suggested the following functions: (1) to provide an internal membrane surface for the orderly distribution of enzymes, (2) to divide the cytoplasm into compartments so as to facilitate segregation of metabolites, and (3) to transmit impulses in structures such as muscle and nerve cells. Except for the association with protein synthesis, there is no very good experimental evidence for the other functions mentioned.

## MICROSOMES

The microsomes are small, particulate components of the cytoplasm which were first isolated from liver homogenates by differential centrifugation by Claude (1941). It now seems clear that this fraction (Figure 3-26 (a) and (b)) consists of membrane fragments of the endoplasmic reticulum with their associated small granules of Palade, or ribosomes (Palade and Siekevitz, 1956). Biochemical studies have shown that both the microsomal fraction and the small granules of Palade have a high RNA content. The concept that RNA is implicated in protein synthesis was first postulated by Brachet (1941) and Caspersson (1941). This is based largely on the observation that cells, such as liver cells and meristematic cells in growing roots, which synthesize large amounts of protein are also relatively rich in RNA. On the other hand, muscle and

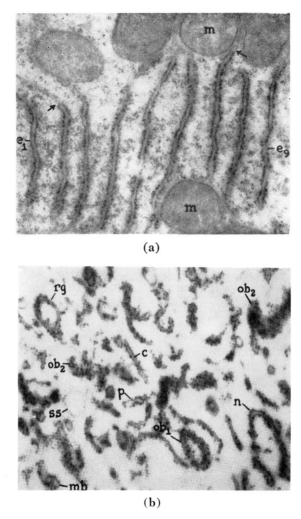

(a)

(b)

**Figure 3-26.** (a) Electron Micrograph of Small Portion of Cytoplasm
of Parenchymatous Liver Cell, showing array of nine elongated profiles
($e_1$, $e_9$) of the rough-surfaced variety which in three dimensions corresponds
to a pile of preferentially oriented cisternae. Numerous small particles of
high electron density (small granules of Palade, ribosomes) are attached to
the outside surface of the membrane limiting the cisternae. Similar particles
appear freely scattered in the intervening cytoplasm. Profiles of five mitochondria (m) are also visible. (b) Electron Micrograph of Section of
Microsomal Fraction Isolated from Liver Homogenate. This fraction con-

(*Contin.* on opposite page.)

kidney cells which have a high physiological activity synthesize very little protein and have a relatively low RNA content. The RNA content of cells varies under different physiological conditions. This variation appears to be reflected in varying capacities for protein synthesis. For example, during development of the reticulocyte or immature mammalian erythrocyte there is a simultaneous reduction in RNA content and incorporation of labeled amino acids into protein. Likewise, in growing bacterial cultures, especially during the logarithmic phase, the RNA content is proportional to the growth rate and RNA synthesis parallels that of protein.

Brachet and his group were the first to suggest that specific cytoplasmic structures may function in protein synthesis. It is now known that the RNA content of the microsomes, like that of the whole cytoplasm, is closely correlated with the cells' capacity for protein synthesis. Furthermore, the initial site of incorporation of isotopically labeled amino acids into cytoplasmic protein is generally assumed to be the microsomal fraction, or more specifically, the ribonucleoprotein granule component of this fraction (Figure 3-27). The first step in amino acid incorporation into the ribonucleoprotein granules is considered to be the enzyme-catalyzed activation of amino acids. This reaction leading to formation of an activated amino acid is considered to be as follows:

$$AA + ATP + E \rightleftharpoons [AA \sim AMP] - E + PP$$

AMINO      ENZYME      ACTIVATED
ACID                    AMINO ACID

The reaction, which is reversible, involves the natural amino acids (L-forms) and has a specific requirement for ATP. The second step is considered to be the addition of specific nucleotides to end groupings of RNA in the soluble portion of the cytoplasm. The third step involves the binding of the activated amino acid to the RNA of the soluble

---

**Figure 3-26.** (*Contin.*)

sists of fragments of the rough-surfaced membrane elements of the endoplasmic reticulum. Many of the fragments still retain the characteristic, flattened appearance of the cisternae in intact tissue as illustrated in Fig. (a) above. A normally sectioned fragment of the endoplasmic reticulum is shown at **n**, fragments cut at increasing degrees of obliquity are marked **ob**, and **ob₂**. Particles attached to membranes (**p**); ring-shaped profiles (**rg**); rough-surfaced membranes (**mb**); matrix or content of membrane fragments or vesicles (**c**); smooth-surfaced profiles (**ss**). (From Palade, G. E. and Siekevitz, P. 1956. "Liver Microsomes. An Integrated Morphological and Biochemical Study," *J. Biophys. Biochem. Cytol.*, 2, Fig. 4, Plate 29, and Fig. 10, Plate 32.)

fraction, which now possesses specific nucleotide end groupings. The final step is believed to involve the transfer of this complex to the ribonucleoprotein of the microsomes, followed by polymerization of the amino acids to produce protein (Stephenson, et al., 1959).

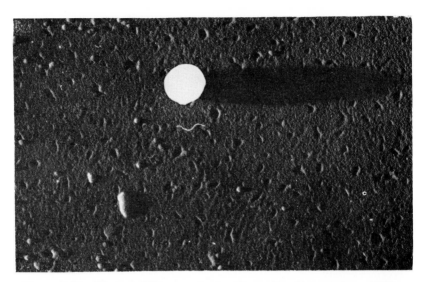

**Figure 3-27.** Electron Micrograph of a Freeze-Dry Preparation of Microsomal Particles (Ribosomes) from Pea Seedlings. The polystyrene sphere is 2600 Å in diameter and serves to show the relative size of the ribosomes. (From Ts'o, P. O. P., 1958. "Structure of Microsomal Nucleoprotein Particles from Pea Seedlings," *in* "Microsomal Particles and Protein Synthesis," R. B. Roberts (Ed.), *1st Symposium Biophys. Soc.*, Pergamon Press, Fig. 1. Courtesy of Dr. P. O. P. Ts'o, California Institute of Technology.)

Microsomes exhibit a small amount of respiratory activity involving DPN- and TPN-linked cytochrome reductases as well as an extramitochondrial cytochrome (cytochrome $b_5$) which can transfer electrons to molecular oxygen. In most cases, there is no evidence that microsomal respiration or electron transport is coupled to phosphorylation of ADP to yield ATP; however, the microsomes of the bacterium, *Azobacter*, appear to be capable of some oxidative phosphorylation (Brachet, 1957). Although most of the glycolytic reactions in carbohydrate breakdown presumably occur in the soluble fraction of the cytoplasm, the hexokinase reaction catalyzing the phosphorylation of glucose to glucose-6-phosphate appears to be confined, at least in some cells, to the microsomes and mitochondria (Lehninger, 1959).

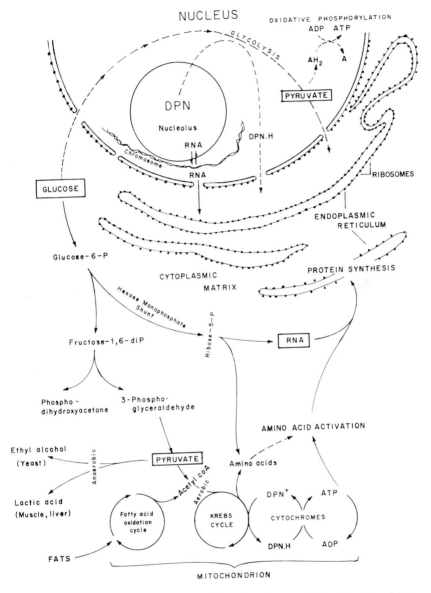

**Figure 3-28.** Schematic Diagram Showing Some of the Possible Inter-relationships That May Exist Between the Various Components of the Cell with Respect to Metabolic Function. Metabolic pathways which have not been definitely established are indicated by dashed arrows.

## CYTOPLASMIC MATRIX

The cytoplasmic matrix is the ground substance in which the organelles of the cell (nucleus, mitochondria, plastids, endoplasmic reticulum, etc.) are embedded. In the biochemical sense, this component of the cell roughly corresponds to the subcellular fraction isolated from homogenates after removal of all cellular particulates, and contains enzymes in the soluble form which are involved in a number of important metabolic pathways (Lehninger, 1959).

Among the important enzymes found in the soluble fraction are those associated with degradation of carbohydrate to pyruvate (Embden-Meyerhof cycle of glycolysis). Also, this is apparently the primary location of the enzymes concerned in the hexose monophosphate shunt which leads to the production of pentose units for nucleotide and nucleic acid (RNA) synthesis. In addition, this fraction is also considered to be the major site of fatty acid synthesis in the cell.

What has been said concerning the mitochondria, endoplasmic reticulum, microsomes, and matrix provides an excellent illustration of the subtle interrelationships that may exist between various cellular components with respect to metabolic function (Figure 3-28). It is quite clear that we cannot really consider any one organelle as functionally independent of the others. One should therefore consider *in vitro* experiments, particularly those involving subcellular fractions, as providing clues to potential, rather than as reflecting *in vivo,* operations. For example, if we consider the problem of protein synthesis it becomes apparent that a variety of cytoplasmic components are involved in this activity (Figure 3-28): the soluble fraction in activation of amino acids, the microsomal fraction in their polymerization, the matrix as a source of specific RNA, and the mitochondria as an energy supply in the form of ATP. Likewise, as noted, the mitochondria are capable of oxidizing fatty acids (Figure 3-11) but their synthesis is dependent on the cytoplasmic matrix. Therefore, fatty acid metabolism in general is determined by interaction between these two cell components.

## GOLGI COMPLEX

In certain animal cells, particularly those which have a secretory function (epididymus, liver, pancreas) a system of fibrous or globular bodies which stain with osmic acid is readily apparent (Figure 3-29). This system or organelle was first described by Golgi in 1898, and has since been known as the Golgi complex. Recent evidence indicates that a similar structure (see Chapter 4, Figure 4-5) may also occur in certain specialized plant cells (Whaley, *et al.*, 1960). Both the function and reality of the Golgi complex have long been debated. So far as light

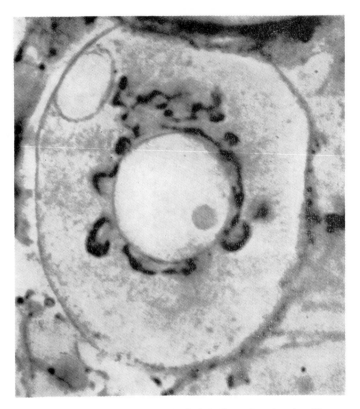

**Figure 3-29.** Photomicrograph of Golgi Complex in the Neuron of a Normal Albino Rat. Note filamentous structure of the anastomosing strands of the complex. (From Bourne, G. H., 1951. "Mitochondria and the Golgi Complex," *in* "Cytology and Cell Physiology," G. H. Bourne (Ed.), 2nd ed., Oxford University Press, London, Fig. 1, Plate 5.)

microscope studies are concerned, the complex in animal cells can at least be differentiated into two parts: (1) an outer osmiophilic component, and (2) an inner osmiophobic component.

In recent years, electron microscopy studies have indicated that the complex has a generalized structural pattern made up of a system of membrane-bound vesicles of varying size, associated with smooth mem-

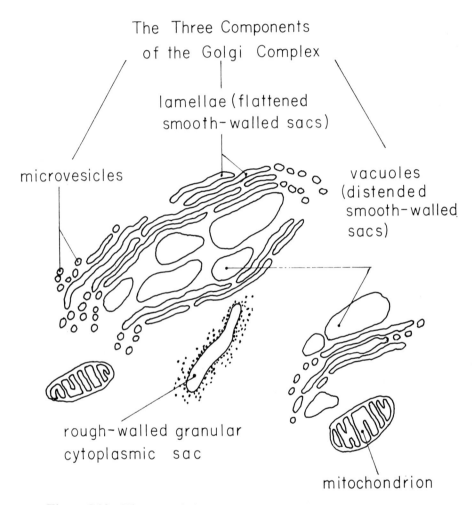

The Three Components
of the Golgi Complex

lamellae (flattened
smooth-walled sacs)

microvesicles

vacuoles
(distended
smooth-walled
sacs)

rough-walled granular
cytoplasmic sac

mitochondrion

**Figure 3-30.** Diagram of the Golgi Complex, Showing the Three Main Components. The rough-surfaced cytoplasmic vesicle is not part of the complex, but is shown for comparison with the smoth-surfaced vesicles of the Golgi region. Two mitochondria are also shown. (From Howatson, A. F. and Ham, A. W., 1957. "The Fine Structure of Cells," *Can. J. Biochem. and Physiol.*, **35**, Fig. 9, p. 555.)

brane elements arranged in more or less parallel fashion (Figures 3-30 and 3-31). Present evidence suggests that this complex is a separate organelle of the cytoplasm and not a part of the endoplasmic reticulum. In support of this view, the following facts may be cited: (1) The mem-

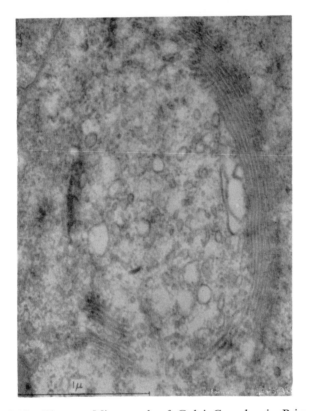

**Figure 3-31.** Electron Micrograph of Golgi Complex in Primary Spermatocyte of Japanese Viviparid Snail, *Viviparus*. The Golgi complex appears as an array of parallel smooth-surfaced membranes enclosing a number of membrane-bound vesicles of variable size. (From Pollister, A. W. and Pollister, P. F., 1957. "The Structure of the Golgi Apparatus," *Intern. Rev. Cytol.*, **6**, Fig. 6b, p. 101.)

brane system has no associated granules; (2) the general morphology of the complex is remarkably similar in cells of very diverse types; (3) the membranes, although resembling certain elements of the endoplasmic reticulum, are markedly thicker; and (4) the complex appears to be specifically capable of reducing osmium tetroxide. There is some evidence of continuity between the smooth membranes of the Golgi and certain elements of the endoplasmic reticulum.

Because the complex is somewhat difficult to isolate from other cellular components, its exact function is not precisely known. The fact that the complex is most readily revealed in cells which have a specialized function in connection with secretion, combined with the observation that there is a general parallel between the morphological changes in the complex and the level of secretory activity, has led to the notion that the Golgi functions as a region for the collection of specialized products. The association between the endoplasmic reticulum and the complex provides a logical means of transport to the cell exterior. It is also tempting to draw an analogy between the proposed function of the Golgi and the contractile vacuole of the protozoa, although some protozoa may have both organelles.

As in the case of the mitochondria and endoplasmic reticulum, electron microscopy studies have also revealed consistent changes in the Golgi complex which are associated with developmental sequences during the maturation of mammalian germ cells (Fawcett, 1959). In primary spermatocytes, the Golgi is typical in its fine structure. As development continues, the interior of the complex is altered to produce, finally, a dense body called the acrosome, which is bounded by a single membrane.

## CELL MEMBRANE

Even cells which appear to be syncitial by ordinary histological methods have in most cases been demonstrated by electron microscopy to be compartmentalized by membranes which are presumably similar in structure and function to those normally forming the outer boundary of free cells. In cross-section, these boundaries appear as osmiophilic lines about 60 Å thick, adjacent membranes being separated from each other by a space of the order of 100 Å. Current opinion appears to be that the cell membrane is actually a double structure having a lipoidal and protein component.

A number of interesting modifications or specializations of the cell membrane have been classified by Selby (1959) as follows: (1) narrow evaginations, (2) local thickenings, (3) deep infoldings compartmentalizing the cytoplasm, (4) interlocking of adjacent cells, and (5) narrow invaginations of the cell surface. Adoption of any of these specializations by the cell membrane serves to increase cellular surface area, facilitate transport of materials in and out of the cell, and modify the degree to which adjacent cells are associated with each other.

The narrow evaginations or finger-like projections distributed at random along most cell surfaces and in continuity with the cytoplasm of the cell, are called "microvilli." It has been suggested that these may represent the fixed, static profiles of active cell surfaces such as those seen in phase-contrast movies of living cells. In the striated border of intestinal epithelium, the microvilli are constant in diameter and length and are closely packed to form a continuous surface structure. The brush border in the proximal convoluted tubule of the kidney is made up of a series of closely spaced membrane extensions arranged in a hexagonal pattern.

Recent electron microscopy studies have demonstrated that cilia such as those of epithelial cells have a characteristic, highly organized internal structure. In their simplest form, they are slender extensions of the cell surface, usually about 0.2 microns in diameter and of variable lengths up to many microns. The individual cilium is made up of a ring of nine peripheral and two centrally located filaments, all of which run in the direction of the long axis (Figure 3-32). The protoplasm in which the entire system of peripheral and central filaments is embedded is continuous with the cytoplasm and enclosed by the cell membrane. In longitudinal sections, the filaments can be seen to terminate in a dense, transverse plate, called the *basal body,* or *kinetosome,* located at the base of each cilium in the cortex of the cell. In some cell types, striated fibers appear to originate from the basal bodies and to extend for some distance into the interior of the cell. The basal body itself is cylindrical and is also composed of a peripheral ring of nine loci continuous with the ciliary filaments. So far, most evidence indicates that the architecture of cilia is basically the same in all forms from protozoans to primates. There is a rather striking similarity of structure between the centrioles, cilia, and basal bodies. The centriole, like the cilium and basal body, is essentially cylindrical in form and shows in cross-section a ring of nine peripheral filaments.

Localized thickenings of closely apposed cell membranes have been reported in a variety of cell types. The thickened portions of each membrane are generally so close together that they appear at low magnification as a single structure, which has been called the *desmosome.* These contiguous regions constitute a sort of bridge between adjacent cells. This bridge is not continuous as is presumed to be the case with the plasmadesmata between adjacent cells in many plant cells or the intercellular bridges between groups of developing mammalian germ cells.

Extensive infoldings of the cell membrane into the interior of the cell are commonly found in a variety of epitheliums. The points along the cell surface where the membrane has invaginated to divide the cytoplasm into compartments are considered to be regions of active transport.

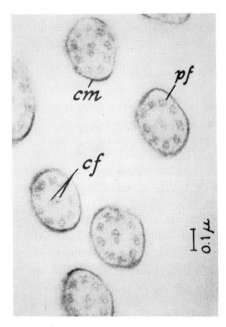

**Figure 3-32.** Electron Micrograph Showing Five Body Cilia of *Paramecium multimicronucleatum* in cross section. The individual cilium consists of nine peripheral filaments (**pf**) evenly spaced in a circle around a central pair of filaments (**cf**), and surrounded by the cell membrane (**cm**). Each of the nine peripheral filaments is, itself, double with each member of the pair measuring 150 to 200 Å in diameter, which is equivalent in size to one of the central filaments. (From Sedar, A. W. and Porter, K. R., 1955. "The Fine Structure of Cortical Components of Paramecium Multimicronucleatum." *J. Biophys. Biochem. Cytol.*, 1, Fig. 6, Plate 153.)

## VACUOLES

It is a debatable matter whether a vacuole should be treated as a cell organelle. It consists essentially of an aggregation of solid or fluid substances. The question of whether or not it is delimited by a membrane or a protoplasmic interface is open, as are the questions of its origin and function. Vacuoles vary in size from virtually submicroscopic to almost the entire cell volume (Figure 3-33). The contractile vacuoles of lower forms appear to serve an excretory function, while the large ones of the conducting tissues of plants may provide necessary turgor for support. Most evidence would suggest that vacuoles simply provide a suitable substrate for metabolic reactions. In any event, they seem to be of universal occurrence in both plant and animal cells.

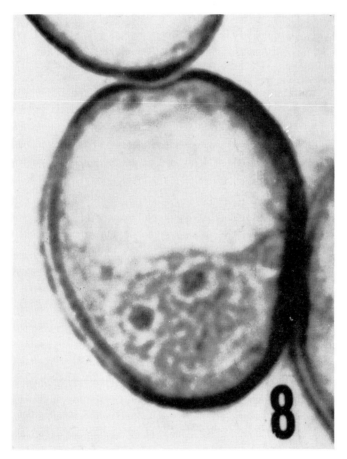

**Figure 3-33.** Photomicrograph of Large Vacuole in Microspore Cell of *Tradescantia paludosa*. Note eccentric position of vacuole and nucleus containing two nucleoli. (From Leak, L. V. and Wilson, G. B., 1960. "Relative Volume Changes of the Nucleolus in Relation to Cell and Nucleus in *Pisum sativum* and *Tradescantia paludosa*," *Trans. Am. Microscop. Soc.,* **79**, Fig. 8, p. 157. Courtesy of Mr. L. V. Leak, Michigan State University.)

# BIBLIOGRAPHY

Allfrey, V., Daly, M. M., and Mirsky, A. E., 1953. "Synthesis of Protein in the Pancreas. II. The Role of Ribonucleoprotein in Protein Synthesis," *J. Gen. Physiol.,* **37**, 157-175.

Baker, J. R., 1957. "The Golgi Controversy," *Symposia Soc. Exptl. Biol.,* **10**, 1-10.

Beaufay, H., Bendall, D. S., Baudhuin, P., Wattiaux, R., and deDuve, C., 1959. "Analysis of Mitochondrial Fractions from Rat Liver by Density-Gradient Centrifuging," *Biochem. Jour.,* **73**, 628-637.

Belt, W. D. and Pease, D. C., 1956. "Mitochondrial Structures in Sites of Steroid Secretion," *J. Biophys. Biochem. Cytol., Suppl.,* **2**, 369-374.

Bennett, H. S., 1956. "The Concepts of Membrane Flow and Membrane Vesiculation as Mechanisms for Active Transport and Ion Pumping," *J. Biophys. Biochem. Cytol., Suppl.,* **2**, 99-105.

Bernhard, W., Gautier, A., and Rouiller, C., 1954. "La notion de 'microsomes' et le problème de la basophilie cytoplasmique," *Arch. anat. microscop. et morphol. exptl.,* **43**, 236-275.

Bowen, R. H., 1924. "On a Possible Relation Between the Golgi Apparatus and Secretory Products," *Am. J. Anat.,* **33**, 197-218.

Brachet, J., 1941. "La localisation des acides pentosenucleiques dans les tissus animaux et les oeufs d'amphibiens en voie de developpement," *Arch. biol.,* **53**, 207-257.

Brachet, J., 1944. "Embryologie Chimique," Desoer, Liege, Belgium.

Brachet, J., 1957. "Biochemical Cytology," Academic Press, New York, N. Y.

Caspersson, T. O., 1941. "Studien uber den Eiweissumsatz der Zelle," *Naturwissenschaften,* **28**, 33-43.

Caspersson, T. O., 1950. "Cell Growth and Cell Function," W. W. Norton & Co., New York, N.Y.

Chance, B. and Williams, G. R., 1956. "The Respiratory Chain and Oxidative Phosphorylation," *Adv. Enzymol,* **17**, 65-134.

Chantrenne, H., 1947. "Hétérogénéite des granules cytoplasmiques du foie de souris," *Biochim. et Biophys. Acta.,* **1**, 437-448.

Claude, A., 1941. "Particulate Components of Cytoplasm," *Cold Spring Harbor Symposia Quant. Biol.,* **9**, 263-271.

Claude, A., 1943. "The Constitution of Protoplasm," *Science,* **97**, 451-456.

Claude, A., 1943. "Distribution of Nucleic Acids in the Cell and the Morphological Constitution of Cytoplasm," *in* "Frontiers of Cytochemistry," N. L. Hoerr (Ed.), *Biological Symposia,* **10**, 111-129, Jaques Cattell Press, Lancaster, Pa.

Crane, R. K. and Soles, A., 1953. "The Association of Hexokinase with Particulate Fractions of Brain and Other Tissue Homogenates," *J. Biol. Chem.,* **203**, 273-292.

Dalton, A. J. and Felix, M. D., 1956. "A Comparative Study of the Golgi Complex," *J. Biophys. Biochem. Cytol., Suppl.,* **2**, 79-84.

Dalton, A. J. and Felix, M. D., 1957. "Electron Microscopy of Mitochondria and the Golgi Complex," *Symposia Soc. Exptl. Biol.,* **10**, 148-159.

DeDuve, C., 1959. "Lysosomes, a New Group of Cytoplasmic Particles," in "Subcellular Particles," T. Hayashi (Ed.), Ronald Press, New York, N.Y., pp. 128-159.

DeDuve, C., 1960. "Intracellular Localization of Enzymes," *Nature,* **187,** 836.

DeDuve, C., Pressman, B. C., Gianetto, R., Wattiaux, R., and Appelmans, F., 1955. "Intracellular Distribution Patterns of Enzymes in Rat Liver," *Biochem. Jour.,* **60,** 604-617.

DeHarven, E. and Bernhard, W., 1956. "Etude au microscope electronique de l'ultrastructure du centriole chez les vertèbres," *Zeit. für Zellforsch. und Mikr. Anat.,* **45,** 378-398.

Dempsey, E. W., 1956. "Variations in the Structure of Mitochondria," *J. Biophys. Biochem. Cytol., Suppl.,* **2,** 305-312.

Dempsey, E. W. and Peterson, R. R., 1956. "Electron Microscopic Observation on the Thyroid Glands of Normal, Hypophysectomized, Cold-exposed and Thiouracil-treated Rats." *Endrocinol.,* **56,** 46-58.

Farquhar, M. G. and Wellings, R. S., 1957. "Electron Microscopic Evidence Suggesting Secretory Granule Formation Within the Golgi Apparatus," *J. Biophys. Biochem. Cytol.,* **3,** 319-322.

Fawcett, D. W., 1958. "The Structure of the Mammalian Spermatozoan," *Intern. Rev. Cytol.,* **7,** 195-234.

Fawcett, D. W., 1959. "Changes in the Fine Structure of Cytoplasmic Organelles During Differentiation," *in* "Developmental Cytology," D. Rudnick (Ed.), Ronald Press, New York, N.Y., pp. 161-189.

Fawcett, D. W. and Ito, S., 1958. "Observations on the Cytoplasmic Membranes of Testicular Cells, Examined by Phase Contrast and Electron Microscopy," *J. Biophys. Biochem. Cytol.,* **4,** 135-142.

Fawcett, D. W. and Porter, K. R., 1954. "A Study of the Fine Structure of Ciliated Epithelia," *J. Morphol.,* **94,** 221-282.

Fawcett, D. W., Ito, S., and Slautterback, D. B., 1959. "The Occurrence of Intercellular Bridges in Groups of Cells Exhibiting Synchronous Differentiation," *J. Biophys. Biochem. Cytol.,* **5,** 453-460.

Garnier, C., 1899. Thèse méd., Nancy.

Gatenby, J. B., Dalton, A. J., and Felix, M. D., 1955. "The Contractile Vacuole of Parazoa and Protozoa, and the Golgi Apparatus," *Nature,* **176,** 301-306.

Granick, S., 1955. "Plastid Structure, Development and Inheritance," *Handbuch der Pflanzenphysiologie,* **1,** 507-564.

Green, D. E., 1958. "Studies in Organized Enzyme Systems," Harvey Lectures (1956-1957), **58,** 177-227.

Green, D. E., 1957. "Chemical Interrelationship Between Fatty Acid Oxidation Cycle and Citric Acid Cycle," *Symp. Soc. Exptl. Biol.,* **10,** 30-49.

Green, D. E., 1959. "Mitochondrial Structure and Function," *in* "Subcellular Particles," T. Hayashi (Ed.), Ronald Press, New York, N.Y., pp. 84-103.

Green, D. E., 1959. "Electron Transport and Oxidative Phosphorylation," *Adv. Enzymol.,* **21,** 73-129.

Hackett, D. P., 1955. "Recent Studies on Plant Mitochondria," *Intern. Rev. Cytol.,* **4,** 143-196.

Haguenau, F., 1958. "The Ergastoplasm. Its History, Ultrastructure, and Biochemistry," *Intern. Rev. Cytol.,* **7,** 425-483.

Hoagland, M. B., 1955. "A Enzymic Mechanism for Amino Acid Activation in Animal Tissues," *Biochim. et Biophys. Acta,* **16,** 288-289.

Hoagland, M. B., Stephenson, M. C., Scott, J. F., Hecht, L. I., and Zamecnik, P. C., 1958. "A Soluble Ribonucleic Acid Intermediate in Protein Synthesis," *J. Biol. Chem.,* **231,** 241-257.

Hogeboom, G. H. and Schneider, W. C., 1955. "The Cytoplasm," *in* "The Nucleic Acids," Vol. 2, E. Chargaff and J. N. Davidson (Eds.), Academic Press, New York, N.Y., pp. 199-246.

Holt, S. J., 1954. "A New Approach to the Cytochemical Localization of Enzymes," *Proc. Roy. Soc. London, B,* **142,** 160-169.

Junqueira, L. C. U. and Hirsch, G. C., 1956. "Cell Secretion: A Study of Pancreas and Salivary Glands," *Intern. Rev. Cytol.,* **5,** 323-364.

Kamen, M. D. and Newton, J. W., 1959. "Particles in Photosynthetic Phosphorylation," *in* "Subcellular Particles," T. Hayashi (Ed.), Ronald Press, New York, N.Y., pp. 104-113.

Keller, E. B., Zamecnik, P. C., and Loftfield, R. B., 1954. "The Role of Microsomes in the Incorporation of Amino Acids into Proteins," *J. Histochem. Cytochem.,* **2,** 378-388.

Krebs, H. A., 1954. "Considerations Concerning the Pathways of Synthesis in Living Matter," *Bull. Johns Hopkins Hosp.,* **95,** 19-33.

Krebs, H. A., 1957. "Control of Metabolic Processes," *Endeavour,* **63,** 125-132.

Lacy, D. and Challice, C. E., 1957. "The Structure of the Golgi Apparatus in Vertebrate Cells Examined by Light and Electron Microscopy," *Symp. Soc. Exptl. Biol.,* **10,** 62-92.

Langdon, R. G., 1957. "The Biosynthesis of Fatty Acids in Rat Liver," *J. Biol. Chem.,* **226,** 615-630.

Langdon, R. G. and Weakley, D. R., 1955. "The Effect of Hormonal Factors and of Diet upon Hepatic Glucose-6-phosphatase Activity," *J. Biol. Chem.,* **214,** 167-174.

Lehninger, A. L., 1956. "Physiology of Mitochondria," *in* "Enzymes: Units of Biological Structure and Function," O. H. Gaebler (Ed.), Academic Press, New York, N.Y., pp. 217-234.

Lehninger, A. L., 1959. "Metabolic Interactions in Cell Structures," *in* "Developmental Cytology," D. Rudnick (Ed.), Ronald Press, New York, N.Y., pp. 191-209.

Lehninger, A. L., Wadkins, C. L., Cooper, C., Devlin, T. M., and Gamble, J. L., Jr., 1958. "Oxidative Phosphorylation," *Science,* **128,** 450-456.

Lever, J. D., 1956. "Physiologically Induced Changes in Adrenocortical Mitochondria," *J. Biophys. Biochem. Cytol., Suppl.,* **2,** 313-318.

Mühlethaler, K., 1955. "The Structure of Chloroplasts," *Intern. Rev. Cytol.,* **4,** 197-220.

Novikoff, A. B., 1956. "Electron Microscopy: Cytology of Cell Fractions," *Science,* **124,** 969-972.

Novikoff, A. B., 1959. "The Intracellular Localization of Chemical Constituents," *in* "Analytical Cytology," R. C. Mellors (Ed.), Blakiston Division, McGraw-Hill Book Co., New York, N.Y., pp. 69-168.

Novikoff, A. B., Beaufay, H., and deDuve, C., 1956. "Electron Microscopy of Lysosome-rich Fractions from Rat Liver," *J. Biophys. Biochem. Cytol., Suppl.,* **2**, 179-184.

Oberling, C., 1959. "The Structure of Cytoplasm," *Intern. Rev. Cytol.,* **8**, 1-31.

Palade, G. E., 1952. "The Fine Structure of Mitochondria," *Anat. Rec.,* **114**, 427-453.

Palade, G. E., 1955. "A Small Particulate Component of the Cytoplasm," *J. Biophys. Biochem. Cytol.,* **1**, 59-68.

Palade, G. E., 1956. "The Endoplasmic Reticulum," *J. Biophys. Biochem. Cytol., Suppl.,* **2**, 85-99.

Palade, G. E., 1958. "Microsomes and Ribonucleoprotein Particles," *in* "Microsomal Particles and Protein Synthesis," R. B. Roberts (Ed.), Pergamon Press, New York, N.Y., pp. 36-61.

Palade, G. E. and Siekevitz, P., 1956. "Liver Microsomes. An Integrated Morphological and Biochemical Study," *J. Biophys. Biochem. Cytol.,* **2**, 171-200.

Palade, G. E. and Siekevitz, P., 1956. "Pancreatic Microsomes. An Integrated Morphological and Biochemical Study," *J. Biophys. Biochem. Cytol.,* **2**, 671-690.

Palay, S. L., 1956. "Synapses in the Central Nervous System," *J. Biophys. Biochem. Cytol., Suppl.,* **2**, 193-203.

Pease, D. C., 1956. "Infolded Basal Plasma Membranes Found in Epithelia Noted for Their Water Transport," *J. Biophys. Biochem. Cytol., Suppl.,* **2**, 203-209.

Pollister, A. W., 1939. "Structure of the Golgi Apparatus in the Tissues of Amphibia," *Quart. J. Microscop. Sci.,* **81**, 235-271.

Pollister, A. W. and Pollister, P. F., 1957. "The Structure of the Golgi Apparatus," *Intern. Rev. Cytol.,* **6**, 85-105.

Porter, K. R., 1953. "Observations on a Submicrocsopic Basophilic Component of Cytoplasm," *J. Exptl. Med.,* **97**, 727-750.

Porter, K. R., 1954. "Electron Microscopy of Basophilic Components of Cytoplasm," *J. Histochem. Cytochem.,* **2**, 346-373.

Porter, K. R., 1957. "The Submicroscopic Morphology of Protoplasm," *Harvey Lectures* (1955-56), **51**, 175-228.

Porter, K. R. and Kallman, F., 1953. "The Properties and Effects of Osmium Tetroxide as a Tissue Fixative with Special Reference to Its Use for Electron Microscopy," *Exptl. Cell Res.,* **4**, 127-141.

Porter, K. R. and Machado, R. D., 1960. "Studies on the Endoplasmic Reticulum. IV. Its Form and Distribution During Mitosis in Cells of Onion Root Tip," *J. Biophys. Biochem. Cytol.,* **7**, 167-180.

Porter, K. R. and Thompson, H. P., 1947. "Some Morphological Features of Cultured Rat Sarcoma Cells as Revealed by the Electron Microscope," *Cancer Res.,* **7**, 431-438.

Porter, K. R., Claude, A., and Fullam, E. F., 1945. "A Study of Tissue Culture Cells by Electron Microscopy," *J. Exptl. Med.,* **81**, 233-246.

Price, W. H., 1952. "Phage Formation in *Staphylococcus muscae* Cultures. XI. The Synthesis of Ribonucleic Acid, Desoxyribonucleic Acid, and Protein in Uninfected Bacteria," *J. Gen. Physiol.,* **35**, 741-759.

Rose, G. G. and Pomerat, C. M., 1960. "Phase-Contrast Observations of the Endoplasmic Reticulum in Living Tissue Cultures," *J. Biophys. Biochem. Cytol.,* **8,** 423-430.

Rouiller, C., 1954. "Les canalicules biliaires. Etude au microscope electronique," *Comp. rend. Soc. Biol.,* **148,** 2008-2011.

Rouiller, C. and Bernhard, W., 1956. " 'Microbodies' and the Problem of Mitochondrial Regeneration in Liver Cells," *J. Biophys. Biochem. Cytol.,* **2,** 355-360.

Sager, R. and Palade, G. E., 1957. "Structure and Development of the Chloroplast in *Chlamydomonas.* I. The Normal Green Cell," *J. Biophys. Biochem. Cytol.,* **3,** 463-488.

Schneider, W. C. and Hogeboom, G., 1956. "Biochemistry of Cellular Particles," *Ann. Rev. Biochem.,* **25,** 201-224.

Sedar, A. W. and Porter, K. R., 1955. "The Fine Structure of Cortical Components of *Paramecium multimicronucleatum,*" *J. Biophys. Biochem. Cytol.,* **1,** 583-604.

Sedar, A. W. and Rudzinska, M. A., 1956. "Mitochondria of Protozoa," *J. Biophys. Biochem. Cytol., Suppl.,* **2,** 331-336.

Selby, C. C., 1959. "Electron Microscopy: Techniques and Applications in Cytology," *in* "Analytical Cytology," R. C. Mellors (Ed.), Blakiston Division, McGraw-Hill Book Co., New York, N.Y., pp. 273-341.

Siekevitz, P. and Palade, G. E., 1958. "A Cytochemical Study on the Pancreas of the Guinea Pig. I. Isolation and Enzymatic Activities of Cell Fractions," *J. Biophys. Biochem. Cytol.,* **4,** 203-218.

Siekevitz, P. and Watson, M. C., 1956. "Cytochemical Studies of Mitochondria. II. Enzymes Associated with a Mitochondrial Membrane Fraction," *J. Biophys. Biochem. Cytol.,* **2,** 653-670.

Sjöstrand, F. S., 1953. "Electron Microscopy of Mitochondria and Cytoplasmic Double Membranes," *Nature,* **171,** 30-32.

Sjöstrand, F. S., 1956. "Electron Microscopy of Cells and Tissues," *in* "Physical Techniques in Biological Research," G. Oster and A. W. Pollister (Eds.), Vol. 3, Academic Press, New York, N.Y., pp. 241-298.

Sjöstrand, F. S., 1956. "The Ultrastructure of Cells as Revealed by the Electron Microscope," *Intern. Rev. Cytol.,* **5,** 456-529.

Sjöstrand, F. S. and Hanzon, V., 1954. "Ultrastructure of Golgi Apparatus of Exocrine Cells of Mouse Pancreas," *Exptl. Cell Res.,* **7,** 415-429.

Slautterback, D. B., 1953. "Electron Microscope Studies of Small Cytoplasmic Particles (Microsomes)," *Exptl. Cell Res.,* **5,** 173-186.

Slautterback, D. B. and Fawcett, D. W., 1959. "The Development of the Cnidoblasts of *Hydra.* An Electron Microscope Study of Cell Differentiation," *J. Biophys. Biochem. Cytol.,* **5,** 441-452.

Stephenson, M. L., Hecht, L. I., Littlefield, J. W., Loftfield, R. B., and Zamecnik, P. C., 1959. "Intermediate Reactions in Protein Synthesis," *in* "Subcellular Particles," T. Hayashi (Ed.), Ronald Press, New York, N.Y., pp. 160-171.

Strittmatter, P. and Velick, S. F., 1956. "The Isolation and Properties of Microsomal Cytochrome," *J. Biol. Chem.,* **221,** 253-264.

Swanson, C. P., 1957. "Cytology and Cytogenetics," Prentice-Hall, Inc., Englewood Cliffs, N.J.

Swift, H., 1958. "Cytoplasmic Particulates and Basophilia," *in* "Chemical Basis of Development," W. D. McElroy and B. Glass (Eds.), Johns Hopkins University Press, Baltimore, Md., pp. 174-213.

Tahmisian, T. N., Powers, E. L., and Devine, R. L., 1956. "Light and Electron Microscope Studies of Morphological Changes of Mitochondria During Spermatogenesis in the Grasshopper," *J. Biophys. Biochem. Cytol., Suppl.,* **2**, 325-330.

Watson, M. L. and Siekevitz, P., 1956. "Cytochemical Studies of Mitochondria. I. The Separation and Identification of a Membrane Fraction from Isolated Mitochondria," *J. Biophys. Biochem. Cytol.,* **2**, 639-652.

Webster, G. C., 1957. "Amino Acid Incorporation by Intact and Disrupted Ribonucleoprotein Particles," *J. Biol. Chem.,* **229**, 535-546.

Wettstein, D. von, 1957. "Genetics and the Submicroscopic Cytology of Plastids," *Hereditas,* **43**, 303-317.

Wettstein, D. von, 1959. "Developmental Changes in Chloroplasts and Their Genetic Control," *in* "Developmental Cytology," D. Rudnick (Ed.), Ronald Press, New York, N.Y., pp. 123-160.

Whaley, W. G., Mollenhauer, H. H., and Leech, J. H., 1960. "The Ultrastructure of the Meristematic Cell," *Am. J. Botan.,* **47**, 401-449.

Zebrun, W. and Mollenhauer, H., 1960. "Electron Microscopic Observations on Mitochondria of Rat Testis Fixed in Potassium Permanganate," *J. Biophys. Biochem. Cytol.,* **7**, 311-314.

# 4

# Structure and Function
# of the Nucleus

THE NUCLEUS has received very much more attention since its discovery by Robert Brown in 1835 than has any other part of the cell. While the bulk of these investigations have been concerned with morphology, particularly of the chromosomes in division, the development and use in recent years of new cytological techniques for study of the nucleus have contributed greatly to our knowledge of the biochemistry and physiology of this cell structure.

## GENERAL MORPHOLOGY AND CHEMISTRY

In general the nucleus tends to be spherical, but may be fusiform, ellipsoidal, flattened, or irregular, depending to some extent on cell shape and function. Its size tends to bear a constant relation to the cytoplasmic volume (O. Hertwig, 1906), but there are many exceptions. In young cells it is more often spherical and centrally located, but in differentiated ones it may be displaced and irregular in shape.

The interphase nucleus (a nucleus not in the process of active division) consists of (1) a *nuclear envelope* surrounding (2) a nonstaining or slightly chromophilic mass, the *nucleoplasm,* in which are dispersed (3) the *chromosomes,* which are considered to be nucleoprotein structures, (4) the *chromocenters,* and (5) one or more basophilic bodies called *nucleoli.* The following discussion is concerned with the structure and chemical makeup of the several parts (Figure 4-1).

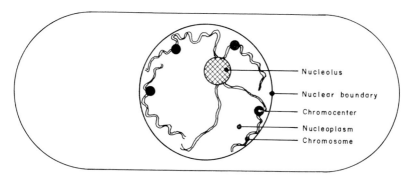

Figure 4-1. Schematic Representation of the Interphase Nucleus. Note association of parts of the chromosomes with the nuclear boundary and nucleolus.

## Nuclear Envelope

There is considerable question as to whether or not the nuclear envelope is actually a semipermeable structure. The available evidence relating to its permeable properties does not preclude the passage

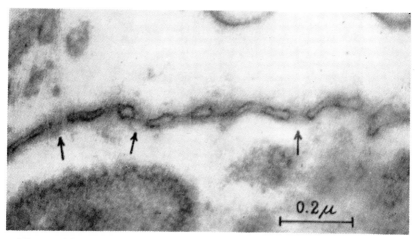

Figure 4-2. Electron Micrograph of Section of Nuclear Envelope of Macronucleus of *Paramecium multimicronucleatum*. The nuclear envelope is a double structure formed by two membranes spaced apart by about 300 Å and surrounding the contents of the nucleus. Between the membranes is the perinuclear space. At points indicated by arrows, pores are formed where the inner and outer membranes of the envelope are joined with one another. (From Watson, M. L., 1955. "The Nuclear Envelope. Its Structure and Relation to Cytoplasmic Membranes," *J. Biophys. Biochem. Cytol.*, **1**, Fig. 3, Plate 71.)

through this structure of relatively large units by diffusion, as in the case of the oocyte nucleus which appears to be freely permeable to molecules up to the size of proteins. Also in the light of what is known regarding ultrastructure it is not impossible that its permeable properties are subject to considerable variation. A number of electron microscopy

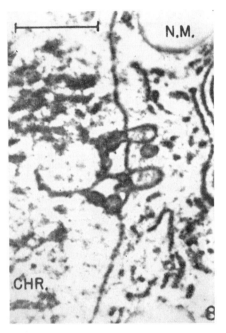

Figure 4-3. Electron Micrograph of *Drosophila* Salivary Gland Cell Showing Outpocketings (Blebs) of the Nuclear Membrane. Note association of highly differentiated chromosomal material with the developing blebs. Approximately 45,000×. (From Gay, H., 1956. "Chromosome-Nuclear Membrane-Cytoplasmic Interrelations in *Drosophila*," *J. Biophys. Biochem. Cytol.*, **2**, Fig. 8, Plate 137. Courtesy of Dr. Helen Gay, Carnegie Institute of Washington.)

studies have shown the nuclear envelope to be a double-layered structure containing pores formed by continuities between the outer and inner layers of the envelope (Figure 4-2). In certain cells, a thin membrane extending across the pores and separating the contents of the nucleus from those of the cytoplasm has been observed. The presence of annuli or rings of electron-dense granules surrounding the pores of the envelope has also been reported. These annuli appear to be associated with extensions (annular tubules) which project into the nucleus and out into the cytoplasm. Projections or blebs from the nuclear membrane (Figure 4-3) and the delamination of segments of it into the cytoplasm has also been described. The association of electron-dense granules with the outer

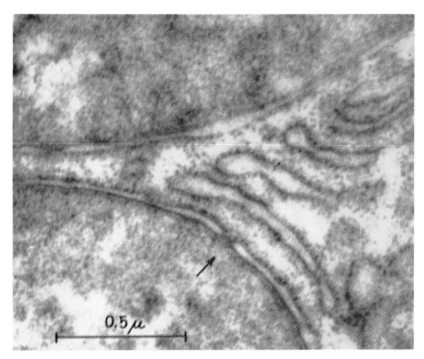

Figure 4-4. Electron Micrograph Showing Parts of Two Nuclei in a Binucleate, Acinar Cell of Rat Pancreas. Small, electron-dense cytoplasmic particles are shown associated with the membrane elements of the endoplasmic reticulum and the outer membrane of the nuclear envelope. The appearance of the outer nuclear membrane and its associated particles makes it indistinguishable essentially from the rough-surfaced membranes of the endoplasmic reticulum. A pore in one nuclear envelope is marked by an arrow. (From Watson, M. L., 1955. "The Nuclear Envelope. Its Structure and Relation to Cytoplasmic Membranes," *J. Biophys. Biochem. Cytol.*, 1, Fig. 5, Plate 73.)

layer of the nuclear envelope (Figure 4-4) and continuity between this layer and certain elements of the endoplasmic reticulum have been observed in both plant and animal cells (Figure 4-5). The morphological similarity and apparent continuity between the nuclear envelope and various elements of the endoplasmic reticulum have been interpreted as indicating either that the nuclear envelope is a modification of the cytoplasmic membrane system or that certain membrane components of the

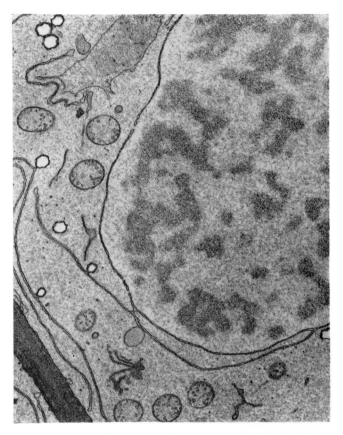

**Figure 4-5.** Electron Micrograph of Portion of a Meristematic Rootcap Cell of Maize, Showing a Double-layered Nuclear Envelope with Distinct Pores. Note continuity of the outer membrane of the nuclear envelope with double membrane element of the endoplasmic reticulum. Mitochondria, a Golgi apparatus (lower left in figure), and unidentified cytoplasmic inclusions are shown. (From Whaley, W. G., Mollenhauer, H. H., and Leech, J. H., 1960. "The Ultrastructure of the Meristematic Cell," *Am. J. Botany,* **47,** Fig. 3, p. 425. Courtesy of Dr. W. Gordon Whaley, University of Texas.)

cytoplasm are of nuclear origin. The observations made on the ultrastructure of the nuclear envelope indicate a complex structural organization which may correspond to regions of different permeable properties.

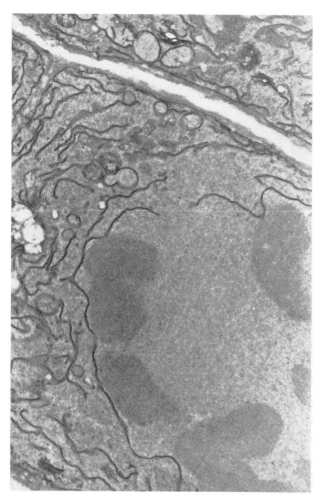

**Figure 4-6.** Electron Micrograph of Portion of Late Prophase Nucleus in a Cell from the Outer Cortex of Onion Root Tip. Three sectors of the nuclear envelope are visible, one of which still retains a connection with a membrane element of the endoplasmic reticulum. Outside the remnants of the nuclear envelope and encircling the nucleus is a zone from which mitochondria and plastids are excluded. Large vesicles with a limiting membrane and homogeneous content, called phragmosomes, begin to appear with increasing frequency at this stage of cell division. (From Porter, K. R. and Machado, R. D., 1960. "Studies on the Endoplasmic Reticulum. IV. Its Form and Distribution During Mitosis in Cells of Onion Root Tip," *J. Biophys. Biochem. Cytol.,* **7,** Fig. 5, Plate 84. Courtesy of Dr. Keith R. Porter, The Rockefeller Institute.)

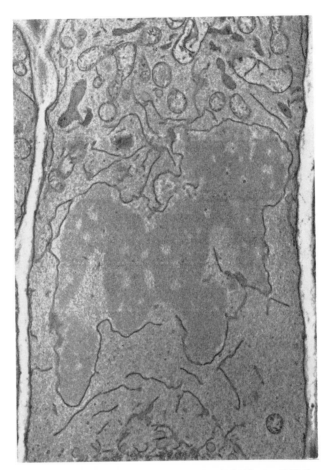

Figure 4-7. Electron Micrograph of Early Telophase Cell from Onion Root Tip. Membrane elements of the endoplasmic reticulum at this stage of cell division appear to orient themselves along the surfaces of the chromosomes to form the nuclear envelope. The envelope is almost complete in this cell, with the exception of the discontinuity shown in lower half of figure. Note that fragments of membrane elements of the endoplasmic reticulum and small vesicles measuring some 20 mμ in diameter have become enclosed, along with the chromosomes, by the nuclear envelope. Polar organization of elements of the endoplasmic reticulum is shown in upper middle of figure. Across the lower margin of the figure numerous phragmosomes are seen in close association with the forming cell plate. (From Porter, K. R. and Machado, R. D., 1960. "Studies on the Endoplasmic Reticulum. IV. Its Form and Distribution During Mitosis in Cells of Onion Root Tip," *J. Biophys. Biochem. Cytol.*, **7**, Fig. 15, Plate 93. Courtesy of Dr. Keith R. Porter, The Rockefeller Institute.)

It has long been known that the nuclear boundary either disappears or undergoes major reorganization during cell division, and that a new boundary is formed around each of the two daughter nuclei. Since the structures concerned are well below the resolving power of the light microscope it has been only recently, with the aid of electron microscopy, that information has been obtained concerning the structures and sequence of events involved in re-establishment of the nuclear envelope at cell division. Recent work has indicated that during mitotic prophase the nuclear envelope breaks up into a number of separate vesicles which become dispersed in the cytoplasm and are indistinguishable from the membrane elements of the endoplasmic reticulum (Figure 4-6).

The new envelope is formed at the end of the mitotic process around each of the daughter nuclei. This involves migration of membrane elements of the endoplasmic reticulum onto the surface of the chromosomes where they eventually coalesce and become reorganized into a double-layered membrane structure (Figure 4-7). The selection of membrane elements in formation of the nuclear envelope appears to be quite random and not to involve necessarily those which arose during the breakdown process in the previous prophase stage.

### Nucleoplasm

This component of the nucleus appears in electron micrographs as consisting of a pattern of irregular-shaped particles or granules. Little is known regarding its chemical makeup. However, ultracentrifugation studies indicate that it is essentially protein in character. It contains some RNA and gives positive cytochemical reactions for glycoproteins. A number of hydrolytic enzymes (i.e., ribonuclease, alkaline phosphatase, dipeptidase) occur in the nucleus and may be specific constituents of the nucleoplasm (Brachet, 1957).

### Nucleolus

Depending on the species, interphase nuclei may contain one or more nucleoli and the number may be constant or variable (Figure 4-8 (a)). Present evidence indicates that in the somatic and reproductive cells of many organisms, both plant and animal, nucleoli are formed during the telophase of mitosis in association with specific regions of specific chromosomes of the complement. For the sake of convenience, such chromosomes are referred to simply as *nucleolar chromosomes* to distinguish them from other members of the complement not displaying this activity (Figure 4-8 (b)). A number of diploid species of plants have a single pair of nucleolar chromosomes, in which case the nucleolus organized

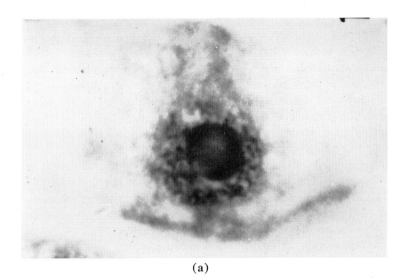

(a)

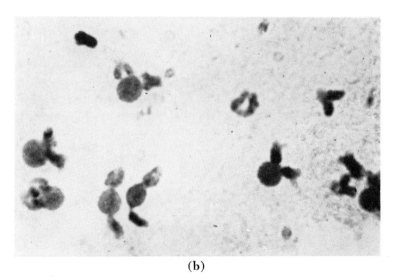

(b)

**Figure 4-8.** (a) Photomicrograph of Nucleolus in Microspore Cell of *Tradescantia*. (b) Nucleolar Chromosomes as Seen at Diakinesis of Meiosis in *Spinacia oleracea* L. Two pairs of chromosomes are associated with each nucleolus. (Fig. (a), courtesy of Mr. L. V. Leak, Michigan State University, E. Lansing, Michigan. Fig. (b) from Bemis, W. P. and Wilson, G. B., 1953. "A New Hypothesis Explaining the Genetics of Sex Determination in *Spinacia oleracea* L.," *J. Heredity,* **44,** Fig. 1C, p. 90.)

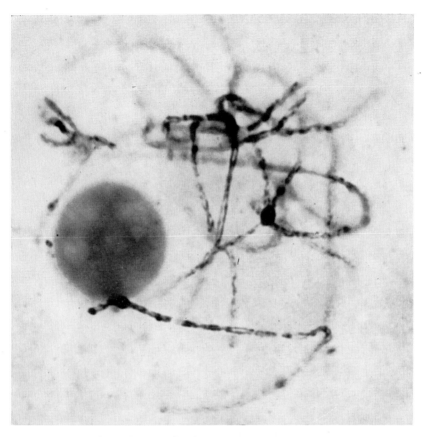

**Figure 4-9.** Photomicrograph of Microsporocyte of *Zea mays* in the Mid-prophase of 1st Meiotic Division. The nucleolus is shown in close association with the dark-staining nucleolar-organizing body of chromosomes 6. Both chromosomes are in close opposition along their length, and possess a terminal satellite which is separated from the nucleolar-organizing body by a thin, faint-staining thread. (From McClintock, B., 1934. "The Relation of a Particular Chromosomal Element in the Development of the Nucleoli in *Zea mays*," *Zeits. für Zellforsch. u. Mik. Anat.*, **21**, Fig. 1, p. 297. Courtesy of Dr. Barbara McClintock, Carnegie Institute of Washington.)

in association with each of the two homologous chromosomes often may fuse with the other to form a single fusion nucleolus in interphase. There are diploid species known, however, which have more than one pair of chromosomes which function in nucleolar formation. The region of the nucleolar chromosome most frequently involved in the production of the nucleolus is the *secondary constriction,* though organisms are known in which nucleoli are formed in association with chromosomes which do not exhibit any such constriction. The specific region of the chromosome active in nucleolar formation is usually designated as the *nucleolar zone* or *nucleolar-organizing region*. In those cases in which the secondary

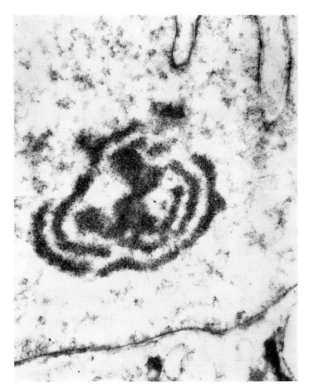

**Figure 4-10.** Electron Micrograph of Nucleolus in Tissue Culture Fibroblast Cell. The filamentous and granular character of the nucleolus is clearly evident. In the center of the nucleolus is a more homogeneous area corresponding to the "pars amorpha." The double-layered nuclear membrane is shown indented at the top of the figure. (Courtesy of Dr. Françoise Haguenau, College de France, Paris.)

constriction is involved, the nucleolar zone may exhibit a morphology distinct from that usually shown by other secondary constrictions of the chromosome complement. For example, in pachytene stages of *Zea mays* (McClintock, 1934) and certain other plant species, a large, darkly staining body (the *nucleolar-organizing body*) is associated with the nucleolar zone (Figure 4-9). Many other organisms, however, fail to show any such morphological differentiation in this particular chromosomal region. It has been claimed that the interphase nucleolus is formed of two different parts: one amorphous, the other filamentous, called the *nucleoloneme* (Estable and Sotelo, 1952). According to this view, the amorphous part undergoes the characteristic cycle of formation at telophase and disappearance at prophase. The nucleoloneme is regarded as a permanent structure which persists throughout mitosis in association with the chromosomes. The presence of filamentous structures within the nucleolus has been revealed by both phase-contrast and electron microscopy (Figure 4-10). It has also been reported that Feulgen-positive granules and threads are sometimes visible in the nucleolus of certain cells. Brachet (1957) suggested that the presence of such Feulgen-positive material could result from penetration of chromosome segments into the substance of the nucleolus. The existence of intranucleolar structures corresponding, morphologically, to the so-called nucleoloneme has been known for some time. The question of intranucleolar material was discussed over twenty years ago by Kaufmann (1938) in relation to his studies on nucleolar formation in *Drosophila* salivary gland nuclei. Kaufmann (1938) pointed out that the substance of the nucleolus presents a medium in which elongation and opening out of the constituent parts of the chromosome may occur, and gave evidence to indicate that the network of threads and granules sometimes visible within the nucleolus is probably composed of separated chromonemata with their associated chromomeres.

The nucleolus in the interphase nucleus of many somatic animal cells is associated with a layer of condensed, Fuelgen-positive material which Thorell (1944) has termed the "nucleolus-associated chromatin." According to both Thorell (1944) and Caspersson (1950), the nucleolus is a product of the chromocenter of the interphase nucleus (Figure 4-11). Basic proteins (histones) and RNA are supposedly produced within the chromocenter during interphase to form the main bulk of the nucleolus. The subsequent accumulation of nucleolar material expands the chromocenter, with the result that the latter takes on the appearance of a ring of Feulgen-positive material surrounding the nucleolus. This perinucleolar ring of chromatin constitutes the nucleolus-associated chromatin (Figure 4-11). As already mentioned, present evidence favors the view that nucleoli are formed at telophase in association with specific nucleolar chromosomes and, contrary to the view of Caspersson and Thorell, suggests that the nucleolus-associated chromatin is probably best interpreted as representing parts of these same chromosomes which, in the fixed cell, have collapsed around the periphery of the nucleolus

(Monty, *et al.,* 1956). The model of the interphase nucleus and the scheme involving formation of the nucleolus from the chromocenter proposed by Caspersson (1950) is based largely on the salivary gland nucleus of *Drosophila.* Apart from the fact that this type of nucleus is highly specialized in terms of development of the chromosomes, there is little evidence to indicate a close morphological relationship between the nucleolus and chromocenter in such nuclei. Kaufmann (1938) demonstrated that the single nucleolus in the salivary gland nucleus of *Drosophila melanogaster* is formed by the fusion of two nucleoli which are

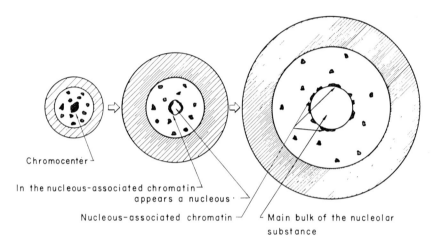

Chromocenter

In the nucleous-associated chromatin
appears a nucleous·

Nucleous-associated chromatin ⌐ Main bulk of the nucleolar
substance

Figure 4-11. Schematic Diagram Showing Development of the Nucleolus from the Nucleolus-associated Chromatin. (From Caspersson, T. O., 1950. "Cell Growth and Cell Function," W. W. Norton & Co., Inc., New York, N.Y., Fig. 48, p. 104.)

organized independently in association with the sex chromosomes. He also pointed out that, because of the tendency of the heterochromatic regions of the chromosomes of this species to fuse and form a single large chromocenter, the fusion nucleolus may sometimes come to occupy a position within the chromocenter and thereby simulate a direct association with this structure. In *Drosophila busehii,* the chromocenter is almost entirely absent, the nucleolus in this species apparently being connected to the central regions of the chromosomes by a series of chromatic strands (White, 1954). It is also well known that in many other cell types a nucleolus is present where no chromocenters are visible (Barigozzi, 1950; Darlington, 1947).

The nucleolus is generally described as being either a fluid, or a semi-solid body. Most evidence favors the view that it is a colloidal structure with the properties of a complex concervate. It may, however, possess a relatively high density and protein content and should, in such cases, be a more or less solid structure. RNA may exist in both a stable and a labile form, and is apparently a consistent but variable component of the nucleolus (Vincent, 1955). It also contains protein and lipid but there is disagreement as to the amounts and types present. Its chemical composition probably varies widely from one cell type to another and with the metabolic activity of the cell. Isotope-incorporation studies of both plant and animal cells indicate a high rate of uptake of isotope into the RNA of the nucleolus (see Figure 4-26), suggesting that this structure is an active site of RNA synthesis in the cell (Brachet, 1957). The nucleolus is apparently also a center of some protein synthesis as indicated by its uptake of labeled amino acids. In certain cells, the enzyme involved in the synthesis of the coenzyme diphosphopyridine nucleotide (DPN) is located in the nucleolus (Baltus, 1954), which may implicate this structure in the synthesis of nucleotide coenzymes (Brachet, 1957).

## Chromocenters

There is some confusion between so-called *prochromosomes,* which are specific segments of the chromosomes and appear as condensed, deeply staining bodies during interphase, and true chromocenters, which appear to be more or less separate globular bodies of similar staining reaction scattered throughout the interphasic nucleus. Whether the latter structures are continuous with or separated from the chromosomes is by no means clear. In some species (e.g., the plant *Trillium sessile*) their number and size are relatively stable, while in others both are highly variable. There is some evidence that the total volume of chromocenter material is constant and increases with an increase in number of chromosomes.

## Chromosomes

### Morphology

When a cell is viewed in the living state, aside from nucleoli, the nucleus frequently appears to be optically empty. In the fixed state, however, coiled threads usually appressed to the inside of the nuclear envelope may be detected quite readily (Figure 4-1). These structures are the chromosomes. The detailed morphology of the chromosome varies from cell to cell and major changes are associated with the cell division process. Regardless of differences in their detailed morphology, both direct and indirect evidence makes it clear that each chromosome is an individual entity which, barring accidents, is retained throughout the life of the cell. Earlier ideas suggesting that chromosomes arose during interphase as the result of coalescence of individual particles or that they were joined together to form a continuous chain or spireme, have had to be discarded. The electron microscope has not, so far, provided any good basis for detailed description of the submicroscopic structure of the chromosome either at interphase or any other stage. The best pictures to date indicate that the individual strands (chromonemata) of the chromosome are made up of many microfibrils which measure about 60 Å units. The total number of these microfibrils is the subject of some controversy, although it seems likely that it is upwards of 64 in number. Indirect evidence suggests that each chromosome at interphase is made up of at least two bundles of microfibrils. As already noted, parts of some chromosomes appear as highly condensed areas in the interphase nucleus which are known as heterochromatic segments (prochromosomes, chromocenters) and are usually thought to represent tightly coiled chromosome regions.

The detailed morphology of the chromosomes is best studied during cell division at the stages of greatest contraction, such as metaphase and anaphase. By the usual methods of fixation and staining the chromosomes at these stages appear as somewhat cylindrical bodies constricted at one or more places along their length (Figure 4-12 (a) and (b)). The positions of these constrictions are a constant characteristic of any particular chromosome of the complement. In the older literature they were frequently referred to as primary and secondary constrictions; the former representing a specialized region of the chromosome which plays a major role in movement of the chromosomes during division, while the latter occur only in certain chromosomes—being associated in some, but not necessarily all, cases with the production of nucleoli (nucleolar zone). The primary constriction, which is known by many terms, the commonest of which are "centromere" and "kinetochore," is obviously an essential part since chromosomes which lack it fail to orient or move properly during mitosis.

With appropriate treatment the chromosome may be seen to consist of one or more helically coiled threads apparently embedded in a *matrix* (Figure 4-12). The coiled threads are called the *chromonemata* (singular, *chromonema*) and are considered to represent the permanent part of the chromosome. The reality of the matrix has been challenged by a number of workers, including both Darlington and Ris, but there are many reasons for believing that it does actually exist and even that it is bounded by a membrane or interface.

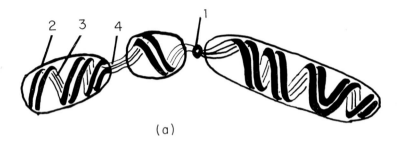

(a)

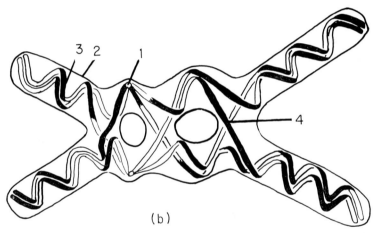

(b)

Figure 4-12. (a) Somatic Chromosome at Anaphase: (1) kinetochore; (2) matrix; (3) chromonema; (4) secondary constriction. (b) Meiotic Chromosome at Diakinesis: (1) kinetochore; (2) matrix; (3) chromonema; (4) chiasma. (From Wilson, G. B., 1952. "Outline of Genetics," Michigan State University Press, East Lansing, Mich., Fig. 1, p. 4.)

Numerous attempts to analyze the nucleus, and thus the chromosomes, chemically have been made since Miescher's pioneering work in that direction in the 1870's. Although considerable progress has been made in recent years through the application of spectrophotometric methods, chemical analysis of both isolated nuclei and chromosomes, and cytochemical techniques, the physiology of the chromosome is still incompletely known. The most constant chemical fraction appears to be DNA. This finding has played a major role in establishing the now widely held concept that DNA is the most significant part of the chromosome genetically. The protein fraction of the chromosome is variable, both in amount and kind, but in most cases it can be divided into basic and nonbasic protein types. In addition to DNA, the chromosome can be demonstrated to contain some RNA as well as lipid substances.

## Heterochromatin

The chromosome is obviously a very complex organelle and no doubt serves a number of functions other than the purely genetic in the accepted sense. Despite this complexity, with very few exceptions the chromosomes are remarkably similar in all kinds of cells, tissues, and organisms. As a result, cytologists and cytogenetisists have been forced to look for different "kinds" of chromatin which may be revealed either naturally or under experimental conditions in terms of morphological differentiation. Two major kinds have been recognized generally, namely, *euchromatin* and *heterochromatin*. This distinction is by no means a happy one, for no single definition of either can be considered all-embracing. From the genetic point of view, euchromatin is considered to be that part of the chromosome which can be shown to contain genetic material by classical methods of genetic analysis, while heterochromatin represents segments of, or whole, chromosomes which are relatively inert. Cytologists have attempted to distinguish these two types on a morphological basis, usually by looking for differential staining. As has already been noted, the chromosomes in interphase frequently show segments which are deeply staining and markedly condensed. During division, however, this distinction frequently disappears. Cytological recognition of a distinction between heterochromatin and euchromatin depends exclusively on the two kinds being out of phase with respect to staining reaction at different stages of the mitotic cycle. Such discordance is not always apparent and even when the distinction can be made frequently there is no certainty that the cytological and genetic distinctions are the same. Probably a reasonable definition of heterochromatin would be that segment of a chromosome which can be deleted without producing any obvious phenotypic change. In many chromosomes, segments near or adjacent to the kinetochore are covered by this definition and are also frequently heteropycnotic in the purely cytological sense. For example, in the X-chromosome of *Drosophila melanogaster,* all of the short arm and about one-third of the proximal part of the long arm are heterochromatic by any definition, as is almost all of the Y-chromosome in the same organism (Figure 4-13 (a) and (b)). On genetic test, the Y-chromosome cannot be considered entirely inert. Aside from a short region, which contains one or more standard genetic loci, elements on the distal ends of the long and short arms are essential for male fertility.

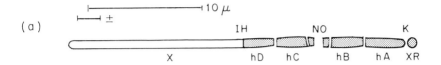

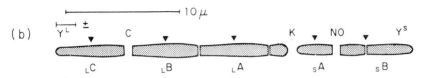

**Figure 4-13.** Diagrammatic Representation of the X and Y Chromosomes of *Drosophila melanogaster:* (a) X chromosome with heteropycnotic regions shaded: **IH**, junction of isopycnotic and heteropycnotic regions; hA—hD, main segments of Xh with the "paranucleolar bodies" set off to each side of the nucleolus organizer; **K**, kinetochore; **NO**, nucleolus organizer; **XR**, genetic right limb of X. (b) Y chromosome with heteropycnotic segments shaded: small triangles indicate uncertain points of subdivision; **C**, main secondary constriction of long arm; **K**, kinetochore; $_L$A-$_L$C, main segments of long arm; **NO**, nucleolus organizer; $_s$A, $_s$B, main segments of short arm; **Y$^L$**, long arm; **Y$^s$**, short arm. (From Cooper, K. W., 1959. "Cytogenetic Analysis of Major Heterochromatic Elements (Especially Xh and Y) in *Drosophila melanogaster,* and the Theory of Heterochromatin," *Chromosoma,* **10,** Fig. 9, p. 541, and Fig. 25, p. 543.)

In the plants, *Trillium* and *Paris,* and in the newt, *Triturus,* exposure to low temperature for some period of time results in the differentiation of the chromosomes during division with respect to staining capacity. This reaction was termed differential reactivity by Darlington and La Cour. Certain specific regions of specific chromosomes are understained relative to the rest, that is, they are negatively heteropycnotic (Figure 4-14 (a) and (b)). Wilson and Boothroyd (1941, 1944) have also shown, at least in *Trillium,* that the pattern of these unstained regions is a species characteristic and that they represent areas which are under-contracted relative to the rest of the chromosome. Whether such regions are heterochromatic in the genetic sense is not known. There is some evidence that they can be deleted without producing any obvious effect on viability.

In a number of plants and animals individuals in a population may contain a number of chromosomes in addition to the normal complement. These extra chromosomes are known as supernumeraries. As a rule, they are smaller than normal, appear to be genetically inert, since variation in their numbers is not accompanied by any marked phenotypic

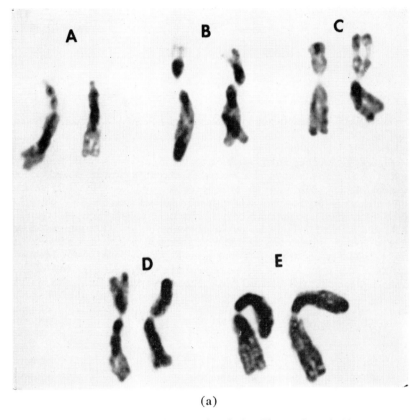

(a)

Figure 4-14. (a) Photomicrograph of the Five Pairs of Chromosomes from a Single Cell of *Trillium grandiflorum,* showing the pattern of differentially reactive segments produced by prolonged cold treatment. Note differences between homologues with respect to degree of expression. (b)

(*Contin.* on opposite page.)

variation, and frequently show the cytological staining reaction characteristic of heterochromatin. There are, however, many cases in which a distinction on the basis of staining reaction is impossible. In *Tradescantia* and *Trillium,* for example, supernumeraries appear to be largely euchromatic and in maize they contain both kinds of chromatin (Figure 4-15). Since they tend to persist in a population with a rather constant average frequency per individual, it has been suggested that they perform some rather subtle function which is of value to the species as a whole. In many cases, their behavior during both mitotic and meiotic divisions is erratic. Such behavior not infrequently leads to random elimination and fragmentation. In general, their origin is not known, although it is presumed that they represent kinetochore-containing heterochromatic segments from normal chromosomes.

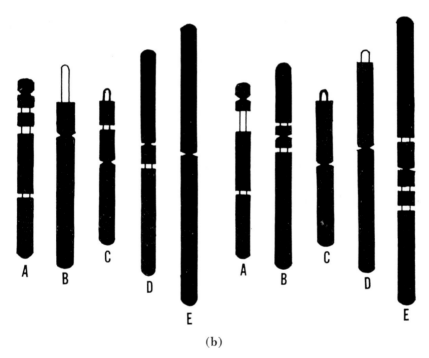

(b)

Figure 4-14. (*Contin.*)

Schematic Representation of the Differentially Staining Regions Typically Found in *Trillium grandiflorum* (left) and *T. flexipes* (right) After Prolonged Cold Treatment. (From Giles, R. A. and Wilson, G. B., 1956. "A Cytological and Morphological Study of Two Populations of *Trillium grandiflorum* (Michx.) Salisb.," *Cytologia,* 21, Fig. 5, p. 381, and Fig. 4, p. 380.)

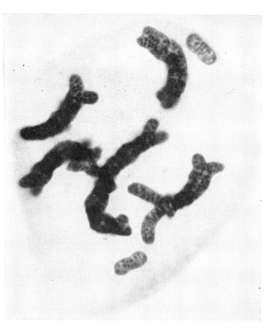

**Figure 4-15.** Photomicrograph of First Meiotic Metaphase in Microsporogenesis of *Trillium erectum* Showing Two Supernumerary or Fragment-like Chromosomes. (From Sparrow, A. H., Pond, V., and Sparrow, R. C., 1952. "Distribution and Behavior of Supernumerary Chromosomes during Microsporogenesis in a Population of *Trillium erectum* L.," *Am. Naturalist,* **86,** Fig. 4, p. 282. Courtesy of Dr. A. H. Sparrow, Brookhaven National Laboratory.)

### Chromomeres

At certain stages, most notably prophase of the first meiotic division, the chromosome often may be seen to be differentiated longitudinally by chromatic thickenings known as *chromomeres* (see Chapter 5, Figure 5-7). The question of their functional significance is somewhat debatable, although the fact that the number, and to some extent, even the size is constant suggests the tempting hypothesis that they represent the genetically significant part of the chromosome. No conclusive proof of this idea has ever been provided and it should be noted that heterochromatic regions are not without chromomere-like structures. The exact structure of the chromomeres has not yet been worked out to the point where there is any general agreement. Belling considered them to be chromatic thickenings surrounding a small granule which he referred to as the ultimate chromomere. More recent work involving micromanipulation and treatment with uncoiling agents such as KCN have indicated that the chromomeres simply represent regions of tight coiling.

### Special Chromosomes

*"Salivary Gland" Type Chromosomes.* In certain tissues of the dipteran larva such as the salivary gland and some regions of the gut and trachea, the chromosomes are of a size and morphological structure

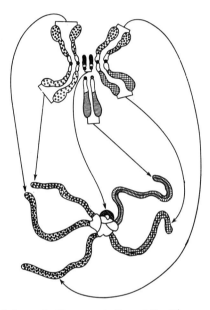

**Figure 4-16.** A Schematic Representation of the Chromosomes of *Drosophila melanogaster,* as Seen at Metaphase of Mitosis in Dividing Cells (above) and in the Cells of the Salivary Glands of Fully Grown Larvae (below). Each chromosome "limb" is shown with different shading. The heterochromatic segments of the metaphase chromosomes, which form the chromocenter in the salivary gland nucleus, are shown in white. The kinetochores of the metaphase chromosomes (invisible in the salivary gland cells) are shown in black. (From Sinnott, E. W., Dunn, L. C., and Dobzhansky, T., 1950. "The Principles of Genetics," 4th ed., McGraw-Hill Book Co., Inc., New York, N.Y., Fig. 106, p. 245.)

which makes them strikingly different from those characteristically found in the more typical somatic cells of the same organism. Such chromosomes were reported in 1881 by Balbiani but received comparatively little attention until Kostoff (1930), Painter (1933), and Heitz and

Bauer (1933) demonstrated their cytogenetic importance. Since that time they have received an enormous amount of attention, much of it, however, having to do with cytogenetic analyses rather than with the question as to their origin, detailed morphology, and physiological significance.

On examination, the salivary gland type of chromosome can be seen to be composed of *two homologous chromosomes* which are more or less closely paired and loosely twisted around each other (Alfert, 1954). Since these chromosomes are really *paired units* or *bivalents,* they are

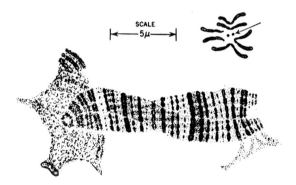

**Figure 4-17.** Drawing of Salivary Chromosome 4 (below) of *Drosophila melanogaster* and, on the Same Scale, the Entire Group of Eight Chromosomes at Metaphase in Gonial Cells of the Same Organism (upper right). In the gonial group, the fourth chromosomes (paired and highly multistranded in the salivary gland nucleus) are indicated by the arrow. Comparison of the salivary chromosomes with those seen in the gonial nucleus reveals the greater wealth of detail visible in the former. (From Bridges, C. B., 1935. "Salivary Chromosome Maps," *J. Heredity,* **26,** Fig. 4, p. 62.)

present in the diploid number in the tissues in which they are found (Figure 4-16). The salivary type chromosomes are often of enormous size, having lengths which may be more than 100 times those of the corresponding somatic chromosomes at metaphase (Figure 4-17). Individual chromosomes are differentiated along their length into a series of alternating chromatic and achromatic regions of variable width which are referred to as the "bands" and "interbands," respectively (Figure 4-18). The pattern of banding, which constitutes a morphological marking system of profound cytogenetic utility, is a constant feature of any particular segment of any particular chromosome. Since certain bands can be associated with specific genes, it has been thought that the bands represent genetic loci but, so far, no cytogenetic analysis can be brought to the state of refinement necessary to exclude the possibility that genetic material may also lie in the interband regions.

Not all features of the developmental sequence of the salivary chromosomes are known with certainty. It is generally considered that the following events occur: (1) intimate synapsis of homologous chromosomes, each of which is double and longitudinally differentiated into a series of chromomeres, and (2) increase in length and in diameter. The mechanism of length increase is not known. It may involve some form of "molecular stretching" or actual growth by intussusception. Increase in diameter is quite clearly the result of replication of the component strands to a degree variably estimated to be from 500 to 16,000. The bands on this view would consist of side-by-side association of the replicated chromomeres. Not all workers agree with this *multistranded* or *polytene* hypothesis. The most common alternative hypothesis, which has several variants, proposes that there are in reality only four strands —swollen especially in the interband regions but not otherwise consisting of any more basic units than more typical chromosomes.

The salivary chromosomes of many species show local variations in the degree of condensation of the bands, some bands being discrete and sharply defined, while others appear as diffuse "puffs." Such modifications in chromosomal structure occur in different cell types and at specific times during larval growth. The formation of puffs or diffuse swellings generally occurs at single bands or interbands. Puffing is apparently not confined to a single band in the chromosome since adjacent loci may form puffs simultaneous with, or independent of, other loci (Pavan, 1958). In the salivary gland cell the chromosomes are also known to develop puffs called *Balbiani rings* which are larger than the more typical puffs formed by the giant chromosomes in nuclei of both the salivary gland and other dipteran larval tissues (Figure 4-19). According to Beermann (1956) the chromonemata running through a specific band of the salivary chromosome are spun out laterally to form a series of small loops which together form the Balbiani ring (Figure 4-20 (a) and (b)). Pavan (1958) favors the view that most puffs are the result of interaction of a specific locus of the chromosome and the nuclear environment. According to this view, the production of chromosomal material increases the diameter of the chromosome at a specific point or band and tends to spread adjacent bands apart. The band involved in puff formation reacts actively with the nuclear sap to produce the main body of the puff. The formation of puffs, particularly Balbiani rings, has been interpreted as indicating differential gene activity taking

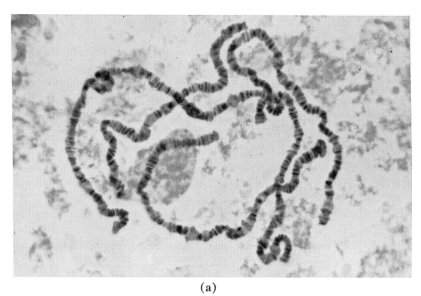

(a)

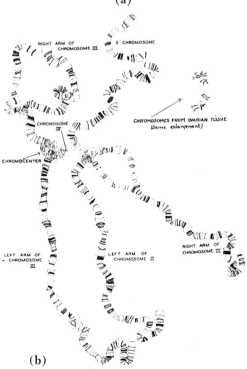

RIGHT ARM OF
CHROMOSOME III

X CHROMOSOME

CHROMOSOMES FROM OVARIAN TISSUE
(same enlargement)

CHROMOSOME
IV

CHROMOCENTER

LEFT ARM OF
CHROMOSOME
III

LEFT ARM OF
CHROMOSOME II

RIGHT ARM OF
CHROMOSOME II

(b)

Figure 4-18.     (*Contin.* on opposite page.)

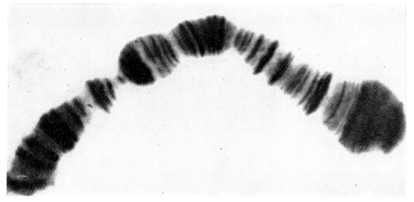

(c)

Figure 4-18. (a) Photomicrograph of Giant Polytene Chromosomes in Salivary Gland Cell of *Drosophila*. (b) Drawing of *Drosophila* Salivary Gland Giant Chromosomes and Those of the Gonial Cells on the Same Scale (upper right). Note longitudinal differentiation of the salivary gland chromosomes into a series of transverse chromatic and achromatic bands, and the incomplete pairing between homologues in the right arm of chromosome II. (c) Photomicrograph of Part of a Salivary Gland Chromosome in *Chironomus*. The pattern of the bands is particularly well shown. (Fig. (a), courtesy of General Biological Supply House, Inc., Chicago. Fig. (b), from Painter, T. S., 1934. "Salivary Chromosomes and the Attack on the Gene," *J. Heredity,* **25**, Fig. 1, p. 466. Fig. (c), from White, M. J. D., 1951. "Nucleus, Chromosomes, and Genes," *in* "Cytology and Cell Physiology," G. H. Bourne (Ed.), 2nd ed., Oxford University Press, London, England, Fig. 4, Plate 1.)

place at the chromosomal level (Beermann, 1956; Ficq, *et al.,* 1959; Pavan, 1958). This view is based largely on the finding that puff formation takes place at particular bands or interbands in different cell types at specific times during larval growth and is, for the most part, a reversible process. Also disproportionate increases in DNA are sometimes detectable in bands previously involved in puff formation (Pavan, 1958).

*Lampbrush Chromosomes.* The nuclei of many vertebrate oocytes, particularly those rich in yolk, possess chromosomes which become enormously enlarged in length and assume a brush-like appearance during meiotic prophase. This type of chromosome was first described by Flemming in 1882 and given the name "lampbrush" by Rückert in 1892.

The brush-like appearance is most obvious at the late stage of the first meiotic prophase. These chromosomes are generally described as having a central chromosomal axis from which project a series of lateral loops

**Figure 4-19.** Photomicrograph of Salivary Chromosome 4 of *Chironomus tentans* Showing One Large Balbiani Ring and Two Smaller Rings Located Near the Terminal Ends of the Chromosome. (From Beermann, W., 1959. "Chromosomal Differentiation in Insects," *in* "Developmental Cytology," D. Rudnick (Ed.), Ronald Press, New York, N.Y., Plate VI, p. 94. Courtesy of Dr. Wolfgang Beermann, Zoologisches Institut, Universität Marburg, Germany.)

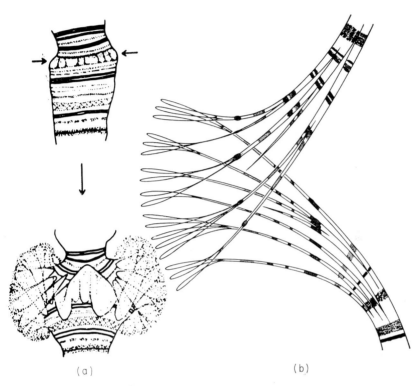

(a)                                        (b)

**Figure 4-20.** (a) Drawing Showing the Normal Banded Appearance of
a Portion of a Salivary Chromosome (above) and Its Appearance After
Formation of a Balbiani Ring (below) at the Point Marked by the Arrows.
(b) Diagrammatic Representation of Part of a Helically Wound Bundle of
Chromonemata in a Salivary Chromosome at the Location of a Fully Developed Balbiani Ring. Hypothetical loop formation of the ultimate chromonemata at the periphery is shown. (Fig. (a) from Gall, J. G., 1956. "On
the Submicroscopic Structure of Chromosomes," *Brookhaven Symp. Biol.,*
**21,** Fig. 15, p. 29. Fig. (b) from Beermann, W., 1956. "Nuclear Differentiation and Functional Morphology of Chromosomes," *Cold Spring Harbor
Symposia Quant. Biol.,* **21,** Fig. 6, p. 227; courtesy of Dr. Wolfgang Beermann, Zoologisches Institut, Universität Marburg, Germany.)

(Figure 4-21). The axis usually appears optically single but there is some evidence that it is at least double. The loops appear to project out from dense regions which are comparable to the chromomeres of other meiotic prophase chromosomes (Figure 4-22). Only the kinetochore, which resembles an enlarged chromomere morphologically, bears no lateral projections. The loops appear to be continuous with the central axis, that is, the axis itself forms the loops (Gall, 1958; Ris, 1957).

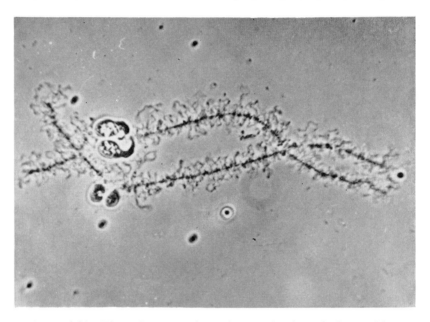

**Figure 4-21.** Phase-Contrast Photomicrograph of a Bivalent With Homologous Lampbrush Chromosomes Joined by Two Chiasmata in 1st Meiotic Prophase of the Newt, *Triturus cristatus carnifex*. Note the numerous lateral loops associated with the central chromosomal axis of each lampbrush chromosome. (Courtesy of Dr. H. G. Callan, The University, St. Andrews, Scotland.)

The lampbrush chromosomes at maximum development are even longer than the longest salivary gland chromosome, but unlike the latter they are no greater in number of strands than more typical chromosomes. The brush-like characteristic, as noted, reaches maximum development in the late prophase of the first meiotic division (diplotene) and thereafter the chromosomes begin to revert to a more typical aspect, until by first metaphase they are quite usual in appearance. While the lateral loops have been shown to contain both protein and RNA, their exact

function is not known (Gall, 1958; Ris, 1957). Loop formation is interpreted by Gall (1958) as a reversible physiological change which is
probably nongenetic. However, he points out that loops exhibit variations in their morphology which suggests that perhaps each loop, or
loop pair, represents a different genetic locus responsible for the formation of some particular cell product.

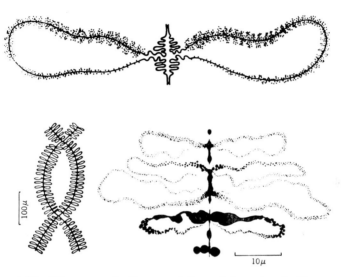

Figure 4-22. Diagrammatic Representation of Lampbrush Chromosome
Structure. Top, enlargement of portion of single chromosome showing chromonemata and chromomere with attached lateral loops. Bottom left, a
bivalent with homologous chromosomes joined by two chiasmata, and
showing paired lateral loops. Bottom right, enlargement of section of single
chromosome illustrating the variation in morphology of the chromomeres
and loops. (From Gall, J. G., 1956. "On the Submicroscopic Structure of
Chromosomes," *Brookhaven Symp. Biol.*, **21**, Fig. 7, p. 22, and Fig. 1, p. 18.)

## SOME BIOCHEMICAL CONSIDERATIONS

As already mentioned, the nucleus contains four major chemical
constituents: (1) DNA, (2) RNA, (3) proteins, and (4) lipids.

### DNA

Of the chemical constituents of the nucleus, DNA has been the most
extensively studied in terms of its molecular organization, localization,
and function within the nucleus. Biochemical studies have established
that the amount of DNA per somatic nucleus is approximately the same

in various tissues of the same organism and is twice that found in the nucleus of the haploid sperm cell (Boivin, *et al.*, 1948; Mirsky and Ris, 1949). Furthermore, cytophotometric measurements made on individual Feulgen-stained nuclei have shown that the amount of nuclear DNA is directly proportional to the number of chromosomes in the nucleus of any given cell of the organism (Swift, 1953). Somatic interphase nuclei with DNA content approximately two or four times the more common diploid amount, are encountered in tissues such as liver where polyploidy is known to occur (Pollister, 1952). Variations in the quantity of DNA would also be expected to occur, particularly in differentiated tissues, as a consequence of polyteny. Cytophotometric studies have also indicated that the amount of nuclear DNA is the same at the late interphase (following DNA synthesis preparatory to cell division) and metaphase stages of the mitotic cycle (Swift, 1953). Present evidence suggests that in many cells the quantity of DNA is doubled at a specific time during the interphase (Howard and Pelc, 1951; Walker and Yates, 1952), but replication of DNA may occur in some cells as early as the previous telophase (Brachet, 1957) or as late as prophase (Moses and Taylor, 1955). In brief, the diploid telophase nucleus in somatic mitosis contains half the DNA content (2C value) of the subsequent prophase (4C) and twice the amount of DNA present in the haploid (C) sperm nucleus of the same species.

The finding that the amount of nuclear DNA was related to ploidy and was doubled during the mitotic process, has led to the belief that DNA is a relatively stable and more or less metabolically "inert" component of the cell nucleus. In support of this view is the negligible rate of incorporation of radioactive phosphorus into the DNA of nondividing cells (Ris, 1957). There are, however, a number of observations which suggest that the DNA of the nucleus is not quite so stable and metabolically inert as was once believed. For example, disproportionate increases in DNA content of specific bands of giant dipteran chromosomes have been demonstrated (Ficq, *et al.*, 1959; Pavan, 1958; Rudkin and Corlette, 1957; Stich and Naylor, 1958). These studies, especially those in which uptake of DNA precursors was followed, suggest that there is a fraction of the DNA which shows a high turnover as well as a fraction which is relatively stable (Figure 4-23). Further evidence comes from the fact that a small but detectable uptake of isotopically labeled DNA precursors occurs in some nondividing cells (Koenig, 1958; Pelc, 1959). Also it has been shown that fractions of DNA isolated from different tissues differ in chemical composition and metabolic activity (Bendich, *et al.,* 1956). That the amount of DNA per nucleus may be affected by changes in metabolic activity is suggested by several studies in which it has been shown that reduction occurs in root tip cells following exposure to low temperatures (Chayen, 1959; Evans, 1956; Heyes and Shaw, 1958; LaCour, *et al.,* 1956). There is no evidence of a similar relationship in animal cells nor in bacteria (Allfrey, *et al.,* 1955; Evans, 1956). It should be noted in passing that the phrase "constant amount

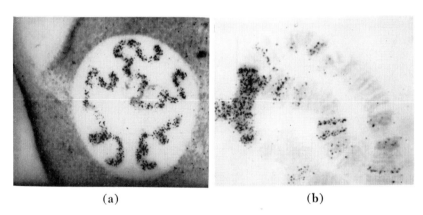

(a)                                             (b)

**Figure 4-23.** (a) Autoradiograph of Nucleus of a Cell from Intestinal Wall of Fully Grown Larva of *Rhynchosciara angelae,* Injected with Tritiated Thymidine 24 Hours Prior to Fixation. Film developed after seven days' exposure to the radiation from the chromosomes. The entire set of chromosomes (A, B, C, and X) is clearly shown. (b) Autoradiograph of Salivary Chromosome from Intestinal Wall Cell of a Larva of *R. angelae,* showing incorporation of tritiated thymidine only in specific regions of the chromosome, mainly in the heterochromatic chromocenter and a few of the euchromatic bands. (Fig. (a) from Ficq, A. and Pavan, C., unpublished results. Fig. (b), from Pavan, C., 1958. "Morphological and Physiological Aspects of Chromosomal Activities," *Proc. X. Intern. Congress Genetics,* **1**, Fig. 2, p. 324; courtesy of Dr. C. Pavan, Universidade de São Paulo, São Paulo, Brazil.)

of DNA" is by no means an absolute since the recorded variations between cells appear to be considerably greater than can be accounted for either by random errors in measurement or changes in chromosome number.

The results of short-term labeling of plant cells with tritiated thymidine (Figure 4-24 (a) and (b)) by Taylor, *et al.* (1957), indicate that chromosomal DNA replicates as if it were a double-stranded macromolecule of the type originally proposed for DNA by Watson and Crick

(1953). Essentially what these workers found was that by exposing cells in interphase to tritiated thymidine for short intervals, it was possible to obtain chromosomes at metaphase which had both of their daughter chromatids labeled. By allowing such cells to go through a second division in the absence of the label, it was discovered that when they again reached metaphase the chromosomes had only one of their chromatids

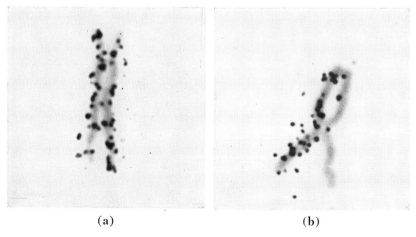

(a)                                                    (b)

**Figure 4-24.** (a) Autoradiograph of Chromosomes of *Vicia faba* at the First Mitotic Division After Duplication in the Presence of Tritiated Thymidine. The isotope is equally distributed between both chromatids (daughter chromosomes). (b) Autoradiograph of Chromosomes of *V. faba* at the Second Mitotic Division After Labeling by One Duplication with Tritiated Thymidine. The isotope is confined to only one daughter chromosome of each sister pair. (From Woods, P. S. and Schairer, M. V., 1959. "Distribution of Newly Synthesized Deoxyribonucleic Acid in Dividing Chromosomes," *Nature,* 183, Fig. 1, p. 303. Courtesy of Dr. Philip S. Woods, Brookhaven National Laboratory.)

labeled. The results of this study are diagrammed in Figure 4-25. The sequence begins with two complementary nonlabeled strands in a chromosome, each of which separates and forms a complementary labeled strand along its length in the presence of tritiated thymidine. In the subsequent metaphase, each chromosome will consist of two chromatids, both of which carry a labeled and a nonlabeled strand. Following replication during the next interphase in the absence of the labeled thymidine, each chromosome at metaphase will show a nonlabeled and a labeled chromatid. If a third replication occurs, only one half of the chromosomes at the subsequent metaphase will contain a labeled chromatid (Hughes, 1958). Studies using tritiated thymidine as a means of following DNA metabolism during chromosome replication indicate that this label is built into the DNA of the chromosome as a part of a physical entity that remains intact during succeeding replications (Hughes, 1958). The interphase chromosome before replication would be composed of two such entities which are probably complementary to each other. After replication of each entity to give a chromosome with four entities, the whole chromosome then divides so that by metaphase, each chromatid or daughter chromosome regularly receives an "original" and a "new" entity. Whether or not the two physical entities of the interphase

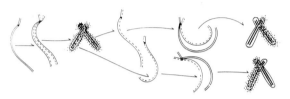

**Figure 4-25.** Diagrammatic Representation of the Structural Organization and Mode of Replication of the Chromosome as Revealed by Labeling with Tritiated Thymidine. The nonlabeled DNA subunits are shown as solid lines, while the labeled subunits appear as dashed lines. The dots represent grains as seen in the autoradiographs. (From Taylor, J. H., Woods, P. S., and Hughes, W. L., 1957. "The Organization and Duplication of Chromosomes as Revealed by Autoradiographic Studies Using Tritium-labeled Thymidine," *Proc. Natl. Acad. Sci.,* **43**, Fig. 3, p. 125.)

chromosome associated with the uptake of tritiated thymidine represent the chromonemata is not known.

While the evidence is fairly good that the major role of DNA is genetic, studies of protein synthesis in isolated nuclei have suggested another possible function, namely, as a cofactor in the nuclear aerobic synthesis of ATP. Allfrey and Mirsky (1959) have shown that when a large fraction of the DNA is removed from isolated nuclei there is a loss of capacity for ATP synthesis, amino acid incorporation, and for RNA synthesis. This loss can be reversed by addition of DNA from almost any source, RNA, polyadenylic acid, and a number of nonnucleotides such as heparin and chondroitin sulfate. These results have been explained on the basis that DNA facilitates ATP synthesis which, in turn, is necessary for production of RNA and protein in the nucleus.

## RNA

The early work of Brachet (1941) and Caspersson (1941) clearly demonstrated that RNA is a universal constituent of all living cells and that the nucleus, particularly the nucleolus, contains appreciable amounts. RNA is also a component of the chromosomes, and in the case of rat liver constitutes as much as 12 per cent of their total nucleic acid (Allfrey, *et al.*, 1955).

As previously indicated, sites of protein synthesis are rich in RNA, notably nucleolus and cytoplasm. Since increase in protein frequently

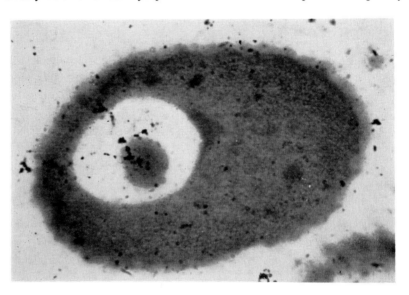

**Figure 4-26.** Autoradiograph Showing Active Incorporation of Adenine —8—C¹⁴ by the Nucleolus of the Starfish Oocyte. (Courtesy of Dr. A. Ficq, Université Libre de Bruxelles.)

accompanies cellular growth, a concomitant increase in nucleolar size might be expected. This relationship appears to hold for nerve cells, growing oocytes, proliferating normal and malignant cells, and for many secretory cells. Further, the nucleolus is reduced in volume in cells of animals fed on low or nonprotein diets. Also cells of the pancreas or gastric mucosa, which are synthesizing large amounts of enzyme protein, have nucleoli which possess a high content of RNA.

Whether nucleolar RNA is synthesized in the nucleolus itself, or elsewhere and then transported to this structure to be bound to protein, is still something of an open question. There is no doubt from autoradiographic studies that labeled RNA precursors appear very rapidly in the nucleolus (Figure 4-26) and prior to their appearance in cytoplasmic RNA. While this suggests that the nucleolus is a site of RNA synthesis, recent studies suggest that such synthesis may be initiated at the surface of the chromosomes with subsequently rapid transfer to either the nucleolus or the cytoplasm (Goldstein and Micou, 1959; Taylor and Woods, 1959).

The fate of nucleolar RNA is somewhat obscure as is its relationship to that of the cytoplasmic RNA. Some studies, however, have indicated that nuclear, and possibly nucleolar, RNA is transported to the cytoplasm presumably across the nuclear boundary (Goldstein and Plaut, 1955; Ficq, 1955; Zalokar, 1959). This idea is at least in accord with the proposed mechanism of transfer of genetic information via an RNA intermediate from the chromosome to cytoplasmic sites of action. Recent labeling and enucleation studies of Prescott (1960) indicate that the cytoplasm may be completely dependent on the nucleus for RNA synthesis.

### Proteins

The nucleus, like the cytoplasm, shows capacity for synthesis of protein. The kinds of proteins produced as well as the sites of production are somewhat controversial topics. Some workers, notably Brachet (1957), have provided what seems to be sound evidence for involvement of the nucleolus, but other work on other kinds of cells indicates that there is little incorporation of labeled protein precursors into this nuclear body (Carneiro and Leblond, 1959). Even Brachet's studies, as he himself has pointed out, may be interpreted as indirect rather than direct involvement of the nucleolus in nuclear protein synthesis. Carneiro and Leblond (1959) have shown that labeled precursors of protein are actively taken up in somatic cells of adult mice only by the chromosomes and cytoplasm and that there is extensive and rapid turnover in both sites. This suggests, but scarcely proves, that the chromosomes themselves represent the major sites of protein synthesis in the nucleus.

It has been known since the days of Kossel and Meischer that the cell nucleus contains basic protein complexed with nucleic acid. Modern chemistry tends to classify basic proteins into two groups: (a) the *histones,* and (b) the *protamines.* The distinction between these two is not always clear-cut. In general, the former are more complex and have a higher molecular weight than the latter, which are found only in sperm nuclei. Both are rich in basic amino acids such as arginine and lysine and contain a smaller variety of amino acids than other types of proteins such as the globulins and albumins.

The basic proteins of the nucleus vary with the cell type and under different physiological conditions. For example, in the salmon the nuclei of both somatic and developing germ cells contain histones, while those of the mature sperm cell in the same animal contain only protamine. Whether this change is a conversion or a replacement process remains to be determined.

The electrochemical properties of DNA are such that it would be expected to complex with both acid and basic proteins. Since both types of proteins occur in the nucleus, it is somewhat surprising to find that in some cases the ratio of DNA to basic protein approaches unity. There is also fairly good correspondence between replication of basic protein and DNA (Bloch and Godman, 1955).

Acid, or at least tryptophane-containing proteins, have been demonstrated in the nucleus, especially by Stedman and Stedman (1947) and Mirsky and Ris (1947). The latter workers digested chromosomes isolated from interphase nuclei and found that about 90 per cent of the mass was accounted for by DNA and histone, with the remaining 10 per cent persisting as a coiled nucleoprotein thread made up largely of a tryptophane-containing protein, 2 to 3 per cent DNA and 12 to 14 per cent RNA. It has been suggested that this thread constitutes the "backbone" or structural framework of the intact chromosome. The amount of protein contained in these residual threads apparently differs greatly between nuclei in different tissues of the same animal. For example, in calf thymus chromosomes it constitutes some 8 per cent, while in calf liver chromosomes the amount is as high as 39 per cent. Use of suitable radioactive isotopes has indicated that the turnover of nuclear protein is greatest in nondividing, metabolically active cells. This turnover seems to be lower in the histones than in other proteins of the nucleus (Allfrey, *et al.,* 1955).

In addition to the proteins mentioned above, the nucleus also contains globulin protein which, in certain cases such as calf liver nuclei, may be present to the extent of some 40 per cent (Dounce, 1955). The nuclear location and functional significance of this protein have not been determined.

## Lipids

The nucleus contains significant amounts of lipid and in some cases may account for as much as 40 per cent of the dry weight of the nucleus. Phospholipids, in particular, have been shown to be present in the nucleolus and to some extent in the chromatin (Serra, 1955). Most nuclear lipids are probably combined with protein as lipoprotein and perhaps also with RNA. In any event, nucleohistone isolated from calf thymus has been reported to contain relatively large amounts of bound phospholipid (Chayen, *et al.*, 1959).

## BIBLIOGRAPHY

Alfert, M., 1954. "Composition and Structure of Giant Chromosomes," *Intern. Rev. Cytol.,* 3, 131-169.

Alfert, M., 1957. "Some Cytochemical Contributions to Genetic Chemistry," *in* "Chemical Basis of Heredity," W. D. McElroy and B. Glass (Eds.), Johns Hopkins University Press, Baltimore, Md., pp. 186-199.

Allfrey, V. and Mirsky, A. E., 1959. "Biochemical Properties of the Isolated Nucleus," *in* "Subcellular Particles," T. Hayashi (Ed.), Ronald Press, New York, N.Y., pp. 186-207.

Allfrey, V., Mirsky, A. E., and Osawa, S., 1957. "The Nucleus and Protein Synthesis," *in* "Chemical Basis of Heredity," W. D. McElroy and B. Glass (Eds.), Johns Hopkins University Press, Baltimore, Md., pp. 200-231.

Allfrey, V., Mirsky, A. E., and Stern, H., 1955. "The Chemistry of the Cell Nucleus," *Adv. Enzymol.,* 16, 411-500.

Anderson, N. G. and Wilbur, K. M., 1952. "Studies on Isolated Cell Components. IV. The Effect of Various Solutions on the Isolated Rat Liver Nucleus," *J. Gen. Physiol.,* 35, 781-796.

Baker, J. R. and Callan, H. G., 1950. "Heterochromatin," *Nature,* 166, 227-228.

Balbiani, E. G., 1881. "Sur la structure du noyau des cellules salivaires chez les larves de *Chironomus*," *Zool. Anz.,* 4, 367-641.

Baltus, E., 1954. "Observations sur le rôle biochimique du nucléole," *Biochim. et Biophys. Acta.,* 15, 263-267.

Barer, R., Joseph, S., and Meek, G. A., 1959. "The Origin of the Nuclear Membrane," *Exptl. Cell Res.,* 18, 179-182.

Barigozzi, C., 1950. "A General Survey on Heterochromatin," *Portugaliae Acta Biol. (Sér. A),* R. B. Goldschmidt Vol., 593-620.

Barnes, B. G. and Davis, J. M., 1959. "The Structure of Nuclear Pores in Mammalian Tissue," *J. Ultrastructure Res.,* 3, 131-146.

Beermann, W., 1956. "Nuclear Differentiation and Functional Morphology of Chromosomes," *Cold Spring Harbor Symposia Quant. Biol.,* 21, 217-232.

Beermann, W., 1959. "Chromosomal Differentiation in Insects," *in* "Developmental Cytology," D. Rudnick (Ed.), Ronald Press, New York, N.Y., pp. 83-103.

Beermann, W. and Bahr, G. F., 1954. "The Submicroscopic Structure of the Balbiani Ring," *Exptl. Cell Res.,* 6, 195-201.

Belling, J., 1928. "The Ultimate Chromomeres of *Lilium* and *Aloe* with Regard to the Number of Genes," *Univ. Calif. Publ. Botany,* 14, 307-318.

Bendich, A., Pahl, H. B., and Beiser, S. M., 1956. "Chromatographic Fractionation of Deoxyribonucleic Acids with Special Emphasis on the Transforming Factor of *Pneumococcus,*" *Cold Spring Harbor Symposia Quant. Biol.,* **21**, 31-48.

Bernhard, W. F., Haguenau, F., and Oberling, C., 1952. "The Ultrastructure of the Nucleolus of Some Animal Cells Disclosed by the Electron Microscope," *Experientia,* **8**, 58-59.

Bloch, D. P. and Godman, G. C., 1955. "A Microphotometric Study of the Synthesis of Desoxyribonucleic Acid and Nuclear Histone," *J. Biophys. Biochem. Cytol.,* **1**, 17-28.

Bloch, D. P. and Godman, G. C., 1955. "Evidences of Differences in the Desoxyribonucleoprotein Complex of Rapidly Proliferating and Non-dividing Cells," *J. Biophys. Biochem. Cytol.,* **1**, 531-550.

Boivin, A. R., Vendrely, R., and Vendrely, C., 1948. "L'acide désoxyribonucléique du noyau cellulaire, dépositaire des caractères héréditaires: Arguments d'ordre analytique," *C. rend. Acad. Sci.,* **226**, 1061-1063.

Brachet, J., 1941. "La localisation des acides pentosenucleiques dans les tissus animaux et les oeufs d'amphibiens en voie de developpement," *Arch. Biol.,* **53**, 207-257.

Brachet, J., 1952. "The Role of the Nucleus and Cytoplasm in Synthesis and Morphogenesis," *Symp. Soc. Exptl. Biol.,* **6**, 173-200.

Brachet, J., 1957. "Biochemical Cytology," Academic Press, New York, N.Y.

Breuer, M. E. and Pavan, C., 1955. "Behavior of Polytene Chromosomes of *Rhynchosciara angelae* at Different Stages of Larval Development," *Chromosoma,* **7**, 371-386.

Bridges, C. B., 1935. "Salivary Chromosome Maps," *J. Hered.,* **26**, 60-64.

Callan, H. G., 1942. "Heterochromatin in Triton," *Proc. Roy. Soc. London, B,* **130**, 324-335.

Carneiro, J. and Leblond, C. P., 1959. "Continuous Protein Synthesis in Nuclei, Shown by Radioautography with H³-labeled Amino Acids," *Science,* **129**, 391-392.

Caspersson, T. O., 1941. "Studien uber den Eiweissumsatz der Zelle," *Naturwissenschaften,* **28**, 33-43.

Caspersson, T. O., 1950. "Cell Growth and Cell Function," W. W. Norton & Co., Inc., New York, N.Y.

Caspersson, T. O., 1956. "Quantitative Cytochemical Determinations on Endonuclear Structures," *Cold Spring Harbor Symposia Quant. Biol.,* **21**, 1-18.

Chayen, J., 1959. "The Quantitative Cytochemistry of DNA and Its Significance in Cell Physiology and Heredity," *Exptl. Cell Res., Suppl.,* **6**, 115-131.

Chayen, J., Gahan, P. B., and LaCour, L. F., 1959. "The Nature of a Chromosomal Phospholipid," *Quart. J. Microscop. Sci.,* **100**, 279-284.

Chayen, J., Gahan, P. B., and LaCour, L. F., 1959. "Masked Lipids of Nuclei," *Quart. J. Microscop. Sci.,* **100**, 325-337.

Clark, W. H., Jr., 1960. "Electron Microscope Studies of Nuclear Extrusions in Pancreatic Acinar Cells of the Rat," *J. Biophys. Biochem. Cytol.,* **7**, 345-352.

Cooper, K. W., 1938. "Concerning the Origin of Polytene Chromosomes," *Proc. Natl. Acad. Sci.,* **24**, 452-458.

Cooper, K. W., 1959. "Cytogenetic Analysis of Major Heterochromatic Elements (Especially Xh and Y) in *Drosophila melanogaster*, and the Theory of 'Heterochromatin,' " *Chromosoma*, **10**, 535-588.

Crick, F. H. C., 1957. "The Structure of DNA," *in* "Chemical Basis of Heredity," W. D. McElroy and B. Glass (Eds.), Johns Hopkins University Press, Baltimore, Md., pp. 532-539.

Daly, M. M., Mirsky, A. E., and Ris, H., 1951. "The Amino Acid Composition and Some Properties of Histones," *J. Gen. Physiol.*, **34**, 439-450.

Darlington, C. D., 1937. "Recent Advances in Cytology," 2nd ed., Blakiston, Philadelphia, Pa.

Darlington, C. D., 1947. "Nucleic Acids and the Chromosomes," *Symp. Soc. Exptl. Biol.*, **1**, 252-269.

Darlington, C. D. and LaCour, L. F., 1940. "Nucleic Acid Starvation of Chromosomes in *Trillium*," *J. Genetics*, **40**, 185-213.

Deeley, E. M., Davies, H. G., and Chayen, J., 1957. "The DNA Content of Cells in the Root of *Vicia faba*," *Exptl. Cell Res.*, **12**, 582-591.

Dounce, A. L., 1955. "The Isolation and Composition of Cell Nuclei and Nucleoli," *in* "The Nucleic Acids," Vol. 2, E. Chargaff and J. N. Davidson (Eds.), Academic Press, New York, N.Y., pp. 93-153.

Duryee, W. R., 1938. "A Microdissection Study of Amphibian Chromosomes," *Biol. Bull.*, **75**, 345.

Duryee, W. R., 1941. "The Chromosomes in the Amphibian Nucleus," *in* "Cytology, Genetics, and Evolution," University of Pennsylvania Press, Philadelphia, Pa., pp. 129-142.

Duryee, W. R. and Doherty, J. K., 1954. "Nuclear and Cytoplasmic Organoids in the Living Cell," *Ann. N.Y. Acad. Sci.*, **58**, 1210-1230.

Ehrenburg, L., 1946. "Influence of Temperature on the Nucleolus and Its Coacervate Nature," *Hereditas*, **32**, 407-418.

Estable, C., and Sotelo, J. R., 1952. "Technical Procedures for the Study of the Nucleoloneme," *Stain Technol.*, **27**, 307-312.

Evans, W. L., 1956. "The Effect of Cold Treatment on the Desoxyribonucleic Acid (DNA) Content in Cells of Selected Plants and Animals," *Cytologia*, **21**, 417-432.

Ficq, A., 1955. "Étude autoradiographique du métabolisme de l'oocyte d'Asterias rubiens au cours de las croissance," *Arch. Biol.*, **66**, 509-524.

Ficq, A. and Pavan, C., 1957. "Autoradiography of Polytene Chromosomes of *Rhynchosciara angelae* at Different Stages of Larval Development," *Nature*, **180**, 983-984.

Ficq, A., Pavan, C., and Brachet, J., 1959. "Metabolic Processes in Chromosomes," *Exptl. Cell Res., Suppl.*, **6**, 105-114.

Flemming, W., 1882. "Zellsubstanz, Kern, und Zellteilung," Vogel, Leipzig.

Frey-Wyssling, A., 1953. "Submicroscopic Morphology of Protoplasm," Elsevier, Amsterdam.

Gall, J. G., 1952. "The Lampbrush Chromosomes of *Triturus viridescens*," *Exptl. Cell Res., Suppl.*, **2**, 95-102.

Gall, J. G., 1954. "Lampbrush Chromosomes from Oocyte Nuclei of the Newt," *J. Morphol.*, **94**, 283-352.

Gall, J. G., 1958. "Chromosomal Differentiation," *in* "Chemical Basis of Development," W. D. McElroy and B. Glass (Eds.), Johns Hopkins University Press, Baltimore, Md., pp. 103-135.

Gates, R. R., 1942. "Nucleoli and Related Nuclear Structures," *Botan. Rev.,* 8, 337-409.

Gay, H., 1956. "Nucleocytoplasmic Relations in *Drosophila,*" *Cold Spring Harbor Symposia Quant. Biol.,* 21, 257-269.

Gay, H., 1956. "Chromosome-Nuclear Membrane-Cytoplasmic Interrelations in *Drosophila,*" *J. Biophys. Biochem. Cytol.,* 2, 407-414.

Giles, R. A. and Wilson, G. B., 1956. "A Cytological and Morphological Study of Two Populations of *Trillium grandiflorum* (Michx.) Salisb.," *Cytologia,* 21, 376-383.

Goldstein, L. and Plaut, W., 1955. "Direct Evidence for Nuclear Synthesis of Cytoplasmic Ribose Nucleic Acid," *Proc. Natl. Acad. Sci.,* 41, 874-880.

Goldstein, L. and Micou, J., 1959. "On the Primary Site of Nuclear RNA Synthesis," *J. Biophys. Biochem. Cytol.,* 6, 301-303.

Haguenau, F. and Bernhard, W., 1955. "Particularities structurales de la membrane nucléaire," *Bull. du Cancer,* 42, 537-544.

Hannah, A., 1951. "Localization and Function of Heterochromatin in *Drosophila melanogaster,*" *Adv. Genetics,* 4, 87-125.

Heitz, E. and Bauer, H., 1933. "Beweise für die chromosomen struktur der Kernschliefen in den Knäuelkernen von *Bibio hortulanus* L. (Cytologische Undersuchungen an Dipteran, I.)," *Zeit. für Zellforsch. und Mikr. Anat.,* 17, 67-82.

Hertwig, O., 1894. "Allgemeine Biologie," 2nd ed., 1906, Gustav Fischer Verlagsbuch-handlung, Jena.

Heyes, J. K. and Shaw, G. W., 1958. "Chemical Determination of Deoxyribonucleic Acid in Root Tips Before and After Cold Treatment," *Nature,* 181, 1337-1338.

Howard, A. and Pelc, S. R., 1951. "Nuclear Incorporation of P[32] as Demonstrated by Autoradiographs," *Exptl. Cell Res.,* 2, 178-187.

Hughes, W. L., 1958. "Chromosomal Replication and the Dynamics of Cellular Proliferation—Some Autoradiographic Observations with Tritiated Thymidine," *in* "The Chemical Basis of Development," W. D. McElroy and B. Glass (Eds.), Johns Hopkins University Press, Baltimore, Md., pp. 136-156.

Kaufmann, B., 1938. "Nucleolus-organizing Regions in Salivary Gland Chromosomes of *Drosophila melanogaster,*" *Zeits. für Zellforsch. und Mikr. Anat.,* 28, 1-11.

Kaufmann, B., 1948. "Chromosome Structure in Relation to the Chromosome Cycle," *Botan. Rev.,* 14, 57-126.

Koenig, H., 1958. "Uptake of Adenine-8-C[14] and Arotic-6-C[14] Acid into Nuclear DNA of Non-dividing Cells in the Adult Feline Neuroxis," *J. Biophys. Biochem. Cytol.,* 4, 664-666.

Kostoff, D., 1930. "Discoid Structure of the Spireme and Irregular Cell Division in *Drosophila melanogaster,*" *J. Hered.,* 21, 323-324.

LaCour, L. F., Deeley, E. M., and Chayen, J., 1956. "Variations in the Amount of Feulgen Stain in Nuclei of Plants Grown at Different Temperatures," *Nature,* **177,** 272-273.

Leak, L. V. and Wilson, G. B., 1960. "Relative Volume Changes of the Nucleolus in Relation to Cell and Nucleus in *Pisum sativum* and *Tradescantia paludosa,*" *Trans. Am. Microsp. Soc.,* **78,** 154-160.

Leuchtenberger, C. and Schrader, F., 1952. "Variations in the Amounts of Desoxyribose Nucleic Acid (DNA) in Cells of the Same Tissues and Its Correlation with Secretory Function," *Proc. Natl. Acad. Sci.,* **38,** 99-105.

Longley, A. E., 1927. "Supernumerary Chromosomes in *Zea mays,*" *J. Agric. Res.,* **35,** 769-784.

Mazia, D. and Prescott, D. M., 1955. "The Role of the Nucleus in Protein Synthesis in *Amoeba,*" *Biochim. Biophys. Acta.,* **17,** 23-34.

McClintock, B., 1934. "The Relation of a Particular Chromosomal Element in the Development of the Nucleoli in *Zea mays,*" *Zeits. für Zellforsch. und Mikr. Anat.,* **21,** 294-328.

McMaster-Kaye, R. and Taylor, J. H., 1958. "Evidence for Two Metabolically Distinct Types of Ribonucleic Acid in Chromatin and Nucleoli," *J. Biophys. Biochem. Cytol.,* **4,** 5-11.

Miescher, F., 1897. "Die Histochemischen und Physiologischen," Arbeiten, Leipzig.

Mirsky, A. E., 1947. "Chemical Properties of Isolated Chromosomes," *Cold Spring Harbor Symposia Quant. Biol.,* **12,** 143-146.

Mirsky, A. E. and Allfrey, V., 1958. "The Role of the Nucleus in Development," *in* "Chemical Basis of Development," W. D. McElroy and B. Glass (Eds.), Johns Hopkins University Press, Baltimore, Md., pp. 94-102.

Mirsky, A. E. and Ris, H., 1947. "Isolated Chromosomes. The Chemical Composition of Isolated Chromosomes," *J. Gen. Physiol.,* **31,** 1-18.

Mirsky, A. E. and Ris, H., 1949. "Variable and Constant Components of Chromosomes," *Nature,* **163,** 666-667.

Mirsky, A. E. and Ris, H., 1951. "The Composition and Structure of Isolated Chromosomes," *J. Gen. Physiol.,* **34,** 475-492.

Monty, K. J., Litt., M., Kay, E. R. M., and Dounce, A. L., 1956. "Isolation and Properties of Liver Cell Nucleoli," *J. Biophys. Biochem. Cytol.,* **2,** 127-146.

Moses, M. J. and Taylor, J. H., 1955. "Desoxypentose Nucleic Acid Synthesis During Microsporogenesis in *Tradescantia,*" *Exptl. Cell Res.,* **9,** 474-488.

Östergren, G., 1947. "Heterochromatic B-chromosomes in Anthoxanthum," *Hereditas,* **33,** 261-296.

Painter, T. S., 1933. "A New Method for the Study of Chromosome Rearrangements and the Plotting of Chromosome Maps," *Science,* **78,** 585-586.

Painter, T. S., 1939. "The Structure of Salivary Gland Chromosomes," *Am. Naturalist,* **75,** 315-330.

Painter, T. S., 1941. "An Experimental Study of Salivary Chromosomes," *Cold Spring Harbor Symposia Quant. Biol.,* **9,** 47-54.

Pavan, C., 1958. "Morphological and Physiological Aspects of Chromosomal Activities," *Proc. X Intern. Congress Genetics*, Montreal, Canada, pp. 321-336.

Pelc, S. R., 1959. "The Participation of the Cell Nucleus and Its DNA in the Formation of Keratin," *Exptl. Cell Res., Suppl.,* **6,** 97-104.

Pelc, S. R. and Howard, A., 1952. "Chromosome Metabolism as Shown by Autoradiographs," *Exptl. Cell Res., Suppl.,* **2,** 269-278.

Plaut, W., 1959. "The Nucleus and Ribonucleic Acid Synthesis in *Amoeba proteus,*" *Exptl. Cell Res., Suppl.,* **6,** 69-77.

Pollister, A. W., 1952. "Nucleoproteins of the Nucleus," *Exptl. Cell Res., Suppl.* **2,** 59-74.

Pollister, A. W. and Leuchtenberger, C., 1949. "Nucleotide Content of the Nucleolus," *Nature,* **163,** 360-361.

Pontecorvo, G., 1944. "Structure of Heterochromatin," *Nature,* **153,** 365-367.

Porter, K. R. and Machado, R. D., 1960. "Studies on the Endoplasmic Reticulum. IV. Its Form and Distribution During Mitosis in Cells of Onion Root Tips," *J. Biophys. Biochem. Cytol.,* **7,** 167-180.

Prescott, D. M., 1957. "The Nucleus and Ribonucleic Acid Synthesis in *Amoeba,*" *Exptl. Cell Res.,* **12,** 196-198.

Prescott, D. M., 1959. "Nuclear Synthesis of Cytoplasmic RNA in *Amoeba proteus,*" *J. Biophys. Biochem. Cytol.,* **6,** 203-206.

Prescott, D. M., 1960. "The Nuclear Dependence of RNA Synthesis in *Acanthamoeba* Sp.," *Exptl. Cell Res.,* **19,** 29-34.

Ris, H., 1945. "The Structure of Meiotic Chromosomes in the Grasshopper and Its Bearing on the Nature of 'Chromomeres' and 'Lamp-brush Chromosomes,' " *Biol. Bull.,* **89,** 242-257.

Ris, H., 1957. "Chromosome Structure," *in* "Chemical Basis of Heredity," W. D. McElroy and B. Glass (Eds.), Johns Hopkins University Press, Baltimore, Md., pp. 23-69.

Ris, H. and Mirsky, A. E., 1949. "The State of the Chromosomes in the Interphase Nucleus," *J. Gen. Physiol.,* **32,** 488-502.

Rückert, J. von, 1892. "Zur Entwicklungsgeschichte des Ovarialeies bei Selachiern," *Anat. Anz.,* **7,** 107-158.

Rudkin, G. T. and Corlette, S. L., 1957. "Disproportionate Synthesis of DNA in a Polytene Chromosome Region," *Proc. Natl. Acad. Sci.,* **43,** 964-968.

Schultz, J., 1947. "The Nature of Heterochromatin," *Cold Spring Harbor Symposia Quant. Biol.,* **12,** 179-191.

Schultz, J., 1952. "Interrelations Between Nucleus and Cytoplasm. Problems at the Biological Level," *Exptl. Cell Res., Suppl.,* **2,** 17-43.

Serra, J. A., 1955. "Chemistry of the Nucleus," *Handbuch der Pflanzenphysiologie,* **1,** 413-444.

Sinnott, E. W., Dunn, L. C., and Dobzhansky, T., 1958. "The Principles of Genetics," 5th ed., McGraw-Hill Book Co., New York, N.Y.

Sparrow, A. H., Pond, V., and Sparrow, R. C., 1952. "Distribution and Behavior of Supernumerary Chromosomes During Microsporogenesis in a Population of *Trillium erectum* L.," *Am. Naturalist,* **86,** 277-292.

Stedman, E. and Stedman, E., 1947. "The Chemical Nature and Functions of the Components of Cell Nuclei," *Cold Spring Harbor Symposia Quant. Biol.*, 12, 244-256.

Stenram, U., 1953. "The Nucleolar Size in the Liver Cell of Rats Fed High and Nonprotein Diets," *Exptl. Cell Res.*, 5, 539-541.

Stich, H. F. and Naylor, J. M., 1958. "Variation of Desoxyribonucleic Acid Content of Specific Chromosome Regions," *Exptl. Cell Res.*, 14, 442-445.

Swift, H., 1950. "The Desoxyribose Nucleic Acid Content of Animal Nuclei," *Physiol. Zool.*, 23, 169-198.

Swift, H., 1953. "Quantitative Aspects of Nuclear Nucleoproteins," *Intern. Rev. Cytol.*, 2, 1-76.

Swift, H., 1958. "Cytoplasmic Particulates and Basophilia," *in* "Chemical Basis of Development," W. D. McElroy and B. Glass (Eds.), Johns Hopkins University Press, Baltimore, Md., pp. 174-210.

Taylor, J. H., 1960. "Autoradiography with Tritium-labeled Substances," *in* "Advances in Biological and Medical Physics," Vol. 7, C. A. Tobias and J. H. Lawrence (Eds.), Academic Press, New York, N.Y., pp. 107-130.

Taylor, J. H. and McMaster-Kaye, R., 1954. "Autoradiographic and Microphotometric Studies of Desoxyribose Nucleic Acid During Microgametogenesis in *Lilium longiflorum*," *Chromosoma*, 6, 489-521.

Taylor, J. H. and Woods, P. S., 1959. "*In Situ* Studies of Polynucleotide Synthesis in Nucleolus and Chromosomes," *in* "Subcellular Particles," T. Hayashi (Ed.), Ronald Press, New York, N.Y., pp. 172-185.

Taylor, J. H., Woods, P. S., and Hughes, W. L., 1957. "The Organization and Duplication of Chromosomes as Revealed by Autoradiographic Studies Using Tritium-labeled Thymidine," *Proc. Natl. Acad. Sci.*, 43, 122-128.

Thorell, B., 1944. "Behavior of the Nucleolar Apparatus During Growth and Differentiation of Normal Blood Cells," *Acta. Med. Scand.*, 117, 335-375.

Thorell, B., 1947. "The Relation of Nucleic Acids to the Formation and Differentiation of Cellular Proteins," *Cold Spring Harbor Symposia Quant. Biol.*, 12, 247-255.

Vendrely, R., 1955. "The Deoxyribonucleic Acid Content of the Nucleus," *in* "The Nucleic Acids," E. Chargaff and J. N. Davidson (Eds.), Vol. 2, Academic Press, New York, N.Y., pp. 155-180.

Vendrely, R. and Vendrely, C., 1956. "The Results of Cytophotometry in the Study of the Deoxyribonucleic Acid (DNA) Content of the Nucleus," *Intern. Rev. Cytol.*, 5, 171-197.

Vincent, W. S., 1955. "Structure and Chemistry of Nucleoli," *Intern. Rev. Cytol.*, 4, 269-298.

Walker, P. M. B. and Yates, H. B., 1952. "Nuclear Components of Dividing Cells," *Proc. Roy. Soc. London, B*, 140, 274-299.

Watson, J. D. and Crick, F. H. C., 1953. "Molecular Structure of Nucleic Acids," *Nature*, 171, 737-738.

Watson, J. D. and Crick, F. H. C., 1953. "Genetical Implications of the Structure of Deoxyribonucleic Acid," *Nature*, 171, 964-967.

Watson, J. D. and Crick, F. H. C., 1953. "The Structure of DNA," *Cold Spring Harbor Symposia Quant. Biol.,* **18,** 123-131.

Watson, M. L., 1955. "The Nuclear Envelope. Its Structure and Relation to Cytoplasmic Membranes," *J. Biophys. Biochem. Cytol.,* **1,** 257-270.

Watson, M. L., 1959. "Further Observations on the Nuclear Envelope of the Animal Cell," *J. Biophys. Biochem. Cytol.,* **6,** 147-156.

Whaley, W. G., Mollenhauer, H. H., and Leech, J. H., 1960. "The Ultrastructure of the Meristematic Cell," *Am. J. Botany,* **47,** 401-449.

Whaley, W. G., Mollenhauer, H. H., and Leech, J. H., 1960. "Some Observations on the Nuclear Envelope," *J. Biophys. Biochem. Cytol.,* **8,** 233-245.

White, M. J. D., 1954. "Animal Cytology and Evolution," 2nd ed., Cambridge University Press, Cambridge.

Wilson, G. B., 1948. "Nucleolar and Cell Volumes in a Polyploid Series of the Musae," *J. Genetics,* **49,** 42-45.

Wilson, G. B., 1950. "Nuclear Cytology," Michigan State University Press, E. Lansing, Mich.

Wilson, G. B. and Boothroyd, E. R., 1941. "Studies in Differential Reactivity. I. The Rate and Degree of Differentiation in the Somatic Chromosomes of *Trillium erectum* L.," *Can. J. Res., C,* **19,** 400-412.

Wilson, G. B. and Boothroyd, E. R., 1944. "Temperature-induced Differential Contraction in the Somatic Chromosomes of *Trillium erectum* L.," *Can. J. Res., C,* **22,** 105-119.

Woods, P. S. and Schairer, M. V., 1959. "Distribution of Newly Synthesized Deoxyribonucleic Acid in Dividing Chromosomes," *Nature,* **183,** 303-305.

Zalokar, M., 1959. "Nuclear Origin of Ribonucleic Acid," *Nature,* **183,** 1330.

# 5

# Mitosis and Meiosis

When a cell divides the nucleus usually does likewise, and by a process which insures that the chromosomes will divide and separate with the mathematical precision necessary to maintain genic uniformity within required limits. There are two common forms of mitosis associated with cell division, namely, *somatic* and *meiotic*. The former is, in general, the process which gives rise to new cells in the growing regions of an organism and maintains continuity of chromosome number and type, while the latter is the modified form which gives rise directly or indirectly to sexual gametes. In meiosis the chromosome number is reduced to half and partner or homologous chromosomes are segregated. A third form of mitotic activity which appears to be fairly common in differentiated tissues is *endomitosis,* and involves progressive duplication of the chromosomes without cell division or any of the usual mitotic events.

## SOMATIC MITOSIS

Somatic mitosis may be defined as a process whereby the chromosomes become duplicated longitudinally into two more or less equivalent parts which separate to opposite poles of the cell. The stages of this process and their chief characteristics (Figures 5-1, 5-2, 5-3), are as follows:

### Interphase

Most nuclei in an organism are in a state of inactivity so far as microscopically resolvable changes are concerned. For this reason one usually finds this state referred to as the resting stage. Since there is reason to believe that this stage is far from "resting" in the physiological sense, but rather that it is the most active period, the term "energic phase" may serve the purpose better (Berril and Huskins, 1936). Nonetheless, the terms "interphase" and "interkinesis" are widely used to designate the stage between two successive nuclear divisions and, in this restricted sense, seem quite adequate even though some other term would appear more suitable for nuclei of differentiated cells.

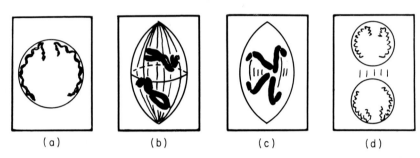

**Figure 5-1.** Diagrammatic Representation of the Stages of Mitosis: (a) prophase; (b) metaphase; (c) anaphase; and (d) telophase. (From Wilson, G. B., 1952. "Outline of Genetics," Michigan State University Press, East Lansing, Mich., Fig. 2, p. 6.)

The nucleus at this stage is as described in Chapter 4. The chromosomes lie in the form of more or less loosely coiled threads, usually somewhat closely appressed to the membrane. Most cytologists consider them to be already duplicated, and some workers believe them to be multipartite. They may or may not stain intensely with standard nuclear stains at this stage, presumably depending on the distribution of nucleoprotein which appears to vary with the species. Nucleoli and Feulgen-positive chromocenters are also conspicuous during this stage.

*Prophase*

At the beginning of division the chromosomes start to contract, thicken, and undo their coiling. Part of this change appears to be associated with the development, at right angles to the old coil, of a new one which grows from a coil of many small gyres to one of relatively few larger ones. This coiling is generally obscured by the development of matrical material. Total end-to-end contraction is to approximately one-fifth the initial length (Sparrow, *et al.,* 1941). About midway through this process, it becomes obvious that each chromosome is at

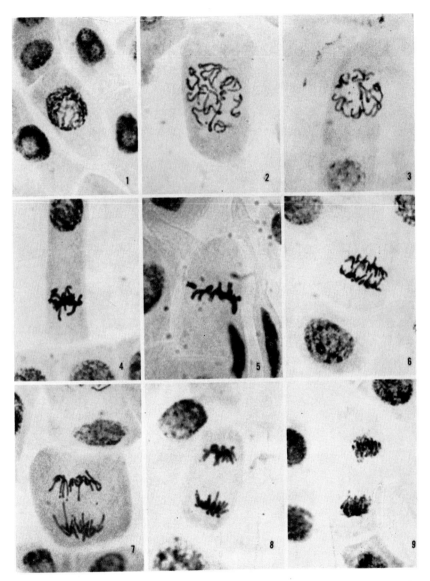

**Figure 5-2.** Stages of Mitosis in Meristematic Cells of *Pisum:* (1) early prophase; (2) mid-prophase; (3) late prophase; (4) prometaphase; (5) metaphase; (6) early anaphase; (7) late anaphase; (8) early telophase; (9) late telophase.

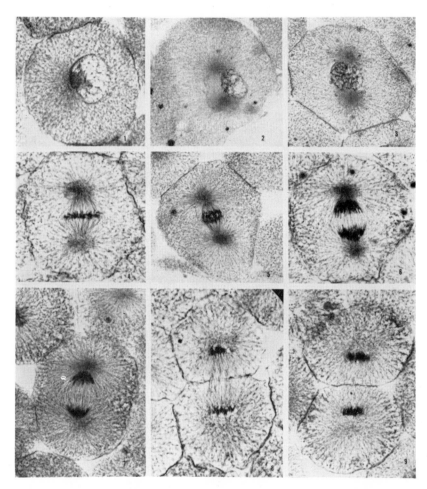

**Figure 5-3.** Stages of Mitosis in Cells of the Whitefish Blastula: (1) interphase, with cell center adjacent to nucleus; (2) early prophase showing development of astral centers; (3) late prophase, with astral centers at opposite ends of the cell; (4) metaphase; (5) early anaphase; (6) late anaphase; (7) early telophase; (8) mid-telophase, showing cleavage furrow; (9) telophase-interphase following separation of daughter cells. (Courtesy of Mr. Philip G. Coleman, Michigan State University.)

least double and that the two halves are intertwined in a relational coil which becomes progressively uncoiled as the prophase advances (Figure 5-4).

During this process the nuclear boundary becomes disrupted, the spindle apparatus begins to form, and the nucleolus and chromocenters generally disappear.

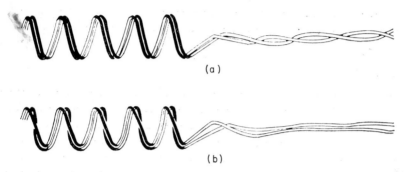

(a)

(b)

**Figure 5-4.** Schematic Representation of Plectonemic and Paranemic Coils Composed of Two Strands: (a) plectonemic coil made up of two interlocking strands which form a relational coil when the gyres are partially drawn out; (b) paranemic coil of two strands which are free to separate as independent units when straightened out. (From Sparrow, A. H., Huskins, C. L., and Wilson, G. B., 1941. "Studies on the Chromosome Spiralization Cycle in *Trillium*," *Can. J. Res., C,* 19, Fig. 1, p. 325.)

### Prometaphase

Following the breakdown or disappearance of the nuclear boundary, the chromosomes tend to aggregate in a central position in the cell. In plant cells, at least, this time corresponds to the first appearance of an organized spindle. Wilson and Hyppio (1955) considered this positioning of the chromosomes to play an important role, both in the development and normal functioning of spindle organization. Motion pictures of the mitotic process (Bajer, 1957) would seem to indicate that prometaphase collapse is characteristic of normal mitoses in plant cells. Similar motion pictures such as those produced by Raymond Zirkle and his colleagues indicate that the same is true for animal cells as well.

### Metaphase

This is the stage of alignment of chromosomes on the equatorial plate, which is the midportion of the spindle apparatus. It appears to be the kinetochores which are particularly attracted towards this region. They tend to line up more or less uniformly on the periphery of a circle or ellipse bounding the central region of the spindle, with the chromosome arms lying at random either within or without the spindle area (Figure 5-1). Each chromosome is independent of the others and in most cases its position bears no discernible relation to that of its homologue.

## Anaphase

This is the stage of separation of half chromosomes, or chromatids, which move toward opposite poles, generally with the kinetochore first and the arms trailing.

## Telophase

On arrival at the poles the chromosomes progressively lose their chromaticity and indications of internal structure can often be seen, though individual chromosomes can rarely be resolved as separate structures. Reformation of the membrane, nucleolus, and chromocenters brings us back to the interphase stage again, with the result that one nucleus has given rise to two which are its genetical and cytological equivalents.

In most cases in plant cells, a cell wall is formed in the region of the equatorial plate to form two daughter cells. In animal cells, daughter cells are usually separated by a process of invagination in the equatorial region. Electron microscope studies of Porter and Machado (1960) indicate that formation of the cell plate is initiated by migration of tubular elements of the endoplasmic reticulum toward the interzonal region of the spindle where they spread out to form a close network along the equator of this region. This network marks the midline of the developing phragmoblast within which the cell plate forms. The cell plate appears first as a series of unconnected vesicles within the meshes of the network, which later increase in size and fuse to complete the separation of daughter cells except at points where continuity is maintained by the plasmodesmata (Figure 5-5). The present concepts concerning cell wall formation in plant cells have recently been reviewed by Whaley and coworkers (1960).

It must be remembered that the process described here is a dynamic affair and that one stage merges into the next without any definite line of demarcation. The names attached are useful only in that they provide a means of designating the part of the process under discussion.

It may also be noted that this description is a generalized one and that there are many variations, some of which are normal in that they occur characteristically in certain tissues of special organisms. Any part

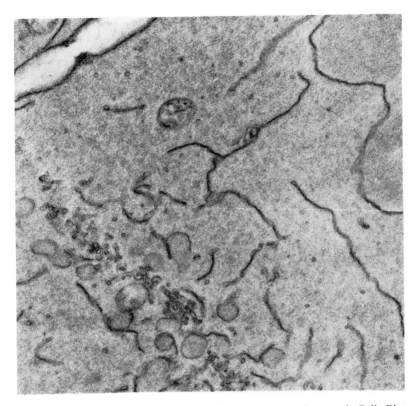

**Figure 5-5.** Electron Micrograph Showing Early State of Cell Plate Formation in Telophase of Dividing Onion Root Tip Cell. A small portion of each telophase nucleus is seen at the upper right and lower left. The developing cell plate extends diagonally from lower right to upper left. Membrane elements of the endoplasmic reticulum with evidence of branching are present on both sides of the cell plate. In the immediate vicinity of the cell plate the elements of endoplasmic reticulum are shorter and form a reticulation composed of a close lattice of tubules along the midline between the two cells. Phragmosomes are seen concentrated on either side of the plate region. Development of the cell plate is more advanced at the center (the early phragmoplast) and grades out toward the margins, where fewer cytoplasmic elements are present. (From Porter, K. R. and Machado, R. D., 1960. "Studies on the Endoplasmic Reticulum. IV. Its Form and Distribution During Mitosis in Cells of Onion Root Tip," *J. Biophys. Biochem. Cytol.,* **7**, Fig. 16, Plate 94. Courtesy of Dr. Keith R. Porter, The Rockefeller Institute.)

of the process may go wrong under certain conditions, occasionally with important cytogenetical consequences which will be discussed later. The process as we have described it should be considered primarily as a norm or base against which to view expected and observed variations.

## MEIOTIC MITOSES

The transition from sporophytic to gametophytic tissue in plants and the formation of gametes in animals is normally accomplished by a special series of divisions known as meiotic mitoses or simply meiosis. It may be defined as *two* divisions of the nucleus accompanied by only one *functional* division of the chromosomes (Darlington, 1937). It characteristically results in the separation of homologous chromosomes and the halving of the chromosome number. The stages of the two divisions and their more fundamental characteristics (Figures 5-6 and 5-7) are as follows:

### First Division

*Prophase I*

As in somatic mitosis, this is in general the stage of contraction. There is, however, evidence that a slight elongation precedes the contraction (Belling, 1928; Wilson, 1939; Sparrow, *et al.,* 1941). Meiotic prophase is usually divided into a number of stages coinciding with the occurrence of several phenomena normally associated with meiosis. These stages and their characteristics are:

*Leptotene.* The chromosomes are long, thin, optically single threads which show little of the relic coiling characteristic of somatic prophase. Presumably the coils unwind rapidly. In good preparations the threads contain a series of chromatic beads called chromomeres which have often been assumed to be representative of gene loci, though there is no direct evidence on this point (Belling, 1928).

*Zygotene.* Homologous chromosomes begin to pair, usually at the ends or the kinetochore or both. General pairing is followed by a closer chromomere-to-chromomere association or synapsis, which may be complete or not, depending on the species in some cases and on conditions within the organism in others. Many factors apart from homology are known to influence synapsis; e.g., temperature, nutrition, and specific genes.

*Pachytene.* Contraction proceeds and synaptic mates tend to separate. Also each chromosome can be seen to be double in some places, but the separation is not as great as between homologues. In certain regions

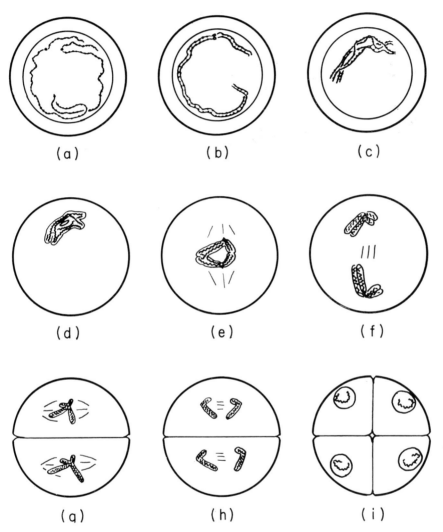

Figure 5-6. Diagrammatic Representation of the Stages of Meiosis.
(a) to (d), Prophase of First Division. (a) leptotene; (b) zygotene; (c)
pachytene; (d) diakinesis; (e) first metaphase; (f) first anaphase; (g) second
metaphase; (h) second anaphase; and (i) tetrad of four spores. (From
Wilson, G. B., 1952. "Outline of Genetics," Michigan State University Press,
E. Lansing, Michigan, Fig. 3, p. 7.)

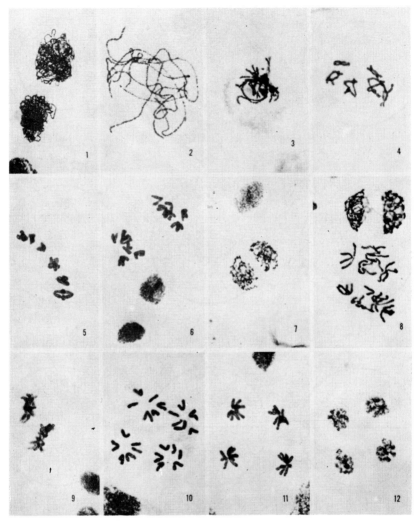

**Figure 5-7.** Stages of Meiosis in Microsporocytes of *Podophyllum:* (1) zygotene; (2) pachytene; (3) diplotene; (4) diakinesis; (5) metaphase I; (6) anaphase I; (7) telophase I; (8) prophase II; (9) metaphase II; (10) anaphase II; (11) early telophase II; (12) late telophase II. (Courtesy of Miss N. Gabriele Mühling, Montana State University.)

there are apparent exchanges of segments between homologous half-chromosomes as indicated by X arrangements known as chiasmata.

It has generally been assumed that chiasmata represent the physical basis of crossing over since it has been demonstrated that genetic exchange also involves chromosome exchange (Stern, 1931; Creighton and McClintock, 1931), and it has also been shown that both chiasmata and crossing over involve only two out of four strands at any one locus. Various theories concerning the origin of chiasmata and their assumed relationship with crossing over will be discussed in Chapter 6.

*Diplotene.* Contraction continues as well as the opening out between homologues, and the chromosomes tend to clump in the center of the cell. Formation of the major coil usually begins at this stage, though in some cases its inception may be slightly earlier. Because of the characteristic clumping, this is a difficult stage to study.

*Diakinesis.* As a rule, this is the best stage for studying chromosome associations. Contraction is near a maximum and the chromosome pairs are well spread throughout the cell as though by mutual repulsion. Pairs of homologous chromosomes are still held together at chiasmata but are elsewhere separated (Figures 5-6 and 5-7). This has given rise to the idea that the chiasmata hold pairs together, but there are a number of cases of continued association in which no chiasmata can be demonstrated. The nucleolus generally disappears during this stage but may persist, usually in reduced size, until anaphase. The major coil is usually completely formed by the end of this stage.

### Metaphase I

Pairs (bivalents, tetrahomads, tetrads) line up on the equatorial plate with homologous kinetochores oriented toward opposite poles.

### Anaphase I

Homologous kinetochores move toward opposite poles. Each kinetochore is attached to two chromatids (half chromosomes) which are sisters in some regions and homologues in others, depending on where crossing over has occurred. The chiasmata are fully resolved, apparently by being pulled off the ends.

### Telophase I

This is a regrouping of the chromosomes at the poles similar to the equivalent stage of somatic mitosis. In some species both this stage and the following one may be virtually eliminated.

*Interkinesis*

This is the interphase stage between the two divisions. It may be of relatively long duration, in which case a cell wall is usually laid down between the two nuclei to give a two-celled or dyad stage. On the other hand it may be of such short duration as to be practically nonexistent. In this case a cell wall is seldom laid down and the chromosomes go through the second division relatively unchanged morphologically. In animals the two cells of the dyad are normally separated except for a thin cytoplasmic connection.

## Second Division

*Prophase II*

If there is no interkinesis, this stage is eliminated. In any event it appears to be rapid, but like any prophase, is essentially a stage of contraction and coiling.

*Metaphase II*

The kinetochores which have been holding the two chromatids together line up as at somatic metaphase, and divide.

*Anaphase II*

Sister kinetochores separate to the poles, pulling with them the chromatids to which they are attached.

*Telophase II*

This stage involves the reconstitution of interphase nuclei and the laying down of cell walls to give four cells, known as a tetrad in plants. In animals there are four separate cells in the male. In the female, a microcyte called the polar body is usually budded off after the first division and a second polar body after the second division so that the end product of meiosis is a "reduced" egg and two or three polar bodies. Thus the final result of these two divisions is four cells, each with a complete chromosome set and half the somatic number of chromosomes.

In animals the end products of meiosis become gametes, while in higher plants a number of purely somatic-type divisions occur to give the gametophytic generation, which is haploid.

As in mitosis, this description should be considered a norm. Variations occur both as accidents and as established processes. For example, chiasma formation appears to be absent in meiosis of the males of certain insects.

## ENDOMITOSIS

Duplication of chromosomes without cell or nuclear division in the usual sense appears to be characteristic of some tissues in both plants and animals. Such duplication gives rise to a state known as polyteny, which means only that the chromosomes are obviously multistranded. The widespread occurrence of this phenomenon has led to the notion that a chromosome is potentially multistranded and that variations in the degree may somehow be bound up with the question of cellular differentiation (Huskins, 1947) and senescence. The general thesis that variation in the number of ultimate or potential strands may be related to nuclear metabolism would appear to warrant extensive consideration.

## VARIATIONS IN MITOSIS

Variations in the mitotic process may be induced by a variety of chemical and physical stimuli. In addition, very similar deviations from the norm occur sporadically and spontaneously and are also characteristic of the cells of some tissues. Berger (1938) and Grell (1946) described a series of "reduction" divisions in certain gut cells of the larva mosquito in which chromosome replication took place to a very high degree and was followed by a rapid series of mitoses with no further replication until the chromosomes again reached the normal diploid strand level. Multiplication of chromosome strands without mitosis appears to be rather common, especially in nuclei of differentiated cells, as first noted by Geitler (1939) in the water skater, *Gerris lateralis*. Later, Geitler (1941) published an extensive review of the subject of multiple chromosome replication (polyteny). In 1947, Huskins provided experimental evidence of the existence of such strand multiplication in plant roots by showing that the average number of chromocenters was correlated with the degree of polyteny. Occasionally such cells enter division either spontaneously or by induction but, instead of going through a series of "reduction" divisions as in the mosquito gut cells, the nuclei become typically polyploid, with each chromosome having the usual two major strands (Figure 5-8).

Another kind of "somatic reduction" division was reported by Huskins (1947, 1948) following treatment of plant meristems with sodium nucleate. He noted that, at stages from prophase to metaphase, there was a strong tendency for whole chromosomes to separate into two groups. This, if followed by a more or less normal anaphase separation of chromatids, would lead to formation of a multinucleate cell and, with cytokinesis, to cells with less than the diploid number of chromosomes. Later, Wilson, Hawthorne, and Tsou (1952) noted similar "reduction" figures in untreated onion roots (Figure 5-9). They referred to these as "split figures" and, in some cases found the metaphase spindle to be double. Usually, since the double spindles were close together and in the same plane, anaphase separation and telophase transformation led to the usual binucleate condition. Occasionally, however, the two spindles

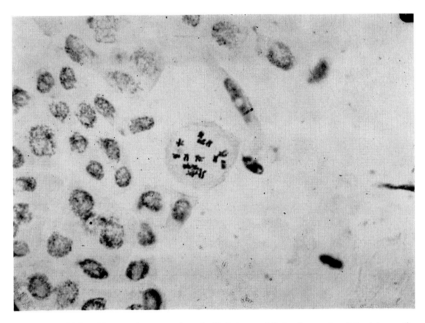

Figure 5-8. Photomicrograph of Polytene Metaphase in Meristematic Cell of Pea Root. (Courtesy of Dr. Jack Van't Hof, Michigan State University.)

were tipped relative to each other, which resulted in tri- or tetra-nucleated cells. Only in rare cases, however, were viable cells with subdiploid numbers found. Whether or not such "split figures" tend to separate homologues is not clear. Wilson and Cheng (1949) did find more cases of homologous separation in *Trillium* than expected on a random basis. Whether such "split figures" result from multiplication of spindle foci or chance alignment of spindle fibers is not known, but the fact that such separations are found before spindle organization suggests the latter.

Deviations from "normal" mitosis appear to be characteristic in some tissues. For example, all of the departures from norm which have been

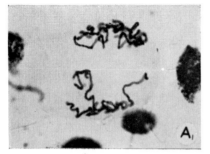

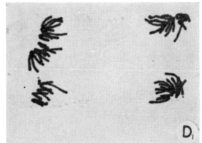

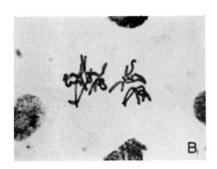

**Figure 5-9.** Series of "Split Figures" in Untreated *Allium* Root Tip Cells. The sequence shown can lead to both segregation and numerical reduction of the chromosomes. (From Wilson, G. B. Hawthorne, M. E., and Tsou, T. M., 1951. "Spontaneous and Induced Variations in Mitosis," *Journal Heredity*, **42**, Fig. 10, pp. 184-185.)

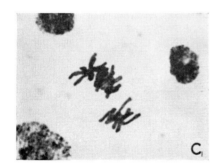

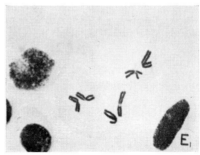

reported as induced by chemical treatment, may be observed in the late divisions of the tapetal cells from anthers in a variety of plants. In *Podophyllum* (the May Apple), for instance, the initial breakdown in mitosis is failure of cytokinesis. Subsequent divisions may be normal

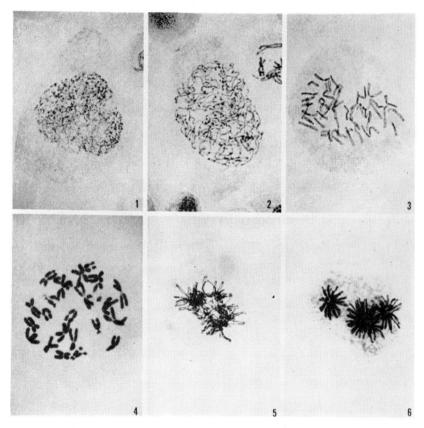

**Figure 5-10.** Plate Showing Some of the Various Types of Aberrant Mitotic Figures in Dividing Tapetal Cells of *Podophyllum peltatum*. (Courtesy of Miss Gabriele N. Mühling, Montana State University.)

so far as chromosome behavior is concerned, but since spindles are more or less randomly oriented and no further cytokinesis occurs, multinucleate cells are produced with the number of chromosomes per nucleus being highly variable. In a number of cases, with or without first establishing a binucleate condition, configurations similar to those induced by colchicine may be produced (Figure 5-10), which lead to varying degrees of polyploidy. In addition, and especially during, the last divisions of the tapetal cells, "star" metaphases and anaphases may be found (Figure 5-10). Similar deviations from typical mitosis are fairly characteristic of developing tumors of various kinds, especially in animals.

## BIBLIOGRAPHY

Bajer, A., 1957. "Cine-micrographic Studies on Mitosis in Endosperm. III. The Origin of the Mitotic Spindle," *Exptl. Cell Res.,* 13, 493-502.

Belling, J., 1928. "Contraction of Chromosomes During Maturation Divisions in *Lilium* and Other Plants," *Univ. Calif. Publ. Botany,* 14, 335-343.

Berger, C. A., 1938. "Multiplication and Reduction of Somatic Chromosome Groups as a Regular Developmental Process in the Mosquito, *Culex pipiens,*" *Carnegie Inst. Wash. Publ.,* 476, 209-232.

Berrill, N. J. and Huskins, C. L., 1936. "The 'Resting' Nucleus," *Am. Naturalist,* 70, 257-260.

Creighton, H. B. and McClintock, B., 1931. "A Correlation of Cytological and Genetical Crossing-over in *Zea mays,*" *Proc. Natl. Acad. Sci.,* 17, 492-497.

Darlington, C. D., 1937. "Recent Advances in Cytology," 2nd ed., Blakiston, Philadelphia, Pa.

Geitler, L., 1939. "Die Entstehung der polyploiden Somakerne der Heteropteren durch Chromosomenteilung ohne Kernteilung," *Chromosoma,* 1, 1-22.

Geitler, L., 1941. "Das Wachstum des Zellkerns in tierischen und pflanzlichen Geweben," *Ergebn. Biol.,* 18, 1-54.

Grell, M., 1946. "Cytological Studies in *Culex.* I. Somatic Reduction Divisions. II. Diploid and Meiotic Divisions," *Genetics,* 31, 60-94.

Huskins, C. L., 1947. "The Subdivisions of the Chromosomes and Their Multiplication in Non-dividing Tissues: Possible Interpretations in Terms of Gene Structure and Gene Action," *Am. Naturalist,* 81, 401-434.

Huskins, C. L., 1948. "Segregation and Reduction in Somatic Tissues," *J. Heredity,* 39, 311-325.

Huskins, C. L., 1952. "Nuclear Reproduction," *Intern. Rev. Cytol.,* 1, 9-26.

Huskins, C. L. and Cheng, K. C., 1950. "Segregation and Reduction in Somatic Tissues. IV. Reductional Groupings Induced in *Allium cepa* by Low Temperature," *J. Heredity,* 41, 13-18.

McLeish, J. and Snoad, B., 1958. "Looking at Chromosomes," St. Martin's Press, New York, N.Y.

Morrison, J. H., 1960. "Meiosis," *in* "Encyclopedia of the Biological Sciences," Peter Gray (Ed.), Reinhold Publishing Corp., New York, N.Y.

Porter, K. R. and Machado, R. D., 1960. "Studies on the Endoplasmic Reticulum. IV. Its Form and Distribution During Mitosis of Onion Root Tips," *J. Biophys. Biochem. Cytol.,* 7, 167-180.

Rhoades, M. M., 1950. "Meiosis in Maize," *J. Heredity,* 41, 59-67.

Richardson, K. C., 1934. "The Golgi Apparatus and Other Cytoplasmic Structures in Normal and Degenerate Cells *in Vitro,*" *Arch. für Exptl. Zellforsch.,* 16, 100-115.

Sparrow, A. H., Huskins, C. L., and Wilson, G. B., 1941. "Studies on the Chromosome Spiralization Cycle in *Trillium*," *Can. J. Res., C.*, **19**, 323-350.

Stern, C., 1931. "Zytologisch-genetische Untersuchungen als Beweise für die Morgansche Theorie des Factorenaustauschs," *Biol. Zbl.*, **51**, 547-587.

Whaley, W. G., Mollenhauer, H. H., and Leech, J. H., 1960. "The Ultrastructure of the Meristematic Cell," *Am. J. Botany*, **47**, 401-449.

Wilson, G. B., 1939. "The Structure and Behaviour of Chromosomes During Meiosis in *Trillium erectum* L.," Ph.D. Thesis, McGill University.

Wilson, G. B., 1950. "Cytological Effects of Some Antibiotics," *J. Heredity*, **41**, 227-231.

Wilson, G. B., 1952. "Outline of Genetics," Michigan State University Press, E. Lansing, Mich.

Wilson, G. B. and Cheng, K. C., 1949. "Segregation and Reduction in Somatic Tissues," *J. Heredity*, **40**, 3-6.

Wilson, G. B., Hawthorne, M. E., and Tsou, T. M., 1951. "Spontaneous and Induced Variations in Mitosis," *J. Heredity*, **42**, 183-189.

# 6

# *Mechanics and Physiology of Cell Division*

THE DESCRIPTION of mitosis which was presented in Chapter 5 dealt only with the question of what happens during more or less typical mitosis. The nature of the functions performed and the manner in which they are performed that enable the product of one mitosis to reach a subsequent division are events that constitute a group of problems the answers to which are of vital importance. A purely morphological description of the mitotic process does not give us very much information concerning its dynamics or how it actually occurs. The dynamics of cell division may well be designated as the problem of the *mitotic cycle*. This problem introduces many questions concerning the physiological factors involved and their interrelationship during the various stages of the cycle. Although the question of the mitotic cycle has been investigated for over three quarters of a century we are still without many major guiding principles. It is hoped that the application of the modern experimental approach and quantitative analysis will ultimately resolve some of the mysteries. Because of the bearing which cell division in general has on growth, both normal and abnormal, this is a very basic and important problem. Consideration of general biological information together with modern biochemistry and physiology allows one to pose some very definite questions and to set up models which may be used in experimental design. It is our purpose in this section to introduce some of these questions and to indicate the type of experimentation which is currently being used in an attempt to provide answers.

# THE MITOTIC CYCLE

Figure 6-1 is a diagrammatic description of the total mitotic cycle. For the sake of simplicity it is divided into three segments, namely: **a-b**, designated as *active mitosis* which includes prophase to telophase; **b-c**, by definition covering that part of interphase during which various *synthetic activities* are either known or assumed to be taking place; and finally **c-a**, a segment termed *antephase*, which represents that period

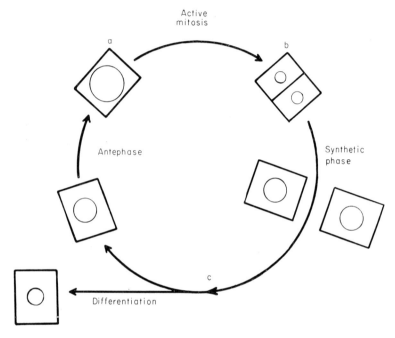

**Figure 6-1.** Diagrammatic Representation of the Mitotic Cycle in Tissues of the Multicellular Organism.

of interphase in which a cell has completed most, if not all, of the synthetic processes necessary to make it competent or "ready" to enter active mitosis. None of these segments are homogeneous either physiologically or morphologically. Theoretically all stages of the mitotic cycle could be subdivided, but for our present purposes, there is no point in further fractionation. Experimental cytology has indicated that the three major segments of the mitotic cycle are sufficiently different in their metabolic characteristics to allow them to be studied separately. Each one of these segments involves a number of problems peculiar to itself.

## Active Mitosis

Wilson and Hyppio (1955) pointed out that active mitosis involves a series of events normally integrated but more or less independent of one another. These include chromosome movement, spindle formation and function, changes in the nuclear membrane, and chromosome morphology. Experimental cytology provides the possibility of considering these various events separately, thus determining their individual roles in the total process. So far, the evidence indicates that a sequence of changes in the nuclear boundary is associated both with the onset of mitosis and with the transition from prophase to prometaphase. This phase of active mitosis apparently occurs independently of an organized spindle. The transition from prometaphase to metaphase to anaphase appears to be, in part at least, a function of the spindle in relation to the kinetochores of the chromosomes. Chemical treatments such as exposure to actidione, colchicine, and iodoacetic acid can all be interpreted as disrupting nuclear membrane changes, spindle organization, kinetochore cleavage, or any combination of these. Morphological changes in the chromosomes themselves, once initiated, appear to go to completion spontaneously.

## Synthetic Phase

In general, following active mitosis, daughter cells are essentially "half" cells. Before such cells can re-enter mitosis they must grow and in the process synthesize many essentials. Exactly what is synthesized and what the location and manner of synthesis may be are questions for which we have no clear answer. The fact that nucleoli reappear in the telophase or early interphase nucleus suggests synthetic activity involving both protein and RNA. The use of radioactive tracers has tended to confirm the synthesis of RNA in the nucleolus during telophase - interphase. Autoradiographic studies using tritium-labeled cytidine have shown that incorporation into the nucleolus occurs in root tip cells of *Vicia faba* as soon as it appears in late telophase, and continues during all stages of interphase and into prophase (Taylor and Woods, 1959). Many experiments with radioactive precursors, especially tritiated thymidine, indicate that DNA synthesis reaches a peak fairly early in interphase. The situation with regard to cytoplasmic or nuclear protein synthesis has not been studied in detail. Cells and nuclei do apparently increase in volume through most of the interphase (Leak and Wilson, 1960); however, how much of this increase is the result of actual synthesis of protein or RNA is not known. The most active period of protein synthesis during meiosis in *Lilium longiflorum,* as measured by incorporation of glycine —$C^{14}$, appears to be during premeiotic interphase and leptotene, with a low level being reached by the beginning of zygotene (Taylor, 1959). The synthesis of DNA was found to occur only during premeiotic interphase, while RNA synthesis took place in both the nucleus and cytoplasm during interphase and up to late leptotene. After late leptotene practically all synthesis of RNA occurred in the nucleus and at a slower rate until the end of prophase.

### Antephase

In the model given in Figure 6-1, c-a is the segment of the mitotic cycle which Bullough (1952) has designated as antephase. This stage would appear to represent, as already noted, the stage at which the cell is competent to enter active mitosis. Experiments with excised pea roots have shown that even in the absence of an exogenous carbohydrate source this fraction of the population does indeed ultimately pass into active mitosis. This presumably means that it is not a stage requiring high energy output, though the rate of entrance of cells into active mitosis can be greatly increased by the addition of a suitable carbohydrate source (i.e., glucose, fructose, sucrose). Furthermore, it should be noted that the conditions which are favorable for rapid entrance of antephase into active mitosis are only moderately suitable for transition from the synthetic phase (b to c) to antephase (c to a). The exact nature of any of these transitions is still largely unknown. Presumably hormonal control plays a role in relation to the utilization of various carbohydrate sources for support of mitotic activity. Bullough (1955) has shown in animal cells that a number of hormones affect the utilization one way or another of glucose but not of fructose. Our own experiments indicate that certain trioses (i.e., D-glyceraldehyde) function very well as carbon sources, but give a quite different pattern of response than the hexoses (Wilson, *et al.,* 1959). The fact that mitotic activity can be initiated and maintained by a variety of carbon sources leads to the possibility that, ultimately, comparative studies will uncover the pathways by which these sources are utilized by the different segments of the mitotic cycle.

## SPINDLE MECHANISM

Historically speaking, the problem of the mechanism of mitosis has been very closely associated with questions concerning the origin, nature, and function of the mitotic spindle. Early work focused attention on the *centrosome* as playing a leading role both in the formation of the spindle and its activity (Wilson, 1900). The centrosome is a highly conspicuous structure in certain animal cells, notably during most maturation divisions and early cleavage stages of embryogeny. Generally, the centrosome consists of a small, dense, refractile body embedded in a clearer area from which fibrillar rays emanate, especially at the onset of division. The central body, usually called the *centriole,* is normally positioned in the cytoplasm just outside the nuclear membrane and

(a)                  (b)

**Figure 6-2.** (a) First Maturation Division Spindle in Living Oöcyte of *Chaetopterus pergamentaceous* Photographed with Polarization Optics. The bright chromosomal and continuous fibers of the spindle and the dark astral rays are all positively birefrigent and appear as dark bodies at the equator of the cell. (b) Tracing of First Maturation Division Spindle of *Chaetopterus* Showing Detail of Component Parts. (From Inoué, S., 1953. "Polarization Optical Studies of the Mitotic Spindle. I. The Demonstration of Spindle Fibers in Living Cells," *Chromosoma,* 5, Figs. 2 and 3, p. 490.)

divides during the early part of mitosis. The products of division migrate until they take up positions opposite each other with the nucleus between them. The so-called *astral rays* normally develop during the time of this migration. What connection these bodies have in the formation of the functional spindle is by no means clear despite many years of study. Proponents of the many versions of the centrosomal theory of spindle organization have been somewhat embarrassed by the finding that no such apparatus can be located in the cells of higher plants and that, furthermore, its existence is doubtful in many animal cells. In plant cells generally, and in many animal cells where there is no apparent centrosomal apparatus, no organized spindle is obvious until prometaphase. The long-debated question as to whether the spindle is a component of the nucleus, cytoplasm, or both is still unanswered. There are many views concerning the nature of the spindle fibers themselves, ranging from the opinion that they are precipitation artifacts to the idea that they represent real fibers presumably protein in composition. They have also been assumed to be lines of force or stress lines and channels. There is very little doubt that they represent real organization (Figure 6-2 (a) and (b)) as indicated by studies with polarized light (Inoué, 1953; Swann, 1951) and by electron micrography (Figure 6-3).

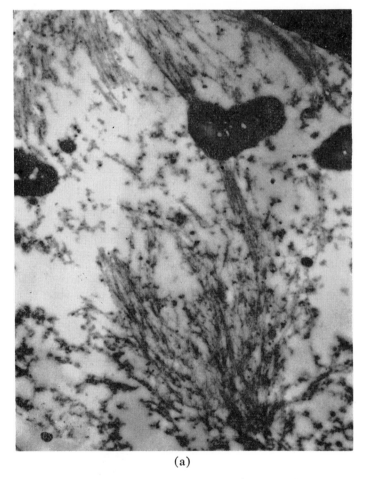

(a)

**Figure 6-3.** (*Contin.* on opposite page.)

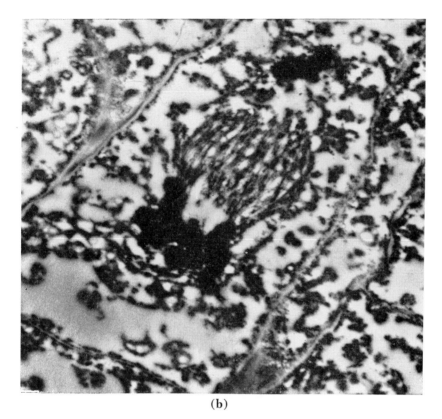

(b)

**Figure 6-3.** Electron Micrographs Showing Spindle Fibers in (a) Pollen Mother Cell of *Lilium speciosum* at Metaphase I, and (b) Meristematic Cell of *Pisum* Root Tip at Somatic Anaphase. (Fig. (a), from Satô, S., 1960. "Electron Microscope Studies on the Mitotic Figure. III. Process of the Spindle Formation," *Cytologia,* **25,** Fig. 8, p. 126. Courtesy of Dr. S. Satô, University of Tokyo. Fig. (b), courtesy of Mr. L. V. Leak, Michigan State University.)

Every physical and physiochemical force which could conceivably bring about movement of the type exhibited by chromosomes in mitosis has been invoked in attempts to explain the mechanism. Most of these are discussed in detail in Franz Schrader's book, *Mitosis* (1953), and will be mentioned here only briefly.

### Elastic Fibers

This is perhaps the oldest idea of all, and many variants of the basic scheme have been proposed. Fundamentally the notion is that the spindle fibers are real and capable of expansion and contraction, and in so doing push and pull the chromosomes into position. There is little positive evidence for this view, and in some cases changes in the spindle are directly contrary to expectation.

### Electrostatic Forces

The idea that the chromosomes may move as a result of the distribution of electric charge was originally advanced by R. S. Lillie (1905). This suggestion has had considerable appeal, but becomes extremely complex when applied to meiosis and almost hopelessly unwieldy in a variety of exceptional cases. That there are areas in the cell bearing different charges is almost certain, and it seems more than probable that electrostatic forces do play some role in chromosome movement.

### Hydrodynamics

The physicist Bjerknes (1902, 1909) made an extensive study of the relationship between pulsating bodies, oscillating bodies, and bodies in their vicinity which were static. He found that (1) two spheres pulsating in phase attract each other and in opposite phase repel; (2) such spheres set up lines of force not unlike a spindle in appearance; (3) a neutral sphere is repelled by a pulsating one if it is lighter than the medium, but is attracted if heavier than the medium; (4) oscillating spheres behave in the same fashion except that they repel when in the same phase and attract when in opposite phase. With these facts it is possible to build up a superficially satisfactory hypothesis of mitosis, but it is difficult to see how the metaphase plate is formed, and it is also unlikely that the forces concerned would act over the necessary distances.

### Tactoids

The fact that long fibers suspended in an unoriented medium will line up in a spindle-like form is well known. The major attempts to apply this fact to mitosis have been made by Bernal (1940), Östergren (1945, and later), and Schrader (1951). Too little is known of tactoids from the physiochemical point of view to allow any reasonable assessment of their potential role in mitosis.

### Other Forces

Such forces as electronic diffusion, sol-gel transformation, and cytoplasmic streaming have been suggested, but though they may play a part, none of them seems capable of giving the organization observed. Likewise autonomous chromosome movement has been stressed as a factor, and while there is no doubt that half chromosomes can separate without any apparent spindle, the nature of the force still remains unexplained.

The biochemical approach to the problem of the spindle seems more

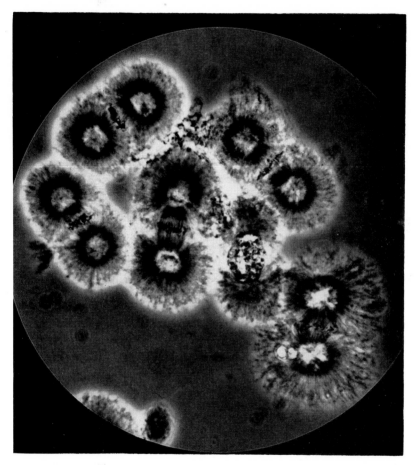

**Figure 6-4.** Phase-contrast Photomicrograph of Mitotic Apparatus Isolated from Eggs of the Sea Urchin, *Strongylocentrotus purpuratus* Using Cold Ethanol-digitonin. (Courtesy of Dr. Daniel Mazia, University of California, Berkeley.)

likely to provide precise information concerning both its nature and function. Mazia and Dan (1952) have developed a method of isolating the mitotic apparatus from sea urchin eggs (Figure 6-4) which has permitted extensive studies to be made on the chemical composition of its component parts (Mazia, 1955, 1957). Mazia (1955) found that the spindle fibers of the isolated mitotic apparatus could be put into solution by reducing agents such as alkaline thioglycollate. On the basis of this observation, he concluded that the spindle fibers were composed essentially of small protein molecules associated end to end by —SS— (disulfide) linkages to form elongate protein chains. Solution of the mitotic apparatus could also be accomplished by the use of urea, which, however, produced a viscous solution. Mazia interpreted this finding as indicating that secondary bonds (presumably hydrogen bonds) had been disrupted and that the —SS— linked protein chains or fibrils of the spindle gel were probably condensed laterally by means of secondary linkages. This could produce oriented clusters of protein chains and so account for the microscopically visible fibers of the spindle. The achromatic component of the mitotic apparatus (asters, spindle), isolated from colchicine-treated sea urchin eggs, is also found in the form of a structureless gel. As pointed out by Brachet (1957), this observation suggests that the protein material which normally constitutes the spindle is present in these eggs, but that the typical fibrillar organization to form the functional spindle is prevented by colchicine. The marked loss of birefrigence of spindle material reported to occur in certain animal cells after colchicine treatment (Inoué, 1952; Swann and Mitchison, 1953) supports this view. Mazia (1955) concluded that colchicine might produce its effect by interfering with the establishment of secondary bonding which he regarded as responsible for the orientation and geometry of the fully formed spindle. Biochemical studies on the isolated mitotic apparatus indicate that the spindle and asters consist of simple proteins of characteristic composition (Mazia, 1955, 1957). It has also been demonstrated that at stages where no organized spindle is evident there are present proteins with characteristics similar to those making up the functional spindle (Mazia, 1957). In summary, the studies on the isolated mitotic apparatus have demonstrated that (1) the spindle fibers are real structures, (2) the spindle protein has a characteristic composition, (3) the linear orientation of the spindle fiber is probably maintained by means of —SS— linkages, and (4) the particular kind of protein from which the spindle is organized is present at prespindle stages.

The idea that an oxidation-reduction cycle might be associated with formation of the mitotic spindle was first proposed by Rapkine (1931) on the basis of studies dealing with variations in the concentration of soluble —SH (sulfhydryl) during cleavage of sea urchin eggs. Rapkine found that the level of soluble —SH decreased during interphase and the early stages of mitosis. At the time of active spindle formation (prometaphase, metaphase) the concentration of soluble —SH then increased rapidly until it reached its initial level at about the time of cytokinesis. These fluctuations in concentration of soluble —SH were interpreted by Rapkine as due to changes in the levels of the oxidized and reduced form of glutathione, and were thought to be accompanied by corresponding changes in the amounts of fixed —SH brought about by a reversible denaturation of proteins during spindle formation. More recently, Nasatir and Stern (1959) have described variations in amounts of soluble —SH during the mitotic cycle of lily microspores similar to those observed by Rapkine. On the basis of Rapkine's view, the decrease in

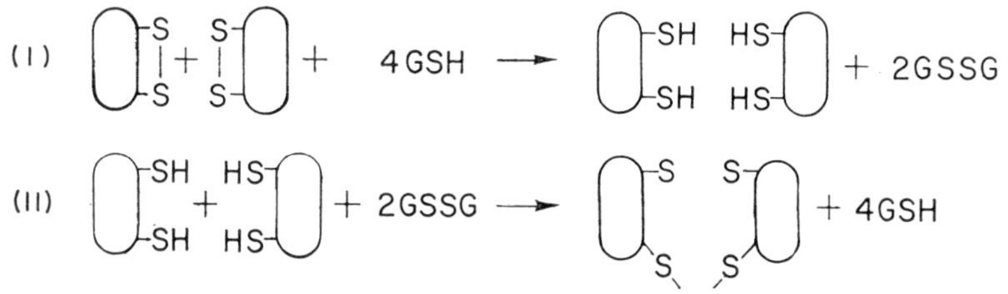

$$(\mathrm{I})\quad \left[\begin{array}{c} -S \\ | \\ -S \end{array} + \begin{array}{c} S- \\ | \\ S- \end{array}\right] + 4\,GSH \;\longrightarrow\; \left[\begin{array}{c} -SH \\ -SH \end{array}\; \begin{array}{c} HS- \\ HS- \end{array}\right] + 2\,GSSG$$

$$(\mathrm{II})\quad \left[\begin{array}{c} -SH \\ -SH \end{array}\; \begin{array}{c} HS- \\ HS- \end{array}\right] + 2\,GSSG \;\longrightarrow\; \left[\begin{array}{c} -S \quad S- \\ S \quad S \end{array}\right] + 4\,GSH$$

Figure 6-5. Schematic Representation of One Possible Mechanism of Polymerization of Protein of the Mitotic Apparatus Through Oxidation-Reduction Cycles of Sulfhydryl Protein and Glutathione. Essentially, intramolecular —SS— is converted to intermolecular —S—. According to this mechanism, oxidized glutathione should be found during the first part of the cycle. (From Mazia, D., 1955. "The Organization of the Mitotic Apparatus," *Symp. Soc. Exptl. Biol.*, 9, Fig. 7, p. 349.)

soluble —SH during the initial stages of mitosis should be accompanied by a corresponding increase in the amount of fixed —SH of the spindle. Likewise, the rise in soluble —SH occurring at metaphase should involve a concomitant decrease in the amount of fixed —SH, presumably as the result of spindle polymerization taking place at this stage. According to Mazia (1955), the variations in protein-bound —SH and soluble —SH actually do follow a course during cell division similar to that proposed by Rapkine; that is, when the protein-bound —SH is high, the soluble —SH is low, and vice versa. This finding has led Mazia (1955) to propose that spindle formation involves an oxidation-reduction cycle between glutathione and protein-bound —SH groups of the spindle protein, and that formation of the gelated spindle is essentially the result of conversion of intramolecular to intermolecular —SS— linkages. In this scheme (Figure 6-5), a decrease in concentration of soluble —SH occurs during the beginning stages of formation of the spindle gel as the result of glutathione being oxidized in the reduction of the intramolecular —SS— bonds of the spindle protein to fixed —SH groups. The rise in soluble —SH accompanying the final stages of gelation of the spindle is the result of the reduction of glutathione accompanying the oxidation of the fixed —SH of the spindle protein to form intermolecular —SS— linkages.

While the variations in soluble —SH observed to occur during cell division seem well documented, it is questionable that such changes can be interpreted as evidence for operation of an oxidation-reduction cycle *specifically* involving glutathione. Several studies have demonstrated that

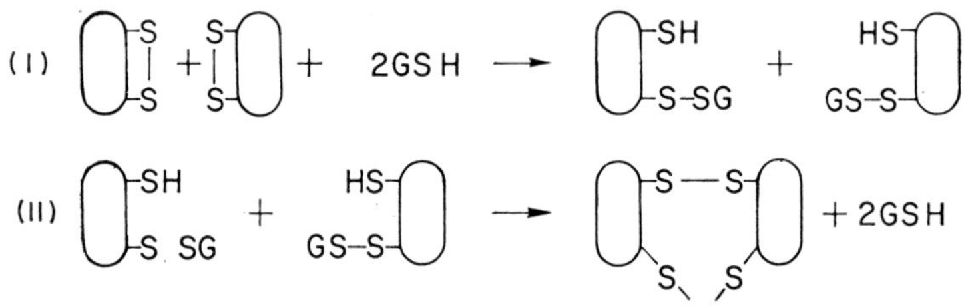

**Figure 6-6.** Schematic Representation of Alternative Mechanism of Polymerization of the Protein of the Mitotic Apparatus. In this scheme oxidized glutathione would not be detected. (From Mazia, D., 1955. "The Organization of the Mitotic Apparatus," *Symp. Soc. Exptl. Biol.,* 9, Fig. 8, p. 349.)

the amount of oxidized glutathione detectable in the sea urchin egg is small and constant in value, and that when reductions in reduced glutathione do occur they are not accompanied by corresponding increases in the amount of oxidized glutathione (Bolognari, 1952; Infantellina and LaGrutta, 1948). To account for this observation, Mazia (1955) has proposed an alternate mechanism for the gelation of the spindle protein, which involves a binding of the oxidized form of glutathione to the protein of the spindle (Figure 6-6). In this scheme, oxidized glutathione would not be detected, and would function in the redox reaction to produce intermolecular —SS— linkages. Barron (1951) has pointed out that variations in soluble —SH during cell division would undoubtedly affect the redox potential of the whole cell and result in marked changes in the activities of various enzymes. Swann (1957) suggested that since many respiratory enzymes are sensitive to oxidation and blocking of their —SH groups, respiration should vary with the amount of soluble —SH, being minimal around the beginning of mitosis. Recent studies of Nasatir and Stern (1959) on the activities of the glycolytic enzymes, aldolase and triosephosphate dehydrogenase, during different stages of the mitotic cycle of lily microspores have shown that the activities of these two enzymes are low during active mitosis. On the other hand, the level of soluble —SH is high during this same period (Figure 6-7).

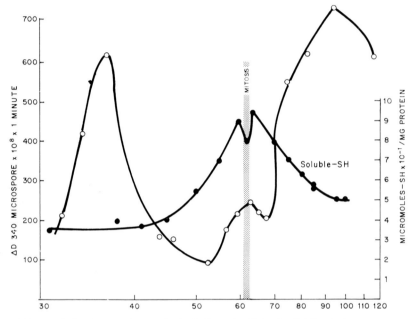

**Figure 6-7.** Comparison of Variations in Soluble Sulfhydryl Concentration (solid circles) in Lily Anther Tissues, and Dehydrogenase Activities (open circles) of Isolated Lily Microspores. (From Nasatir, M. and Stern, H., 1959. "Changes in the Activities of Aldolase and of D-Glyceraldehyde-3-Phosphate Dehydrogenase During the Mitotic Cycle in Microspores of *Lilium longiflorum*," *J. Biophys. Biochem. Cytol.*, **6**, Fig. 2, p. 191.)

The metabolic processes which might be operating to control the redox cycle proposed by Mazia remain to be determined. While the several schemes outlined by Mazia for the gelation of spindle protein do not take into consideration the possible changes involved in dissolution of the spindle during anaphase-telophase, they do, however, suggest ways in which such a breakdown could occur. The progressive dissolution of the spindle following metaphase would appear to involve, in part at least, the cleavage of —SS— bonds. Because the covalent —SS— linkage is relatively stable and not broken under the usual conditions of denaturation, cleavage of such linkages may possibly be enzymatic in character. The finding that glycolytic inhibitors (i.e., iodoacetic acid, iodoacetamide) interfere with cleavage of the kinetochore and, consequently, prevent anaphase movement of the chromosomes (Wilson and Morrison, 1958) suggests that glycolytic activity may be necessary for kinetochore cleavage and that such cleavage may be related in some way to initiation of enzymatic activity necessary for the splitting of the —SS— bonds of the spindle protein. This cleavage would lead to the release of —SH groups as the result of disruption of intermolecular —SS— bonding. Following release of —SH groups, there is then the possibility that folding of the spindle protein molecules occurs, with the subsequent formation of intramolecular —SS— linkages. Disruption of secondary bonding, if such exists, would be expected to occur also as part of the total process involved in spindle breakdown. This sequence of events would result in a progressive folding of the spindle protein and would tend to shorten the spindle.

The conversion of —SH groups to intramolecular —SS— linkages postulated as occurring during anaphase may be an inherent property of the spindle protein and independent of any redox mechanism. This last point is quite compatible with the lack of effect of oxidants and respiratory inhibitors (cyanide, malonic acid, urethane) on cells undergoing active mitosis, particularly those cells in postprophase stages of the mitotic process. The folding process which accompanies the shift of —SH to intramolecular —SS— linkages following metaphase could provide a possible mechanism whereby anaphase movement of chromosomes is accomplished. The decrease in birefrigence of the chromosomal fibers which extends ahead of the moving chromosomes during anaphase (Inoué, 1953; Swann, 1951) suggests that the loss of molecular orientation of the spindle protein is a progressive event and is initiated in the region of the chromosomes. Recent cytochemical studies of Kawamura and Dan (1958) have shown that protein-bound —SH groups are detectable during telophase in only those parts of the spindle immediately adjacent to the chromosomes. This observation is consistent with the idea that kinetochore cleavage and spindle dissolution following metaphase is associated with the cleavage of —SS— linkages and the release of —SH groups.

The vital question of the relation of the spindle to alignment of the chromosomes on the metaphase plate and the subsequent movement of the chromosomes into anaphase, has never been answered satisfactorily. One obvious possibility is that there exists an actual attachment of the spindle fibers to part of the chromosomes, namely, the kinetochore, to provide an oriented field in which forces inherent in the chromosomes themselves contribute to their movement during anaphase. Electron microscope studies carried out recently by Satô (1960) on cell division in pollen mother cells of *Lilium* indicate that the chromosomal fibers of

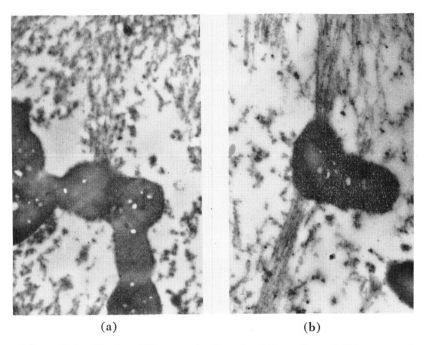

(a)                           (b)

**Figure 6-8.** Electron Micrographs Showing Formation of Chromosomal Fiber During Meiosis in Pollen Mother Cells of Lily: (a) beginning of development of chromosomal fiber in first meiotic division of *Lilium lancifolium*. Note granules drawn up in several lines from the kinetochore region of the chromosome and extending toward the pole to form a bundle of fibers. Within this bundle short fibrils are formed; 6500×. (b) Part of complete chromosomal fiber in metaphase I of pollen mother cell of *Lilium speciosum*. The chromosomal fiber is made up of a bundle of fibrils, about 15 in number; 6500×. (From Satô, S., 1960. "Electron Microscope Studies on the Mitotic Figure. III. Process of the Spindle Formation," *Cytologia,* **25,** Figs. 6 and 7, p. 126. Courtesy of Dr. S. Satô, University of Tokyo.)

the spindle are developed from the kinetochore of each chromosome and grow toward the pole of the cell (Figure 6-8 (a) and (b)). The fact that akinetic chromosome fragments at metaphase do not undergo anaphase movement supports the view that there is an actual attachment of the chromosomes to the spindle apparatus. Also, the abortive attempts to move poleward of metaphase chromosomes which have failed to undergo kinetochore cleavage in the presence of iodoacetic acid (Wilson and Morrison, 1958) suggest that the chromosomes themselves possess some capacity for autonomous movement. No matter what kind of model one proposes to explain chromosome movement, the assumption cannot be reasonably entertained that the chromosomes are merely inert bodies which are pulled around by the spindle fibers. In the last analysis, one must look at the postprophase part of active mitosis as a changing equilibrium between the chromosomes and spindle.

## SYNAPSIS AND CHIASMA FORMATION

### Synapsis

Any satisfactory theory of mitotic mechanisms must be able to explain not only the ordinary and extraordinary movements of chromosomes but also pairing, synapsis, and resultant chiasma formation. To date there is no reasonable explanation of these phenomena. Darlington (1937) has advanced the theory that a chromosome must necessarily exist in a double condition, and that pairing of homologous chromosomes is an attempt to satisfy this requirement at a stage when each individual chromosome is single. Aside from the fact that this theory is dependent on the singleness of the leptotene chromosome, which is by no means generally accepted, it dodges the issue of the actual force involved. It has been assumed generally that the force of attraction is electrostatic in nature, but even a casual analysis of the conditions is sufficient to show that this idea leads to very great complexity. The authors' opinion is that the force of synapsis is more likely to be truly chemical, and may depend partly on the special arrangement of the chromosomes and their degree of duplication.

### Chiasma Formation

Even if we could solve the question of synapsis, there remains the question of chiasma formation. No really satisfactory hypothesis has yet been advanced. Those mentioned below have gained some support, and some have been widely accepted, but all fail to satisfy some requirements.

#### Torsion Theory

Chiasma formation may be caused by torsion resulting in strain breakage as a result of internal twisting and entwining of homologues (Figure 6-9 (a) and (b)). This idea, proposed by Darlington (1937), depends on the validity of torsion coiling and the relational coiling of homologues, both of which are somewhat doubtful. Furthermore, analysis of types of pairs of chiasmata (Huskins and Newcombe, 1941) in *Trillium* and the grasshopper fail to fit spatial expectations without involving complex and unlikely modifications.

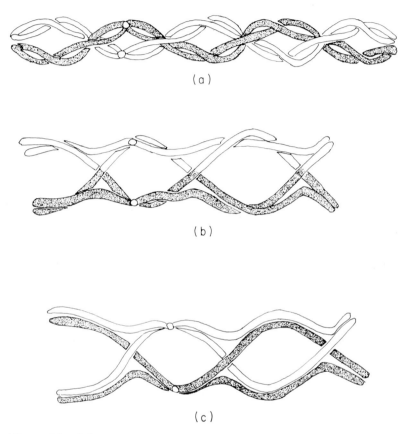

(a)

(b)

(c)

Figure 6-9. Schematic Representation of Chiasmata Formation: (a) relationship of homologous chromosomes prior to chiasmata formation; (b) formation of chiasmata by breakage and rejoining of chromatids; (c) classical mechanism of chiasmata formation as proposed by Sax (1932).

*Duplication Theory*

Duplication of chromosomes followed by longitudinal joining of the chromomeres, which, if overlapping of homologues occurs, may result in the joining of chromosomes from homologues rather than from the same chromosome (Belling, 1927, 1933). Aside from the fact that this hypothesis (Figure 6-10) fails to fit the data on pairs of adjacent chiasmata, it also demands that duplication take place at or shortly after the time of pairing, and it is difficult to see how, in its present form, it can fit the evidence of the multistranded nature of the chromosome. Also, if it is evoked to explain crossing over as well, it fails to account for three- and four-strand double crossovers.

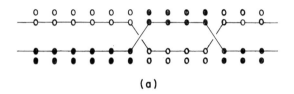

(a)

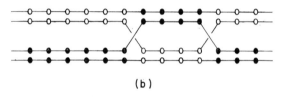

(b)

Figure 6-10. Schematic Representation of Chiasmata Formation According to the Duplication Theory Proposed by Belling.

### Classical Theory

In the classical view proposed by Karl Sax in 1932, chiasmata result from alternate opening out between sister (equational) and homologous (reductional) strands with the kinetic loops being always reductional (Figure 6-9 (c)). On this hypothesis, chiasmata do not represent the result of crossing over, but crossing over may result from breakage and rejoining at points of overlap. In this view also, reduction in the number of chiasmata should be correlated with increase in crossing over since each crossover represents elimination of a chiasma.

### Differential Contraction Theory

Tension set up by differential contraction after pairing may cause breaks at overlaps. This hypothesis is based on measurements which indicate that contraction is greater in paired regions than in those not yet paired. It is difficult to determine whether this mechanism would fit the Huskins and Newcombe data (1941) and by no means certain that any tension would result from differential contraction.

Evidence has been put forth which is supposed to show that chiasma formation and genetical crossing over are independent phenomena even in time. This conclusion is based primarily on genetical studies on re-combinations in microorganisms, which seem more easily explained on a copy-choice hypothesis. If this were so, one could consider the problem of chiasma formation without the concomitant problem of crossing over. While this might simplify the problem, the correlations between chias-mata and crossing over seem too good to be fortuitous and we would be left with lack of a reasonable functional relationship for a readily ob-servable condition. On the whole it would seem that knowledge of the forces involved in pairing is a necessary prerequisite to any analysis of factors involved in chiasma formation.

## ENERGETICS OF CELL DIVISION

Although there is an extensive literature dealing with the physiological aspects of cell division, the metabolic events associated specifically with the initiation of this division and production of energy during the mitotic process are still largely unknown. Critical evaluation of the information concerning this problem can be found in the reviews of Brachet (1957), Bullough (1952), Stern (1956), and Swann (1957).

The major difficulty one encounters in attempting to analyze the energetics of the cell-division process is that much of the available in-formation is indirect and somewhat controversial. It is well established that some cells will undergo mitosis in the absence of oxygen or in the presence of respiratory inhibitors (i.e., carbon monoxide, azide, cya-nide), while others will not (Swann, 1957). Mitosis is not initiated in sea urchin eggs under anaerobic conditions or in the presence of carbon monoxide. On the other hand, egg cells containing large amounts of yolk such as those of the frog and trout, undergo extensive cleavage in the complete absence of oxygen. In the case of the frog egg, cleavage will continue even when 90 per cent of the respiration is inhibited by carbon monoxide. The effect of oxygen lack on mitosis in tissue cultures is no clearer. Some workers have reported rapid inhibition of mitosis in tissue culture cells deprived of oxygen, while others have observed cell division to occur for a time in the absence of oxygen. The effect of oxygen deficiency and metabolic inhibitors on active mitosis, while somewhat more consistent, is almost as difficult to interpret. In the case of sea urchin eggs, it can be demonstrated that mitosis once initiated will go to completion in the presence of carbon monoxide (Swann, 1953). The initiation of mitosis in epidermal cells of the mouse is inhibited under anaerobic conditions or by carbon monoxide, but cells in the process of active mitosis are unaffected under these same conditions (Bullough, 1952). The failure of cyanide to inhibit active mitosis in meristematic cells of the pea root has also been reported (Wilson and Morrison, 1958). A similar effect of malonate and fluoracetate on mitosis in tissue culture cells was observed by Hughes (1950). In contrast, chemicals known to inhibit glycolysis, such as iodoacetic acid and fluoride, selectively block active mitosis in tissue cultures (Hughes, 1950; Pomerat and Willmer, 1939). In plant meristematic cells active mitosis is also selectively inhibited by iodoacetic acid (Wilson and Morrison, 1958). The fact that mitosis, once initiated, will continue in the absence of oxygen and is inhibited by glycolytic inhibitors would seem to implicate glycolysis as a possible source of energy during this particular phase of the mitotic cycle. While most evidence favors this view, it still remains to be determined whether glycolysis is the major and only energy source available to the dividing cell.

Swann (1957) has suggested that an "energy reservoir" may be created prior to cell division, which serves to supply the cell with the energy necessary to carry it through the division process. If such is the case, one would expect to find an increase in oxygen consumption coincident with the onset of cell division. Studies of Erickson (1947) and of Stern and Kirk (1948) on lily and *Trillium* anthers have demonstrated that such a rise in rate of oxygen consumption does actually occur prior to the prophase of microspore mitosis and microsporocyte meiosis, and falls again as soon as cell division is initiated. Stern (1956) interpreted this rise in oxygen uptake preceding mitosis as indicating an increase in energy requirements of the cell in advance of active mitosis. What the exact relationship is between this premitotic metabolism and the establishment of the so-called energy reservoir postulated by Swann is not known. It is quite possible that the increased oxygen uptake preceding mitosis is associated with metabolic events in the nucleus prior to the onset of division rather than with establishment of an energy store to be used specifically for active mitosis. As already pointed out, autoradiographic studies on nucleic acid and protein synthesis during meiosis in *Lilium longiflorum* indicate that active DNA and RNA synthesis occurs in the nucleus during the premeiotic period (Taylor, 1959). The synthesis of DNA is complete before the meiotic prophase is initiated, while RNA synthesis ceases soon after. Protein synthesis in the nucleus is most active during the premeiotic period and declines in the early stages of prophase. These events could well account for the increased oxygen consumption associated with the premitotic period.

Recently, Allfrey and coworkers (1957, and later) have demonstrated that isolated thymus nuclei can synthesize ATP through operation of a coupled oxidation-phosphorylation mechanism. The reaction mechanism mediating this synthesis remains to be investigated. However, their studies indicate that synthesis of ATP by the nucleus requires oxygen and is inhibited by azide, cyanide, and 2,4-dinitrophenol. Carbon monoxide, which is considered to be a specific inhibitor of cytochrome oxidase, has little or no effect on nuclear ATP synthesis. While the studies of the Allfrey group will have to be extended to nuclei of other cell types before their general significance can be determined, they do raise the point that the metabolism of the cell nucleus is probably much more complex than originally supposed. If it should turn out that the capacity of the nucleus for aerobic ATP synthesis is of general occurrence, the high ATP-ase content of nuclei isolated from other tissues (Siebert and Smellie, 1957) and the nuclear synthesis of DPN from nicotinamide mononucleotide and ATP (Hogeboom and Schneider, 1952) would have functional significance in terms of oxidative metabolism in the nucleus. Likewise, the synthesis of nucleotide coenzymes which Brachet (1957) has suggested may be an important activity of the nucleus, would have a basis for interpretation.

It is well established that certain glycolytic enzymes (e.g., lactic dehydrogenase, triosephosphate dehydrogenase, aldolase, enolase) are present in reasonably high concentration in the nuclei of plant and animal cells (Dounce, 1954, 1955; Lang and Siebert, 1951, 1952). On the other hand, the enzyme systems characteristically associated with respiration and oxidative phosphorylation in the cytoplasm are presumably absent (Siebert and Smellie, 1957). A list of the enzymes which cannot be demonstrated in nuclei is shown in Table 6-1. The only known exception to this finding is that the nucleated erythrocyte of the bird has been shown to contain cytochrome oxidase and succinic dehydrogenase in the nucleus. The explanation, as pointed out by Brachet (1957), seems to be that this type of cell does not possess mitochondria. The functional significance of the presence of glycolytic enzymes in the nucleus is not known; however, the possibility exists that a nuclear glycolytic pathway may function in the initial stages of carbohydrate breakdown to produce energy, and operate to reduce DPN (Stern and Mirsky, 1952). Also glycolysis within the nucleus may be necessary to supply certain intermediate metabolites needed for special intranuclear metabolism

(Dounce, 1954), possibly of the type demonstrated by the Allfrey group. The results of Allfrey and coworkers indicating that ATP synthesis is coupled to oxidative processes in the nucleus, are interesting in the light of the finding that isolated plant cell nuclei contain ascorbic acid and glutathione but are lacking in flavoproteins and cytochrome c (Stern and Timonen, 1954). It is conceivable that glutathione and ascorbic acid, with their high capacity for oxidation-reduction, may form part of an electron transport system operating in the nucleus which may in some way be related to the aerobic synthesis of nuclear ATP. The cyclic variations in ascorbic acid reported by Stern and Timonen (1954) to occur during the mitotic cycle certainly merit further investigation.

TABLE 6-I.  Enzymes Absent from Isolated Nuclei.*

| | |
|---|---|
| Succinoxidase | Choline oxidase |
| Cytochrome oxidase | L-Amino acid oxidase |
| Catalase | D-Amino acid oxidase |
| Cytochrome c | Proline oxidase |
| Uricase | Malic dehydrogenase |
| Xanthine oxidase | |

* Data from Siebert, G. and Smellie, R. M. S., 1957. "Enzymatic and Metabolic Studies on Isolated Nuclei," *Intern. Rev. Cytology.*, **6**, Table I, p. 391.

Brachet (1957) has discussed in detail the results of Allfrey's group and has suggested that the aerobic metabolic pathway demonstrated by these workers may be confined, for the most part, to those cells which are in process of preparing for cell division. There are several observations which tend to support this view. The studies of Mazia and Prescott (1954) indicate that uptake of $P^{32}$ in the ameba decreases markedly at the time of cell division, suggesting a reduced capacity to esterify inorganic phosphate at this stage of the mitotic cycle. As already pointed out, the premitotic period, in plant cells at least, is associated with an increase in oxygen consumption (Erickson, 1947; Stern and Kirk, 1948). The metabolic changes reported by Taylor (1959) to occur during the premeiotic period in lily anthers could well be controlled by a metabolic pathway of the type shown by Allfrey and coworkers to be mediated by DNA. According to these workers, DNA controls the synthesis of nuclear ATP which, in turn, controls the incorporation of amino acids into protein and the uptake of purines and pyrimidines into nuclear RNA.

Another observation by the Allfrey group which may be of functional significance in terms of cell division kinetics is that nuclear synthesis of

ATP is markedly affected by changes in environment and that fine structure, nuclear function, and osmotic balance are closely integrated (Allfrey and Mirsky, 1959). The correlation between the presence of a negative electrical charge associated with the chromosomes and biochemical activity of the nucleus has also been stressed by these same workers. As pointed out by Stern (1956), it is obvious that disorganization of the interphase nucleus at the onset of mitosis must have widespread effects on cell activity. The morphological changes in the chromosomes coincident with the development of prophase are well known, and have already been described in detail in Chapter 5. It may well be that the physical and chemical organization of the nucleus is so radically altered at the onset of cell division that some of the metabolic pathways which were operative during the premitotic period are either greatly reduced in activity or made completely inoperative. The decrease in oxygen consumption accompanying the onset of cell division and the apparent lack of synthesis during the postprophase stages of mitosis support this view. It is well known that marked changes in the appearance of the cytoplasm occur during active mitosis. While the nature of these changes is not completely known, it has been found that the basophilic structures characteristic of the cytoplasmic membrane system are altered at the onset of mitosis (Brachet, 1957). The recent electron microscope studies of Porter and Machado (1960) have shown that alterations in the structure and distribution of the endoplasmic reticulum accompany the mitotic process in plant meristematic cells. These workers suggested that the role played by the elements of the endoplasmic reticulum during cell division may be passive relative to chromosome movements in much the same sense that mitochondria and plastids are apparently uninvolved. During mitosis in tissue culture cells and cleavage in sea urchin eggs, the mitochondria lose their motility and fragment into bead-like structures or granules which sometimes completely disappear from view (Agrell, 1955; Chèvremont and Frédéric, 1952). Reconstitution of the mitochondria apparently occurs during the terminal stages of the mitotic process. On the basis of available evidence, it would appear that oxidative processes are minimal during active mitosis and that whatever metabolic activities are associated with this stage of the mitotic cycle are most likely mediated through operation of a glycolytic pathway. Further investigation of nuclear metabolism along lines similar to those employed by the Allfrey group will undoubtedly yield many new and interesting findings which hold promise of contributing significantly to our understanding of the problem of cell division.

# BIBLIOGRAPHY

Agrell, I., 1955. "Mitotic Rhythm in the Appearance of Mitochondria During the Early Cleavages of the Sea-urchin Embryo," *Exptl. Cell Res.,* 8, 232-234.

Allfrey, V. and Mirsky, A. E., 1957. "The Role of Deoxyribonucleic Acid and Other Polynucleotides in ATP Synthesis by Isolated Cell Nuclei," *Proc. Natl. Acad. Sci.,* 43, 589-598.

Allfrey, V. and Mirsky, A. E., 1957. "Some Aspects of Ribonucleic Acid Synthesis in Isolated Cell Nuclei," *Proc. Natl. Acad. Sci.,* 43, 821-826.

Allfrey, V. and Mirsky, A. E., 1959. "Biochemical Properties of the Isolated Nucleus," *in* "Subcellular Particles," T. Hayashi (Ed.), Ronald Press, New York, N.Y., pp. 186-207.

Allfrey, V., Mirsky, A. E., and Osawa, S., 1955. "Protein Synthesis in Isolated Cell Nuclei," *Nature,* 176, 1042-1049.

Allfrey, V., Mirsky, A. E., and Osawa, S., 1957. "The Nucleus and Protein Synthesis," *in* "Chemical Basis of Heredity," W. D. McElroy and B. Glass (Eds.), Johns Hopkins University Press, Baltimore, Md., pp. 200-231.

Allfrey, V., Mirsky, A. E., and Stern, H., 1955. "The Chemistry of the Cell Nucleus," *Advances in Enzymol.,* 16, 411-500.

Barron, E. S. G., 1951. "Thiol Groups of Biological Importance," *Advances in Enzymol.,* 11, 201-266.

Belling, J., 1927. "The Attachments of Chromosomes at the Reduction Division in Flowering Plants," *J. Genetics,* 18, 177-205.

Belling, J., 1933. "Crossing Over and Gene Rearrangements in Flowering Plants," *Genetics,* 18, 388-413.

Bernal, J. D., 1940. "Structural Units in Cellular Physiology," *Publ. Am. Assoc. Advance. Sci.,* 14, 199-205.

Bjerknes, V., 1902. "Hydrodynamische Fernkräfte," Barth, Leipzig.

Bjerknes, V., 1909. "Die Kraftfelder," Vieweg, Braunschweig.

Bolognari, A., 1952. "Variazioni quantitative del contenuto in glutatione nelle uova fecondate di *Paracentrotus lividus,*" *Arch. Sci. Biol.,* 36, 40-47.

Brachet, J., 1957. "Biochemical Cytology," Academic Press, New York, N.Y.

Bullough, W. S., 1952. "The Energy Relations of Mitotic Activity," *Biol. Rev.,* Cambridge Phil. Soc., 27, 133-168.

Bullough, W. S., 1955. "Hormones and Mitotic Activity," *in* "Vitamins and Hormones," Academic Press, New York, N.Y., pp. 261-292.

Cantarow, A. and Schepartz, B., 1954. "Biochemistry," W. B. Saunders Co., Philadelphia, Pa.

Chèvremont, M. and Frédéric, J., 1952. "Evolution des chondriosomes lors de la mitose somatique," *Arch. Biol.,* 63, 259-278.

Darlington, C. D., 1937. "Recent Advances in Cytology," 2nd ed., Blakiston Co., Philadelphia, Pa.

Dounce, A. L., 1954. "The Significance of Enzyme Studies on Isolated Cell Nuclei," *Intern. Rev. Cytol.,* 3, 199-223.

Dounce, A. L., 1955. "The Isolation and Composition of Nuclei and Nucleoli," *in* "The Nucleic Acids," Vol. 2, E. Chargaff and J. N. Davidson (Eds.), Academic Press, New York, N.Y., pp. 93-153.

Erickson, R. O., 1947. "Respiration of Developing Anthers," *Nature,* **159,** 275-276.

Hogeboom, G. H. and Schneider, W. C., 1952. "The Synthesis of Diphosphopyridine Nucleotide by Liver Cell Nuclei," *J. Biol. Chem.,* **197,** 611-620.

Hughes, A. F. W., 1950. "The Effect of Inhibitory Substances on Cell Division. A Study on Living Cells in Tissue Cultures," *Quart. J. Miscroscop. Sci.,* **91,** 251-278.

Hughes, A. F. W., 1952. "The Mitotic Cycle," Academic Press, New York, N.Y.

Huskins, C. L. and Newcombe, H. B., 1941. "An Analysis of Chiasma Pairs Showing Chromatid Interference in *Trillium erectum* L.," *Genetics,* **26,** 101-127.

Infantellina, F. and LaGrutta, G., 1948. "Contenuto in glutatione nella uova di *Paracentrotus lividus* e sue variazione nelle varie fasi dello sviluppo," *Arch. Sci. Biol.,* **32,** 85-106.

Inoué, S., 1952. "The Effect of Colchicine on the Microscopic and Submicroscopic Structure of the Mitotic Spindle," *Exptl. Cell Res., Suppl.,* **2,** 305-322.

Inoué, S., 1953. "The Demonstration of Spindle Fibers in Living Cells," *Chromosoma,* **5,** 487-500.

Inoué, S. and Dan, K., 1951. "Birefrigence of the Dividing Cell," *J. Morphol.,* **89,** 423-451.

Kawamura, N. and Dan, K., 1958. "A Cytochemical Study of the Sulfhydryl Groups of Sea Urchin Eggs During the First Cleavage," *J. Biophys. Biochem. Cytol.,* **4,** 615-620.

Leak, L. V. and Wilson, G. B., 1960. "Relative Volume Changes of the Nucleolus in Relation to Cell and Nucleus in *Pisum sativum* and *Tradescantia paludosa,*" *Trans. Am. Microscop. Soc.,* **79,** 154-160.

Lillie, R. S., 1905. "The Physiology of Cell Division. I.," *Am. J. Physiol.,* **15,** 46-84.

Mazia, D., 1952. "Physiology of the Cell Nucleus," *in* "Modern Trends in Physiology and Biochemistry," E. S. G. Barron (Ed.), Academic Press, New York, N.Y., pp. 77-122.

Mazia, D., 1955. "The Organization of the Mitotic Apparatus," *Symp. Soc. Exptl. Biol.,* **9,** 335-357.

Mazia, D., 1957. "Some Problems in the Chemistry of Mitosis," *in* "Chemical Basis of Heredity," W. D. McElroy and B. Glass (Eds.), Johns Hopkins University Press, Baltimore, Md., pp. 169-185.

Mazia, D. and Dan, K., 1952. "The Isolation and Biochemical Characterization of the Mitotic Apparatus of Dividing Cells," *Proc. Natl. Acad. Sci.,* **38,** 826-838.

Mazia, D. and Prescott, D. M., 1954. "Nuclear Function and Mitosis," *Science,* **120,** 120-122.

Mirsky, A. E. and Allfrey, V., 1958. "The Role of the Nucleus in Development," *in* "Chemical Basis of Development," W. D. McElroy and B. Glass (Eds.), Johns Hopkins University Press, Baltimore, Md., pp. 94-102.

Nasatir, M. and Stern, H., 1959. "Changes in the Activities of Aldolase and of D-Glyceraldehyde-3-phosphate Dehydrogenase During the Mitotic Cycle in Microspores of *Lilium longiflorum*," *J. Biophys. Biochem. Cytol.,* 6, 189-192.

Osawa, S., Allfrey, V., and Mirsky, A. E., 1957. "Mononucleotides of the Cell Nucleus," *J. Gen. Physiol.,* 40, 491-513.

Östergren, G., 1945. "Equilibrium of Trivalents and the Mechanism of Chromosome Movements," *Hereditas,* 31, 498-499.

Östergren, G., 1949. "A Survey of Factors Working at Mitosis," *Hereditas,* 35, 525-528.

Östergren, G., 1950. "Considerations of Some Elementary Features of Mitosis," *Hereditas,* 36, 1-18.

Pomerat, C. M. and Willmer, E. N., 1939. "Studies on the Growth of Tissues *in Vitro*. VII. Carbohydrate Metabolism and Mitosis," *J. Exptl. Biol.,* 16, 232-249.

Porter, K. R. and Machado, R. D., 1960. "Studies on the Endoplasmic Reticulum. IV. Its Form and Distribution During Mitosis in Cells of Onion Root Tip," *J. Biophys. Biochem. Cytol.,* 7, 167-180.

Prescott, D. M., 1955. "Relations Between Cell Growth and Cell Division," *Exptl. Cell Res.,* 9, 328-337.

Rapkine, L., 1931. "Sur les processus chimiques au cours de la division cellulaire," *Ann. physiol. physiochim. Biol.,* 7, 382-418.

Satô, S., 1960. "Electron Microscope Studies on the Mitotic Figure. III. Process of the Spindle Formation," *Cytologia,* 25, 119-131.

Sax, K., 1932. "The Cytological Mechanism of Crossing Over," *J. Arnold Arboretum,* 13, 180-212.

Sax, K., 1936. "Chromosome Coiling in Relation to Meiosis and Crossing-over," *Genetics,* 21, 324-338.

Schrader, F., 1934. "On the Reality of Spindle Fibers," *Biol. Bull.,* 67, 519-534.

Schrader, F., 1951. "A Critique of Recent Hypotheses of Mitosis," *in* "Symposium on Cytology," Michigan State University Press, E. Lansing, Mich., pp. 37-51.

Schrader, F., 1953. "Mitosis," 2nd ed., Columbia University Press, New York, N.Y.

Siebert, G. and Smellie, R. M. S., 1957. "Enzymatic and Metabolic Studies on Isolated Nuclei," *Intern. Rev. Cytol.,* 6, 383-424.

Stern, H., 1955. "On the Intranuclear Environment," *Science,* 121, 144-145.

Stern, H., 1956. "The Physiology of Cell Division," *Ann. Rev. Plant Physiol.,* 7, 91-114.

Stern, H. and Kirk, P. L., 1948. "The Oxygen Consumption of the Microspores of *Trillium* in Relation to the Mitotic Cycle," *J. Gen. Physiol.,* 31, 243-248.

Stern, H. and Mirsky, A. E., 1952. "The Isolation of Wheat Germ Nuclei and Some Aspects of Their Glycolytic Metabolism," *J. Gen. Physiol.,* 36, 181-200.

Stern, H. and Timonen, S., 1954. "The Position of the Cell Nucleus in Pathways of Hydrogen Transfer: "Cytochrome c, Flavoproteins, Glutathione and Ascorbic Acid," *J. Gen. Physiol.,* 38, 41-52.

Swann, M. M., 1951. "The Birefrigence of the Metaphase Spindle and Asters of the Living Sea Urchin Egg," *J. Exptl. Biol.,* 28, 417-443.

Swann, M. M., 1953. "The Mechanism of Cell Division: A Study with Carbon Monoxide on the Sea-urchin Egg," *Quart. J. Microscop. Sci.,* 94, 369-379.

Swann, M. M., 1957. "The Control of Cell Division: A Review. I. General Mechanisms," *Cancer Res.,* 17, 727-757.

Swann, M. M. and Mitchison, J. M., 1953. "Cleavage of Sea Urchin Eggs in Colchicine," *J. Exptl. Biol.,* 30, 506-514.

Swanson, C. P., 1942. "Some Considerations on the Phenomenon of Chiasma Terminalization," *Am. Naturalist,* 76, 593-610.

Taylor, J. H., 1959. "Autoradiographic Studies of Nucleic Acids and Proteins During Meiosis in *Lilium longiflorum,*" *Am. J. Botany,* 46, 477-484.

Taylor, J. H. and Woods, P. S., 1959. *"In Situ* Studies of Polynucleotide Synthesis in Nucleolus and Chromosomes," *in* "Subcellular Particles," T. Hayashi (Ed.), Ronald Press, New York, N.Y., pp. 172-185.

Whaley, W. G., Mollenhauer, H. H., and Leech, J. H., 1960. "The Ultrastructure of the Meristematic Cell," *Am. J. Botany,* 47, 401-449.

Wilson, E. B., 1900. "The Cell in Development and Heredity," 2nd ed., The Macmillan Co., New York, N.Y.

Wilson, G. B., 1959. "Studies on the Control of Mitotic Activity: Fourth Huskins Memorial Lecture," *Can. J. Genet. and Cytol.,* 1, 1-9.

Wilson, G. B. and Hyppio, P. A., 1955. "Some Factors Concerned in the Mechanism of Mitosis," *Cytologia,* 20, 177-184.

Wilson, G. B. and Morrison, J. H., 1958. "Mitotic Activity and Behaviour as an Index of Chemical Effect," *The Nucleus,* 1, 45-56.

Wilson, G. B. and Morrison, J. H., 1959. "The Mitotic Cycle and the Ontogeny of Neoplastic Growth," *Cytologia,* 24, 43-49.

Wilson, G. B., Morrison, J. H., and Knobloch, N., 1959. "Studies on the Control of Mitotic Activity in Excised Roots. I. The Experimental System," *J. Biophys. Biochem. Cytol.,* 5, 411-420.

# 7

# *The Chromosome Coiling Cycle*

A SOMATIC metaphase chromosome consists of two more or less en-twined chromatids, each containing a chromonema (which is probably at least double) in the form of a helical coil (Figure 7-1). The nature and origin of this coil has been the subject of very considerable study and speculation. Most of the more critical studies have been based on the analogous coil of first metaphase and first anaphase of meiosis, especially in plants with large chromosomes. The equivalent meiotic coil (Figure 7-2) is longer-gyred, looser, and more amenable to detailed study. At first anaphase the chromosome consists of two chromatids, relatively widely separated except at the kinetochore. With some mate-rials and by special methods, preparations can be made to reveal the details of coil structure and allow accurate studies of such things as the number of gyres, size, and direction of coiling.

From about 1926 to 1940 a large number of papers were published on this subject. The most active workers were Darlington and his associ-ates (England), Nebel (Geneva, N.Y.), Huskins and his associates (Canada), and Kuwada and his students (Japan). These workers fall fairly neatly into two groups on the question of the origin of this coil. Nebel (1939) refers to them as the *torsional* and *matrical* schools. The basic idea of the former group (Darlington, Kuwada, and Nebel) visu-alizes the coil as being the more or less direct result of the torsion set up by a hypothetical molecular coil. A reasonably adequate model is pro-vided by a twisted elastic band, which tends to relieve the torsion by throwing itself into a large gyred helix. The latter group (Sax, Wilson, and Huskins), on the other hand, favors the idea of a differential length change between the matrix and its enclosed chromonema. A stiff rubber tube forced into a jar of about half its length will serve as a model in this case, for the rubber tube will be forced into a coil.

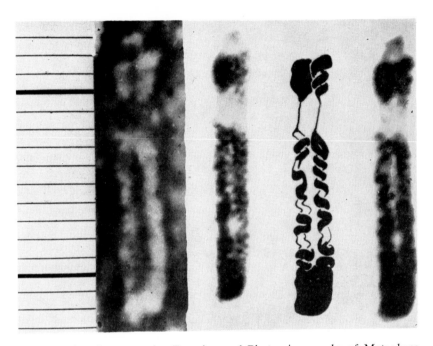

**Figure 7-1.** Interpretative Drawing and Photomicrographs of Metaphase Chromosome from *Allium* Root Tip Showing Nature and Direction of Coiling in Sister Chromatids. (From Wilson, G. B. and Coleman, P. G., 1952. "The Ontogeny of Chromosome and Chromonema Spirals. A Re-evaluation," *Cytologia,* **17,** Figs. 1 and 2, Plate IV.)

The most complete hypothesis of the torsion school has been advanced by Darlington (1937). In brief, his idea is that a molecular coil through torsion gives rise to an internal coil in the opposite direction, which in meiosis produces the major coil. The same mechanism, by assuming uniformity of direction of coiling in the half chromatids, is presumed to explain relational coiling at prophase of mitosis through the tendency of such pairs of coiled strands to reduce tension by entwining in a compensating direction. In meiosis, homologous chromosomes with uniformity in coiling direction would form a relational coil as the two half chromosomes do in mitosis, and Darlington has extended this notion to explain chiasma formation as the result of strain in the twisted homologues. Although the theory is logical in its main outline, it fails to explain a number of known facts: first, homologous chromosomes have

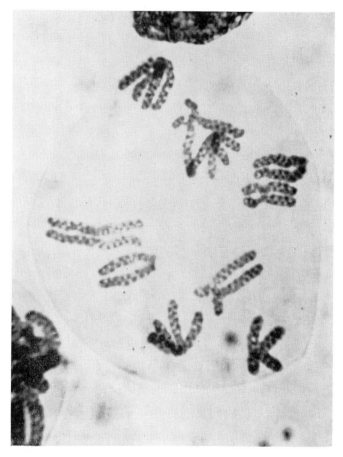

**Figure 7-2.** Photomicrograph Showing Helical Coil in Meiotic Chromosome of *Trillium*. (Courtesy of Dr. A. H. Sparrow, Brookhaven National Laboratory.)

a random direction of coiling with respect to each other; second, the relational coil is not developed at prophase but simultaneously with the development of the helical coils; and third, the direction of coiling is not uniform throughout the chromosome, being random across the kinetochore and subject to reversals within arms (Table 7-1). A number of modifications have been proposed to explain these observations, but though many of them agree superficially with data, they fail to make mathematical agreement.

TABLE 7-1. Frequency of Intrabrachial Reversals at First Anaphase.*

| Observed | | Hypothetical | | | | | |
|---|---|---|---|---|---|---|---|
| | | Intrabrachial reversals | | | Gyres * | | |
| Intrabrachial reversals per cell | Gyres | Within chiasma regions | In other regions | Total | Within chiasma regions | At other loci | |
| 35.9 ± 1.9 | 209.5 ± 1.9 | 31 | 5 | 36 | 125 | 85 | |

| Chiasma frequency | |
|---|---|
| True | Effective |
| 24.36 ± 0.58 | 15.6 ± 0.4 |

* Data from Wilson, G. B. and Hutcheson, I., 1941. "Further Studies on Changes of Direction in the Major Coil of the Chromosomes of *Trillium erectum* L." *Can. J. Research, C,* 19, Table III, p. 389.

The most extensive studies of the matrical group were those made at McGill University from 1935 to 1941. The lead was provided by Wilson and Huskins' discovery (1939) that in *Trillium erectum,* when the major coil is being developed, the over-all length of the chromosome changes only very slightly in the direction of contraction, while the chromonema length increases at least twofold (Table 7-2). All torsion mechanisms demand either contraction of the chromonema or else more or less static conditions. Wilson and Huskins, therefore, proposed the idea that the major coil was the direct result of elongation of the chromonema within a limiting membrane. The general theory is that all chromonema helical coils are the result of differential length changes between the matrix and the contained thread. Later work by Wilson and Hutcheson (1941), Sparrow, *et al.* (1941), and Sparrow (1942) further supported this general hypothesis and showed how it could explain the relational coiling of half chromosomes at prophase. The most important evidence in favor of the hypothesis proposed is the fact that reversals occur with random frequency at chiasmata and the kinetochores and that when these are allowed for, there remain a number correlated with length or, more specifically, with the number of gyres. Such a distribution would be extremely difficult to explain on any torsion theory.

Whether two strands will twist about each other in a relational coil appears to be a function of their distance from each other at the time of formation of the helical coil. If two strands are widely separated and have separate matrices, they will not entwine, and the helical coils formed will be independent in direction. If two strands are clearly separate but within the same matrix, they will not entwine, but their helical coils will be in the same direction at the same loci; if two strands are so close together as to be virtually single, they will be entwined with

TABLE 7-2. Chromosome and Chromonema Lengths in *Trillium erectum*.*

| Stage | Lengths (in microns) | |
|---|---|---|
| | Chromosome | Chromonema |
| Leptotene | — | 920 |
| Zygotene | — | 1040 |
| Pachytene | — | 640 |
| Diakinesis (early) | 86 | 109 |
| Diakinesis (mid) | 125 | 187 |
| Metaphase I | 99 | 320 |
| Anaphase I | 93 | 327 |
| Anaphase II | 76 | 310 |

* Data from Sparrow, A. H., Huskins, C. L., and Wilson, G. B., 1941. "Studies on the Chromosome Spiralization Cycle in *Trillium*," *Can. J. Research, C,* **19**, Table I, p. 325.

one twist for each turn of the helical coil. A bivalent may be considered to consist of two pairs of chromatids, each chromatid a half chromosome, which coil in the same direction but do not entwine. Half chromatids which are very close together entwine to give the relational coiling (Figure 7-3) seen at, for example, the first pollen-grain division in *Trillium* (Figure 7-4). Sparrow, Huskins, and Wilson (1941) and Sparrow (1942) showed a mathematical relationship between the prophase relational coil and the association of half chromatids at the previous anaphase.

In general, the McGill group viewed the coiling cycle as being the result of differential length changes between the matrix and the enclosed chromonemata, with relational coiling being a function of the degree of association of two jointly coiling strands. If two strands are separate and parallel before coiling, they must revolve about each other to form a relational coil. If they are virtually single, then to become relationally coiled requires only that the potentially double strand twist on its own axis. This theory does, however, fail to explain two occasionally reported observations, namely, the development of a minor coil at right angles to the major coil and the relational coiling of homologous chromosomes at zygotene. The former, however, is at the limit of optical reso-

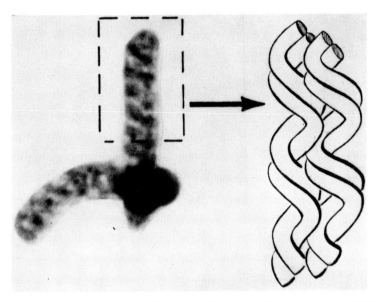

**Figure 7-3.** Photomicrograph of Late Diakinesis Chromosome of *Trillium erectum* with a Schematic Representation of Four-strand Paranemic-Plectonemic Association in a Half-Bivalent. Each strand in the diagram is a half chromatid. (From Wilson, G. B., Sparrow, A. H., and Pond, V., 1959. "Sub-Chromatid Rearrangements in *Trillium erectum*. I. Origin and Nature of Configurations Induced by Ionizing Radiation," *Am. J. Botany,* **46**, Fig. 1, p. 310. Courtesy of Dr. A. H. Sparrow, Brookhaven National Laboratory.)

lution and is considered by many to be either an optical illusion or a zigzag which would be expected in a longitudinally heterogeneous thread. With respect to the latter observation, there is no indisputable evidence that such relational coiling actually exists, since the few cases illustrated seem equally likely to be accidental overlaps.

The electron microscope has so far added little to our knowledge of chromosome geometry beyond indicating that component strands are almost certainly made up of many (probably 64) microfibrils which are

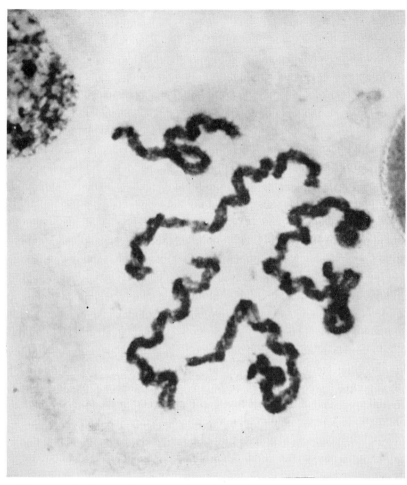

**Figure 7-4.** Photomicrograph Showing Relational Coiling in the B, D, and E Chromosomes of a Giant Microspore of *Trillium grandiflorum* with Nine Chromosomes. (From Sparrow, A. H., Huskins, C. L., and Wilson, G. B., 1941. "Studies on the Chromosome Spiralization Cycle in *Trillium*," *Can. J. Res., C,* 19, Fig. 28, Plate IV. Courtesy of Dr. A. H. Sparrow, Brookhaven National Laboratory.)

presumably in part DNA helices. So far as we are aware the only inter-pretation of electron micrographs which attempts to tie together the submicroscopic picture with that revealed by the light microscope is the

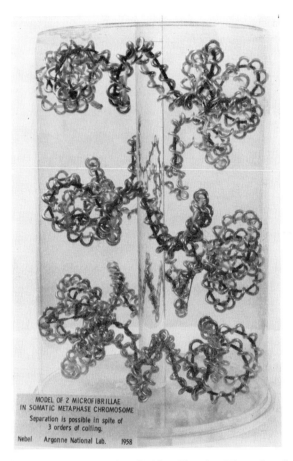

**Figure 7-5.** Model of Two Microfibrillae Showing Three Levels of Coiling in a Somatic Metaphase Chromosome. (From Nebel, B. R., 1960. "On the Structure of Mammalian Chromosomes During Spermatogenesis and After Radiation, with Special Reference to Cores," *in* "Fourth Intern. Conference on Electron Microscopy," Springer-Verlag, Fig. 1, p. 228. Courtesy of Dr. B. R. Nebel, Argonne National Laboratory.)

one offered by Nebel (1959-60). Essentially his model consists of a hierarchy of three levels of coiling, including the minor coil (Figure 7-5). The question of the reality of the minor coil, however, is still open, with the number of workers who flatly deny its existence being pretty well matched by those who defend it on both theoretical and observational grounds. Neither molecular nor supramolecular helices necessarily imply torsion, but they do suggest a rational mechanism for producing length changes in the chromosome which are necessary to explain at least part of the contraction phenomenon as well as being an essential adjunct to either major hypothesis of coiling.

## BIBLIOGRAPHY

Darlington, C. D., 1935. "The Internal Mechanics of Chromosomes," *Proc. Roy. Soc. (London), B.,* 118, 33-96.

Darlington, C. D., 1937. "Recent Advances in Cytology," 2nd ed., Blakiston Co., Philadelphia, Pa.

Huskins, C. L., 1937. "The Internal Structure of Chromosomes—A Statement of Opinion," *Cytologia (Fujii Jubilee Volume),* 2, 1015-1022.

Huskins, C. L., 1941. "The Coiling of Chromonemata," *Cold Spring Harbor Symposia Quant. Biol.,* 9, 13-17.

Huskins, C. L. and Smith, S. G., 1935. "Meiotic Chromosome Structure in *Trillium erectum,*" *Ann. Botany,* 49, 119-150.

Huskins, C. L. and Wilson, G. B., 1938. "Probable Causes of the Changes in Direction of the Major Coil in *Trillium erectum* L.," *Ann. Botany, New Series,* 2, 281-292.

Kaufmann, B. P., 1948. "Chromosome Structure in Relation to the Chromosome Cycle. II," *Botan. Rev.,* 14, 57-126.

Kuwada, Y., 1939. "Chromosome Structure. A Critical Review," *Cytologia,* 10, 213-256.

Nebel, B. R., 1939. "Chromosome Structure," *Botan. Rev.,* 5, 563-626.

Nebel, B. R., 1941. "The Structure of *Tradescantia* and *Trillium* Chromosomes with Particular Emphasis on Number of Chromonemata," *Cold Spring Harbor Symposia Quant. Biol.,* 9, 7-12.

Nebel, B. R., 1960. "On the Structure of Mammalian Chromosomes During Spermatogenesis and After Radiation with Special Reference to Cores," *Fourth Intern. Conf. Electron Microscopy,* 1958. Springer-Verlag, Berlin.

Nebel, B. R., Tyler, S. A., and Murphy, C. J., 1960. "A Note on the Statistical Determination of Shape of Chromatin Elements in Human Spermatid and *Tradescantia* Microsporocyte," *J. Biophys. Biochem. Cytol.,* 7, 377-379.

Ris, H., 1957. "Chromosome Structure," *in* "Chemical Basis of Heredity," W. D. McElroy and B. Glass (Eds.), Johns Hopkins University Press, Baltimore, Md., pp. 23-62.

Sax, H. J. and Sax, K., 1935. "Chromosome Structure and Behavior in Mitosis and Meiosis," *J. Arnold Arboretum,* 16, 423-439.

Sax, K., 1937. "Chromosome Behavior and Nuclear Development in *Tradescantia,*" *Genetics,* 22, 523-533.

Sax, K. and Humphrey, L. M., 1934. "Structure of Meiotic Chromosomes in Microsporogenesis of *Tradescantia,*" *Botan. Gaz.,* 96, 353-362.

Sparrow, A. H., 1942. "The Structure and Development of the Chromosome Spirals in Microspores of *Trillium*," *Can. J. Res., D,* **20**, 257-266.

Sparrow, A. H., Huskins, C. L., and Wilson, G. B., 1941. "Studies on the Chromosome Spiralization Cycle in *Trillium*," *Can. J. Res., C,* **19**, 323-350.

Swanson, C. P., 1942. "Meiotic Coiling in *Tradescantia*," *Botan. Gaz.,* **103**, 457-474.

Wilson, G. B. and Coleman, P. G., 1952. "The Ontogeny of Chromosome and Chromonema Spirals. A Re-evaluation," *Cytologia,* **17**, 270-278.

Wilson, G. B. and Huskins, C. L., 1939. "Chromosome and Chromonema Length During Meiotic Coiling in *Trillium erectum* L.," *Ann. Botany, New Series,* **3**, 257-270.

Wilson, G. B. and Hutcheson, I., 1941. "Further Studies on Changes of Direction in the Major Coil of the Chromonema of *Trillium erectum* L.," *Can. J. Res., C,* **19**, 383-390.

Wilson, G. B., Sparrow, A. H., and Pond, V., 1959. "Sub-chromatid Re-arrangements in *Trillium erectum*. I. Origin and Nature of Configurations Induced by Ionizing Radiation," *Am. J. Botany,* **46**, 309-316.

# 8

# *Cytogenetics*

A MAJOR corollary of the chromosome theory of heredity is that changes in number, structure, or behavior of chromosomes must represent, to some extent, changes in the genetic potential of the organisms involved. The study of the correlation between cytologically observable chromosome change and genetic change constitutes the hybrid discipline of cytogenetics. The present chapter is concerned with those chromosome changes which are of particular significance in this regard. These include increase and decrease in chromosome number, interchanges between chromosomes, and rearrangements within chromosomes.

The basic organism in genetic theory is the true diploid, which may be defined as one possessing two chromosome sets, the chromosomes of one set being of *maternal,* the other of *paternal* origin. The genes associated with the chromosomes making up each set constitute a *genome;* therefore the diploid organism contains two matching genomes, or sets of genes, arranged on two matching sets of chromosomes. The chromosome constitution of an organism may be altered either by spontaneous or induced "accidents." These changes are classifiable and may be related, in theory at least, to their origins.

## CHANGES IN CHROMOSOME NUMBER

### Polyploidy

The simplest and perhaps the most important change in chromosome constitution involves the duplication of one or more complete chromosome sets (Figure 8-1 (a) and (b)) to give a *polyploid* organism. A polyploid may therefore be defined as an organism with more than two complete sets of chromosomes. Regardless of apparent complexity, the origin of any polyploid traces back either to failure of anaphase separation in mitosis or meiosis, or to stimulation of a cell already potentially polyploid through endomitosis.

Polyploids are generally classified according to whether the original stock was a cytological *homozygote* or a cytological *heterozygote*. The

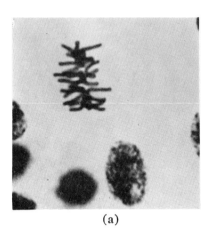 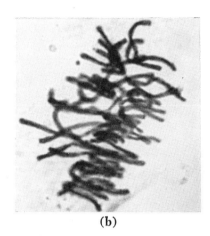

(a)                      (b)

**Figure 8-1.** (a) Photomicrograph of Normal Diploid Metaphase in Dividing Meristematic Cell of *Allium*. (b) Photomicrograph of Tetraploid Metaphase in *Allium* Root Tip Cell Induced by Cyclochlorohexane. (Fig. (a) from Wilson, G. B., Hawthorne, M. E., and Tsou, T. M., 1951. "Spontaneous and Induced Variations in Mitosis," *J. Heredity, 42,* Fig. 12 A, p. 188. Fig. (b) from Wilson, G. B., Tsou, T. M., and Hyppio, P., 1952. "Variations in Mitosis. II. The Interrelation of Some Basic Deviations," *J. Heredity, 43,* Fig. 71, p. 212.)

former gives rise to an *autopolyploid* in which all the chromosome sets are homologous and the latter to an *allopolyploid* in which, ideally, no chromosome has more than one homologue. There are, of course, many theoretical intermediates and complex combinations of these two types (Stebbins, 1950) and in practice most cases are intermediate.

The following illustration may serve to show the essential differences between the two classes. If a diploid containing two *homologous* chromosome sets, AA, has its chromosome number doubled, it will give rise to an organism having four sets of matching chromosomes, AAAA. Pairing at meiosis will therefore tend to be in groups of four (see Figure 8-2). In practice such perfect association may not occur, and we may get associations of 4, 3 + 1, 2 + 2, 2 + 1 + 1, and 1 + 1 + 1 + 1, of which the first two are most likely. The unwieldiness of the first type of association and the random distribution at anaphase of the unassociated chromosome in the second leads to the production of unbalanced gametes which tend to be inviable, and thus a true *autotetraploid* may range from being partially to almost completely sterile.

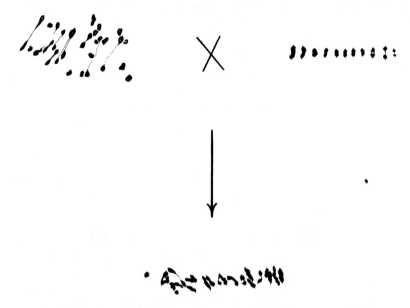

**Figure 8-2.** Diagram of Cross Between Triploid Commercial Banana (Variety Gross Michel, 2n = 33) and Naturally Occurring Diploid (*Musa acuminata,* Variety Zebrina) to Give Tetraploid Seedling (2n = 44). The tetraploid contains three sets of Gros Michel and one set of *M. acuminata* chromosomes. (From Wilson, G. B., 1946. "Cytological Studies in the Musae. I, II, III," *Genetics,* 31, Fig. 3, p. 249; Fig. A, p. 478; Fig. A, p. 484.)

If a diploid containing two more or less *nonhomologous* chromosome sets, AB, has its chromosome number doubled, it will give rise to an *allotetraploid* of constitution AABB. At meiosis in such an organism, A chromosomes will tend to pair with A and B with B to give pairs similar to a normal diploid and thus a mechanically fertile individual. The extreme case is known as an *amphidiploid* and is cytologically and often genetically difficult to distinguish from a diploid except in comparison with its putative parents.

Polyploids are sometimes classified on the basis of origin as *primary* and *secondary*. A primary polyploid (Figure 8-1) is one which arises directly from a given organism by chromosome doubling and must therefore always be even-numbered, while a secondary polyploid is one which arises from crossing—especially, but not necessarily, between organisms of different ploidy levels; for example,

$$2x \xrightarrow{\text{(doubled)}} 4x \text{ (primary)} \times 2x \xrightarrow{\hspace{2cm}} 3x \text{ (secondary)}$$

Since cytological fertility is a function of the degree of association in pairs, even-numbered allopolyploids are more likely to be fertile than even-numbered autopolyploids. Odd-numbered polyploids, however (triploids, pentaploids, etc.), tend to be sterile whether they be allopolyploids or autopolyploids simply because they have a high possibility of giving rise to gametes of unbalanced chromosome constitution.

### Polyploidy in Plants

Polyploidy appears to occur naturally in all groups of plants with the possible exception of the fungi, but as pointed out by Stebbins (1950) the distribution is so irregular that there seems to be little phylogenetic significance. Natural autopolyploids are rather rare, though many polyploid species and races seem to be near-autoploids as judged by frequency of multiple associations. Among such are several tetraploid species of *Tradescantia* and the triploid banana and plantains (Figure 8-2). Presumably such near autoploids have arisen by doubling the chromosome number in a hybrid containing two similar but not strictly homologous sets of chromosomes. Neither artificially induced nor natural autoploids do well above the tetraploid level. While no clear-cut reason for this has so far been established, there is some reason to suspect that the changed surface-volume relationship in the characteristically larger cells of the polyploid may lead to dysfunction. Nonetheless, increase in chromosome number is not always reflected by measurable change in cell size, to say nothing of organ or whole plant size.

Most naturally occurring polyploid plant groups are alloploid or complexes of allo- and autopolyploids and may reach rather high degrees of ploidy. For example, the cotton plant of North American commerce is apparently an allotetraploid of the AABB type derived from a hybrid between *Gossypium arboreum* and *G. rarimondii*. The wheat, *Triticum vulgare,* is an allohexaploid of the AABBCC type derived from two species of wheat and a wheat grass by a successive series of hybridization and chromosome doubling. Polyploid species such as *Phleum protense, Helianthos tuberosum,* and *Solanum nigrum* are hexaploids which, on the basis of pairing relationships between the several genomes, are considered by Stebbins to be autoallohexaploids of the type AAABBB. Most alloploids are either tetra- or hexaploids, but higher levels of ploidy exist or are suspected. Obviously autoploids and alloploids represent extremes of relationship between genomes, and any kind of intermediate may be expected—indeed most cases will represent some deviation from the ideal type.

### Polyploidy in Animals

In contrast to plants, polyploidy is very rare in animals. Nonetheless, some animal groups do contain polyploid members. For example, polyploid species or races have been quite definitely established in flatworms, segmented worms such as the earthworm, crustaceans such as *Artemia,* the Lepidoptera, and the sawfly, *Diprion simile.* Individual animals in many groups may be polyploid, but for a variety of reasons are unlikely to establish a polyploid race. Cases of individual polyploidy have been definitely established in the urodeles, and less satisfactorily in pigs, rabbits, mice, and some birds.

Why the incidence of polyploidy should be so much greater in plants than in animals is still an open question. Certainly there is little reason to believe that the possibility of becoming polyploid is any greater at the cellular level in the former than in the latter. The most commonly accepted explanation is the one originally offered by H. J. Muller in 1925. The essential part of the argument is that polyploidy would be expected to upset the sex chromosome mechanism in bisexual organisms by abolishing the heterogamety on which sex determination depends. Therefore, both in animals and plants, polyploidy would become established only in species which are parthenogenetic, hermaphroditic, or reproduce vegetatively. In general this restriction seems to apply, but there are a number of dioecious species of plants which are polyploid and a number of animal groups, such as the self-fertilizing hermaphroditic molluscs, which appear to be devoid of any polyploid members though there is no obvious cytological barrier to the establishment of such races. A second explanation for the difference in incidence in polyploidy in the two kingdoms is that offered by Stebbins (1950) who suggests that cellular differentiation and presumably intercellular relationships are more complex in animal than in plant embryogeny and thus more liable to reflect disturbance due to polyploidy. For this point of view there is some evidence of the existence of polyploids at pregastrula stages, e.g., in mice (Fischberg and Beatty, 1950), but against it is the fact that polyploidy has become established in animals in which embryogeny is at least as complex a process as in nonpolyploid species. Finally, a partial reason for difference between plants and animals with respect to polyploid incidence may be purely statistical. In most animals there are comparatively few cells which are capable of producing a new organism, namely, those directly in the germ line, while in plants almost any cell not too differentiated to divide may produce another organism either directly by vegetative means or indirectly through production of a flowering branch. Therefore, given the same frequency of suitable mitotic accidents, a plant is much more likely to produce, and perhaps to maintain, a polyploid strain than is an animal. This reasoning does not explain, however, why there should be marked differences between families in incidence of polyploidy. It is probable that all these explanations have some validity.

## Aneuploidy

An organism which contains one or more *incomplete* chromosome sets is known as an *aneuploid*. Such a condition may arise either from union of two gametes at least one of which is unbalanced in chromosome number, or through perpetuation of a cell which has gained or lost one or more chromosomes through failure to divide properly at anaphase of mitosis. As a rule, aneuploids tend to be considerably less viable than the corresponding euploids and accordingly are rather rare in nature. Nevertheless, they do occasionally become established and under certain circumstances may be of some evolutionary significance. Aneuploids near the diploid level are, as a rule, less likely to survive than those near a polyploid level, that is, 2n plus 1 as compared with 4n plus 1. Presumably this difference is correlated in part with the difference in per cent of genic imbalance in the two cases. If an extra chromosome is added to a diploid, it has a greater quantitative effect than if added to a tetraploid.

Specific kinds of aneuploids have names descriptive of the condition: *polysomic* (duplication of one or more chromosomes of a set); *monosomic* (having only one of a pair of chromosomes); *nullosomic* (lacking a pair of chromosomes). Regardless of the exact condition, the principles remain the same and are illustrated by the following example:

If at the first division of a diploid zygote one chromosome fails to divide properly, we may have two cells, one of which has an extra chromosome (2n plus 1) and the other lacking a chromosome (2n minus 1). In fact, neither cell is very likely to survive, but the chances are better for the 2n plus 1 than for its deficient mate. Should the 2n plus 1 cell survive and give rise to the two kinds of gametes, namely, n and n plus 1, fertilization with itself or with one of its kind should produce three kinds of zygotes: 2n, 2n plus 1, and 2n plus 2, in the ratio of 1:2:1. However, because of the differential viability of the three types, this is seldom if ever realized. The two classes of gametes are the result of random distribution of the extra chromosome at first anaphase of meiosis. The best known series of polysomics is in *Datura,* where strains involving duplication of each one of the twelve chromosomes have been found and/or induced (Blakeslee, 1930).

Some distinction should be made between *true* aneuploids and *false* ones. In the former case there are one or more complete genomes plus a fraction of a genome, in the latter, at least two kinds are found: (1) those which are apparent aneuploids by chromosome count because, in addition to one or more complete complements, they contain a certain number of supernumerary chromosomes; and (2) those which are aneuploid by count because they contain two or more complements derived from parents of different chromosome numbers.

As already noted, true aneuploids, by the definition used here, are much less viable than corresponding euploids, as well as being sterile to a considerable degree. So far as the evidence goes aneuploid animals seem to be less viable than plants. For example, the *Datura* trisomics already mentioned vary from moderate to good viability, especially in cultivation. On the other hand, trisomic *Drosophila* are rather inviable except for those involving the small IV chromosome. Before one can rely on such generalities, however, it is necessary to know whether or not one is dealing with true aneuploids, a designation which cannot always be made solely on chromosome counts.

## Variations Within an Organism

It has long been assumed that, apart from accidental exceptions, all somatic cells of an organism are alike in chromosome constitution. Recent work, however, has laid this tenet open to suspicion. It has been known for a long time that occasional polyploid cells may be found in an otherwise diploid organism, and it now appears that varying degrees of polyploidy or polyteny may be the rule rather than the exception, especially in differentiated tissue (Geitler, 1937, 1941; Huskins, 1947). Such variations appear to result from the process of endomitosis, the degree of which may differ between chromosomes and even within chromosomes to provide considerable quantitative variation from cell to cell. In some tissues such divisions appear to be sporadic and in others the rule. Endomitosis appears to be common in specialized tissues such as corn endosperm (Duncan and Ross, 1950) (Figure 8-3), and in the ileum of the mosquito larva (Berger, 1938; Grell, 1946). In the latter case, diploidy is apparently restored by a series of mitoses without further chromosome duplication. Senescent tissues also appear to have many polytene nuclei. It is yet too early to assess the importance of this variation, but it does seem to offer a plasticity which may prove of considerable value in studies of differentiation.

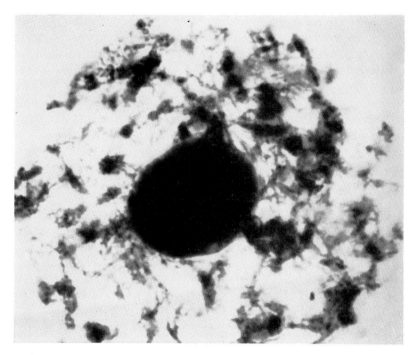

**Figure 8-3.** Photomicrograph of Flattened Nucleus from the Late Milk Stage of Corn Endosperm Showing Multistranded (Polytene) Character of the Chromosomes. (From Duncan, R. E. and Ross, J. G., 1950. "The Nucleus in Differentiation and Development," *J. Heredity,* 41, Fig. 5, p. 261. Courtesy of Dr. Robert E. Duncan, Wisconsin Neurological Foundation, Madison, Wis.)

## CHANGES IN CHROMOSOME STRUCTURE

In addition to changes in whole chromosome sets or parts thereof, alteration in the structure of individual chromosomes may occur spontaneously or by induction. Such changes may result in quantitative alterations of genes (deletions and duplications) or only in spatial rearrangements (translocations and inversions). The cytological significance of the more important of these intrachromosomal alterations are, briefly, as follows:

## Duplication and Deletion

A piece of a chromosome may be *duplicated* or *deleted* to give the intrachromosomal equivalent of aneuploidy. In principle, much of what we had to say concerning aneuploids applies here as well. In general either change reduces viability, the reduction being more marked in the case of a deletion and less effective in a polyploid than in a diploid. Small deletions and duplications cannot usually be detected cytologically and may become confused genetically with gene mutations in the strict sense, for example, bar eye in *Drosophila*. Larger ones may show up in the heterozygous state as a difference in length between homologues or an unpaired loop in pachytene.

As noted by Swanson (1957), duplications may be tandem, reverse tandem, or displaced. How any particular duplication may arise poses a question the answer to which is not generally clear. Tandem duplications may be formed by a process of unequal crossing over or other exchange between homologues.

A deletion may occur in many ways as spontaneous or induced akinetic fragments or as the complementary result of processes leading to duplication. Deletions—no matter how they occur—are frequently lethal, especially when homozygous or hemizygous, and also often have marked phenotypic effects.

## Inversions

When a segment of a chromosome is turned end for end, it is said to be *inverted* relative to the original order. Thus a chromosome in which the gene order is designated as ABCDEFGHI may be changed to the order ABCGFEDHI in which the underlined segment has been inverted. If the homologous chromosome retains the original order, then at meiotic pairing it is subject to a certain degree of difficulty because of the fact that when the homologues are lying side by side homologous regions are not contiguous in all places. If the region involved is short, no pairing will occur within it and this is usually reflected genetically by a decrease in crossing over for the inverted region. If the region is relatively long, pairing may occur through the formation of a loop which involves the inverted region in one or the other of the homologues. It is this form of pairing which leads to cytological difficulties. Two kinds of inversions may be recognized, i.e., *paracentric,* which is confined to

a single chromosome arm and *pericentric,* which includes the kinetochore (Figure 8-4, A and B). In the former case, with loop pairing
and with a chiasma in the loop, the result will be one chromatid with
two kinetochores which on separation at first anaphase forms a chro-

A. When the centromere is
outside the inversion

B. When the centromere is
within the inversion

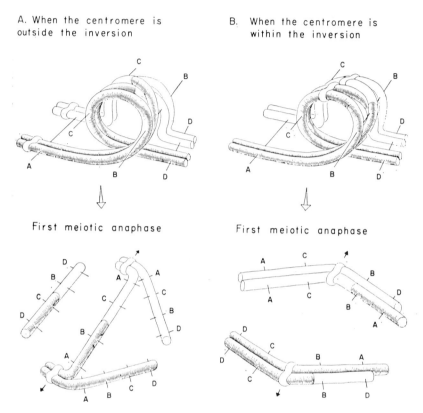

First meiotic anaphase

First meiotic anaphase

**Figure 8-4.** Diagrammatic Representation of a Paracentric (**A**) and pericentric (**B**) inversion. (From Srb, A. M. and Owen, R. D., 1955. "General
Genetics," W. H. Freeman & Co., San Francisco, Calif., Fig. 10-14, p. 197.)

matin bridge, and an akinetic fragment which is generally lost (Figure 8-5). Thus the resultant four end products of meiosis consist of
two normal cells and two cells having deletions as a consequence of the
loss of the fragment. Since the latter two are nearly always inviable,
every gamete mother cell so affected will produce only 50 per cent
viable gametes. Thus if a chiasma is produced in the inversion region,
100 per cent of the time the organism will be only 50 per cent fertile.

The existence of other chiasmata may give rise to more complicated situations or eliminate the effects of the first one, depending on where they occur and what strands are involved. In the case of a pericentric inversion, the position of the kinetochore may be so altered as to change the relative lengths of arms to a detectable degree (Figure 8-4, B);

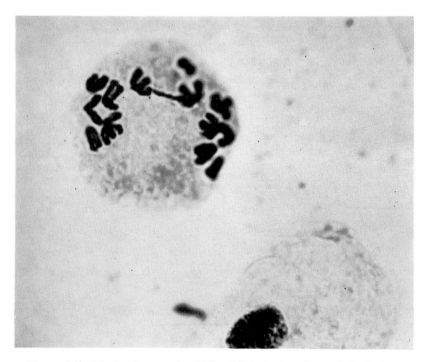

**Figure 8-5.** Photomicrograph of First Meiotic Anaphase of *Podophyllum peltatum,* showing bridge and fragment as a result of crossing over within a region heterozygous for an inversion.

where there is loop pairing and a single chiasma in the loop, no bridge and fragment results at first anaphase, but instead a pair of deficiency-duplication chromatids, which are identical at the two ends (Figure 8-4, B). Pericentric inversions are therefore not as easily diagnosed at first anaphase, unless the lengths of the two chromatids of an anaphase chromosome are detectably different. This, together with the statistically low chance of including any particular point in an inversion, may account for the comparatively low frequency of pericentric as opposed to paracentric inversions.

The causes of inversions are unknown, but it is generally assumed that they result from fortuitous loops which break and rejoin to give the new alignment.

Since an inversion heterozygote will give rise to gametes carrying the normal chromosome and to those carrying the inverted one in equal numbers, it is expected that the progeny from inbreeding such an organism will show a ratio of 1 homozygous normal : 2 heterozygous inversions : 1 homozygous inversion. The relative survival or fertility value of these three types will determine their ultimate concentration in the population.

### Translocations

When a piece of a chromosome becomes transferred to another (usually nonhomologous) chromosome, the process is described as *translocation*. This is generally, and probably always, a *reciprocal* affair caused by the mutual breakage of two overlapping chromosomes followed by rejoining, and may result either in a *dikinetic* (having two kinetochores) and an *akinetic* chromosome, or in two *complete* chromosomes which have exchanged parts. The latter type is the more important and in the heterozygous state results in four chromosomes being partially homologous with one another. If, for example, in an organism, two pairs of chromosomes designated A-B, A'-B' and C-D, C'-D' are involved in a reciprocal translocation, the resulting designations may be A-B, A'-D and C-B', C'-D'. Association at meiosis would give a ring of all four chromosomes or a configuration (e.g., a cross) which would open out into a ring at metaphase (Figure 8-6). Whether balanced gametes result will depend on how the four members of the ring separate at first anaphase. If, for instance, adjacent chromosomes go to the same pole, half the gametes will have a duplication for the A end and a deletion for the C end, while the other half will be the reverse. However, if alternate chromosomes go to the same pole, all the gametes will be genetically balanced, with half having normal chromosomes and the other half having translocated ones. The result on inbreeding is an expectation of 1 homozygous normal : 2 heterozygous for the translocation : 1 homozygous for the translocation, their ultimate concentration being dependent on the relative survival value of the three types. Experience has shown that where the ring is relatively simple, there is a strong tendency for separation of alternate chromosomes to the same pole, and thus fertility in a translocation heterozygote is usually high so far as cytological considerations have a bearing on the question.

An organism may have *more* than one reciprocal translocation. The two best-known examples of *multiple* translocations are *Rhoeo discolor* with twelve chromosomes in a ring (Figure 8-7) and *Oenothera Lamarckiana* with a ring of twelve chromosomes and one bivalent. In both cases separation is preferentially of the alternate type and fertility should be high. Little is known of the genetics of *Rhoeo,* but it is highly sterile. There is no obvious cytological reason, however, why this should be so. *Oenothera,* on the other hand, is about 50 per cent fertile, and nearly all of the offspring are heterozygous for the translocations, as is the parent. Genetical investigations have shown that the homozygotes

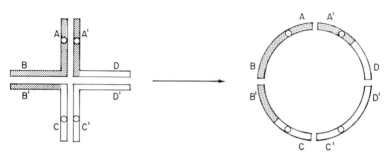

**Figure 8-6.** Diagrammatic Representation of a Reciprocal Translocation Involving Two Pairs of Chromosomes, **A-B, A′-B′,** and **C-D, C′-D′.** Pairing of the chromosomes and their subsequent separation during meiosis results in a ring configuration at first metaphase with the chromosomes designated as **A-B, A′-D,** and **C-B′, C′-D′.** (From Wilson, G. B., 1952. "Outline of Genetics," Michigan State University Press, East Lansing, Mich., p. 25.)

of both types usually fail to develop, apparently because of a balanced lethal condition in which a number of genes prove fatal in the homozygous condition.

Because it may lead to change in the basic number of chromosomes, one kind of translocation is worth special mention. If two chromosomes with subterminal kinetochores are involved in a translocation such that most of the long arm of one exchanges with some of the short arm of the other, the result will be a chromosome with a median or submedian kinetochore and a small chromosome consisting of a kinetochore plus a short region on either side (Figure 8-8). Since in many, if not most cases, the proximal arms of chromosomes are *heterochromatic* and *genetically inert,* and since minute chromosomes run a high risk of being lost, a translocation of the type described can result in decrease in chromosome number without loss of vital genetic material. Such events seem to account very well for the range of chromosome numbers in *Crepis* (Babcock, 1947) especially since interspecific hybrids between species with n = 4 and n = 3 show the latter to have a chromosome partially homologous to two in the former. There is also a good deal of

**Figure 8-7.** Photomicrograph of Ring of 12 Chromosomes in *Rhoeo discolor* Produced as the Result of Multiple Translocation. (From Darlington, C. D. and LaCour, L. F., 1960. "The Handling of Chromosomes," 3rd ed., George Allen & Unwin, Ltd., London, England, Plate XVII.)

evidence that similar translocations have played a phylogenetic role in many animals, especially in grasshoppers, some Diptera, and probably in certain beetles such as the weevils (Smith, 1956). Indeed, much of the difference in basic chromosome number between related species, so conspicuous in many animal groups, may ultimately be explained by such "whole arm" exchange.

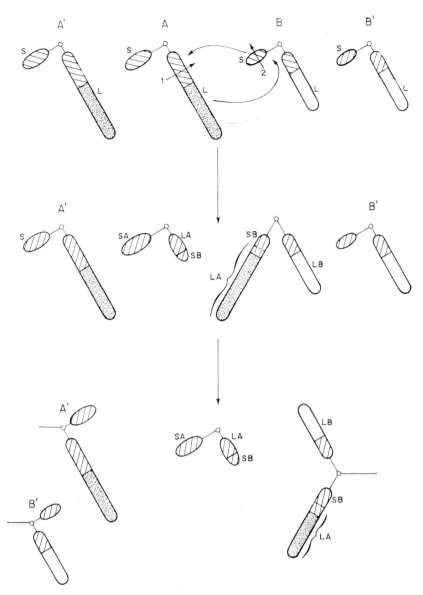

**Figure 8-8.** Diagrammatic Representation of Reciprocal Translocation at Points 1 and 2 Between Heterochromatic Segments (shaded) of Two Chromosomes, **A** and **B**, with Subterminal Kinetochores. Most of the long arm of chromosome **A** (**LA**) exchanges with a part of the short arm of chromosome **B** (**SB**) to give a chromosome with a submedian kinetochore, and a small chromosome consisting of a kinetochore plus a short heterochromatic segment on either side (**SA** and **LA** + **SB**).

## CYTOLOGY OF SEX DETERMINATION

In bisexual species, either plant or animal, it can generally be presumed that one or the other of the two sexes is *heterogametic,* i.e., that it produces two kinds of gametes, one female-determining and the other male-determining. In the majority of bisexual animals as well as in

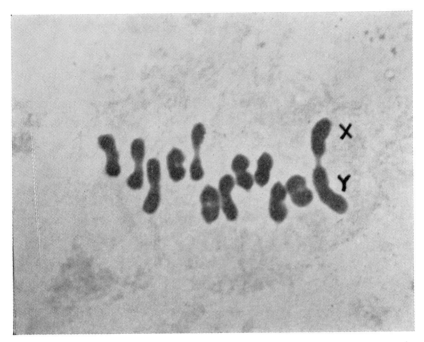

**Figure 8-9.** Photomicrograph of 12 Bivalent Chromosomes at First Meiotic Metaphase in Diploid Male of *Melandrium.* Note heteromorphic XY pair. (From Warmke, H. E., 1946. "Sex Determination and Sex Balance in *Melandrium,*" *Am. J. Botany,* 33, Fig. 1, p. 651.)

many plants, the heterogametic sex may be distinguished cytologically by the fact that it contains a *heteromorphic* pair of chromosomes, the segregation of which at meiosis leads to production of the two kinds of gametes. The heteromorphic pair is generally known as the X-Y pair (Figure 8-9). The Y element is missing from the *homogametic* sex and the X element is represented twice. In some cases, as in several species of grasshopper, the Y element is missing altogether so that the male is XO and the female XX. In other cases, the praying mantid, for example, the X element is compound and consists of two elements which pair with different regions of the Y chromosome in meiosis to give a trivalent $X_1YX_2$ in the male and two bivalents $X_1X_1 \ X_2X_2$ in the female. In a number of dioecious species of plants such as *Spinacia oleracea* with presumed XY systems, there is too little morphological difference between the two elements to allow cytological distinction. In such cases it is assumed that the two elements differ with respect to a limited segment in which crossing over is completely, or at least, largely suppressed. In some cases, *Cannabis sativa,* for example, the X and Y elements are so similar in size and shape that the heteromorphic character can be demonstrated only with difficulty by careful measurement of the two elements. In other cases, as in several species of the marine worm *Bonellia,* bisexuality appears to be largely the result of environmental influences during larval development; and in another marine worm, *Dimophilus,* the female lays two kinds of eggs, small ones which become males and large ones which become females. Since the size difference is established before meiosis, no chromosome mechanism would seem to be involved.

In certain animal groups, especially the Hymenoptera (bees, wasps, etc.), males are haploid derived from unfertilized eggs and females diploid derived from fertilized eggs. Cytologically, therefore, the difference between sexes is ascribable to a difference of an entire chromosome complement. What this difference means in genetic terms is not entirely evident, but from the extensive studies of the Whitings (1943, 1945) on *Habrobracon,* femaleness seems attributable to heterozygosity of a number of loci since inbreeding leads to production of some rather inviable but otherwise normal diploid males.

## CYTOGENETICS AND THE FINE STRUCTURE OF CELLS

In classical genetics, the major problem was the mechanism by which genetic potential was transferred from parent to offspring, so that cytogenetics was concerned with cellular changes, notably in the chromosomes, which influenced such transmission. In recent years geneticists have become increasingly concerned with the problem of translation of genetic information into specific action. By extension, a valid concern of cytogenetics might well be with changes in fine structure which may have a bearing on the transfer of genetic information from the chromosome to sites of action in the cytoplasm in either a general or specific sense. In particular one may attempt to correlate changes in fine structure of chromosomes with genetic activity in a fashion similar to that adopted by Beermann (1956, 1959) in attempting to relate "puffing" of giant Diptera chromosomes to gene activation (see Chapter 4, Figures 4-19 and 4-20). Also one may look for critical changes in the relationship of chromosome, nuclear boundary, and endoplasmic reticulum which may be correlated with differential transfer of genetic information (Gay, 1956) (Figure 4-3). Although so far, few studies have been consciously aimed in this direction, the rapid welding of subcellular structure and cellular biochemistry makes it inevitable that a sort of subcellular cytogenetics will soon evolve.

## BIBLIOGRAPHY

Babcock, E. B., 1947. "The Genus *Crepis,* I and II," *Univ. Calif. Publs. Botany,* Vols. 21 and 22.

Beatty, R. A., 1954. "How Many Chromosomes in Mammalian Somatic Cells?," *Intern. Rev. Cytol.,* 3, 177-197.

Beermann, W., 1956. "Nuclear Differentiation and Functional Morphology of Chromosomes," *Cold Spring Harbor Symposia Quant. Biol.,* 21, 217-232.

Beermann, W., 1959. "Chromosomal Differentiation in Insects," *in* "Developmental Cytology," D. Rudnick (Ed.), The Ronald Press, New York, N.Y., pp. 83-103.

Berger, C. A., 1938. "Multiplication and Reduction of Somatic Chromosome Groups as a Regular Developmental Process in the Mosquito, *Culex pipiens,*" *Carnegie Inst. Wash. Publ.,* 476, 209-232.

Berger, C. A., 1941. "Multiple Chromosome Complexes in Animals and Polysomaty in Plants," *Cold Spring Harbor Symposia Quant. Biol.,* 9, 19-21.

Blakeslee, A. F., 1930. "Extra Chromosomes, a Source of Variations in the Jimson Weed," *Smithsonian Report,* pp. 431-450.

Bridges, C. B., 1925. "Sex in Relation to Chromosomes and Genes," *Am. Naturalist,* 59, 127-137.

Duncan, R. E. and Ross, J. G., 1950. "The Nucleus in Differentiation and Development. III. Nuclei of Maize Endosperm," *J. Hered.,* 41, 259-268.

Fischberg, M. and Beatty, R. A., 1951. "Spontaneous Heteroploidy in Mouse Embryos up to Mid-term," *J. Exptl. Zool.,* 118, 321-336.

Gay, H., 1956. "Nucleocytoplasmic Relations in *Drosophila,*" *Cold Spring Harbor Symposia Quant. Biol.,* 21, 257-269.

Gay, H., 1956. "Chromosome-Nuclear Membrane-Cytoplasmic Interrelations in *Drosophila,*" *J. Biophys. Biochem. Cytol.,* 2, 407-414.

Geitler, L., 1937. "Die Analyse des Kernbaus und der Kernteilung der Wasserläufer *Gerris lateralis* und *Gerris lacustris* (Hemiptera, Heteroptera) und die Somadifferenzierung," *Zeit. für Zellforsch. und Micr. Anat.,* 26, 641-672.

Geitler, L., 1938. "Chromosomenbau," Borntraeger, Berlin.

Geitler, L., 1941. "Das Wachstum des Zellkerns in tierischen und pflanzlichen Geweben," *Ergebn. Biol.,* 18, 1-54.

Grell, M., 1946. "Cytological Studies in *Culex*. I. Somatic Reduction Divisions. II. Diploid and Meiotic Divisions," *Genetics,* 31, 60-94.

Huskins, C. L., 1947. "The Subdivision of the Chromosomes and Their Multiplication in Non-dividing Tissues: Possible Interpretations in Terms of Gene Structure and Gene Action," *Am. Naturalist,* 81, 401-434.

Huskins, C. L. and Steinitz, L. N., 1948. "The Nucleus in Differentiation and Development. I.," *J. Hered.,* 39, 34-43.

Kaufmann, B. P., 1934. "Somatic Mitoses in *Drosophila melanogaster,*" *J. Morphol.,* 56, 125-155.

Muller, H. J., 1925. "Why Polyploidy is Rarer in Animals Than in Plants," *Am. Naturalist,* 59, 346-353.

Müntzing, A., 1936. "The Evolutionary Significance of Autopolyploidy," *Hereditas,* 21, 263-378.

Porter, K. R. and Machado, R. D., 1960. "Studies on the Endoplasmic Reticulum. IV. Its Form and Distribution During Mitosis in Cells of Onion Root Tip," *J. Biophys. Biochem. Cytol.,* 7, 167-180.

Sharp, L. W., 1943. "Fundamentals of Cytology," 1st ed., McGraw-Hill Book Co., New York, N.Y.

Smith, S. G., 1956. "Chromosomal Polymorphism in a Bark Weevil," *Nature,* 177, 386.

Srb, A. M. and Owen, R. D., 1955. "General Genetics," Freeman, San Francisco, Calif.

Stebbins, G. L., Jr., 1950. "Variation and Evolution in Plants," Columbia University Press, New York, N.Y.

Swanson, C. P., 1957. "Cytology and Cytogenetics," Prentice-Hall, Inc., Englewood Cliffs, N.J.

Warmke, H. E., 1946. "Sex Determination and Sex Balance in *Melandrium,*" *Am. J. Botany,* 33, 648-660.

White, M. J. D., 1941. "The Evolution of the Sex Chromosomes. I. The XO and $X_1X_2Y$ Mechanisms in Praying Mantids," *J. Genetics,* 42, 143-172.

White, M. J. D., 1950. "The Chromosomes," 4th ed., Methuen, London.

White, M. J. D., 1954. "Animal Cytology and Evolution," 2nd ed., Cambridge University Press, Cambridge.

Whiting, P. W., 1943. "Multiple Alleles in Complementary Sex Determination of *Habrobracon,*" *Genetics,* 28, 365-382.

Whiting, P. W., 1945. "The Evolution of Male Haploidy," *Quart. Rev. Biol.,* 20, 231-260.

Wilson, G. B., 1946. "Cytological Studies in the *Musae*. III. Meiosis in Some Seedling Clones," *Genetics,* 31, 483-493.

# 9

# *Radiation Cytology*

THE FACT that ionizing radiation of the X-ray type has a marked effect on genetic material was established in the late twenties primarily through the work of H. J. Muller (1928), Altenberg (1928), and Stadler (1928). These workers all showed quite conclusively that there is a marked correlation between exposure to X rays and increase in production of mutant offspring. Their results were quickly confirmed and extended by both genetical and cytological studies. The latter soon provided data indicating that degree of chromosome damage was also quite directly correlated with dosage (Sax, 1938, 1940). Since the dawning of the so-called Atomic Age in 1945, interest in the biological consequences of exposure to ionizing radiations of all sorts has been greatly intensified. Despite all these efforts there are still many blanks in our knowledge, especially concerning the manner in which radiation produces its effects. In this chapter we will outline the salient facts, concepts, and problems with which radiation biology is currently concerned.

## EFFECTIVE RADIATIONS

Ionizing radiations are those which, upon being absorbed, directly or indirectly produce *ion clusters*. These include X rays, gamma rays, alpha particles, beta rays, neutrons, and protons. Despite considerable differences in primary action, all of these waves and particles ultimately induce more or less dense clusters of ion pairs. The consequent local instability is presumably reflected in disruption of many molecules. Nonionizing radiation, especially short waves in the ultraviolet range, pro-

193

duce similar effects, as do many chemicals. The former presumably act by increasing local reactivity and the latter by direct or indirect disruption of molecular integrity.

## THEORIES

There are two major recognized hypotheses concerning mode of action of ionizing radiations. These are commonly referred to as the "Target theory" and the "Biochemical theory." The differences, however, represent differing viewpoints rather than fundamental theoretical ones.

### Target Theory

In its simplest form, this hypothesis views a quantum of emitted radiation as a *projectile,* and the responding structure or element as a *target.* On this basis the relationship between scored biological change and radiation should be similar to the general relationship between physical targets and projectiles. For many kinds of biological effects such a relationship does exist. Mathematical models based on this notion agree well with observed responses such as cell lethality, chromosome breakage, and mutation. The predictive and analytic values of this approach are particularly well illustrated by the theoretical writings of D. E. Lea (1955). The major weakness of the theory lies in the fact that it cannot be extended reasonably to cover the effects of nonionizing radiation, such as the mutagenic capacity of irradiated media for the induction of bacterial mutants (Stone, *et al.,* 1947), or to the modifying effects of many physical and chemical conditions.

### Biochemical Theory

Basically, this hypothesis views radiation-induced biological damage as being the result of generation of highly *reactive radicals* through absorption by suitable molecules of the incident radiation. Such radicals then are presumed to have *secondary* effects on vital macromolecules. In general, such an hypothesis would seem to be more compatible with many modifying effects of chemicals as well as with indirect effects.

## CATEGORIES OF RADIATION EFFECTS

### Physiological

Although this category has become something of a catchall for effects not assignable to disruption of some physical structure, certain commonly observed responses are well worth noting. It is quite clear that radiation interferes with a number of biochemical processes, especially those concerned with protein and nucleic acid synthesis. Presumably this reflects inactivation of essential enzymes. Depolymerization of DNA occurs *in vitro* and probably also *in vivo,* which may well account for chromosome stickiness. Mitosis is generally inhibited and often by comparatively small doses. It seems probable that most of the effects which we term physiological stem from inactivation of enzymes. Such effects may be temporary and reversible, or permanent and usually lethal.

### Mutational

There is a very direct relationship between *exposure* to ionizing radiation and *yield* of mutations. Despite the fact that the mode of operation is still unknown, since both input in terms of energy and output in terms of mutation can be measured, it has been possible to establish a number of fairly definite relationships. Some of the more important are: (1) there is a direct relationship between yield and dose, (2) the yield is independent of wavelength over a fair range and also, within limits, of dose rate, (3) as ion density increases yield of mutations decreases for any given total amount of ionization, and (4) different genes differ in sensitivity.

### Chromosomal

Chromosomal changes resulting from radiation have been of particular interest to cytologists. Differences in both *quantity* and *kind* of chromosomal alterations provide excellent data for the study of differential sensitivity and variations in chromosome organization. While detailed discussion is beyond the technical level of this book, certain principles and results which are of major importance can be outlined. In general, between absorption of the radiant energy and the scored configuration there are three steps: (1) primary effect, (2) chromosome breakage, and (3) healing or union of broken ends. On the target theory the primary effect results from the chromosome being traversed by an ionization track, and on the biochemical theory by production of highly reactive radicals. Breakage presumably results from disruption of bonds important to integrity, either directly or as the result of strain, while healing or union of broken ends might be considered to represent some sort of "satisfaction" of free bonds. In any event it is the resultant rearrangements which can be observed and from which deductions are made. Many analyses of irradiated material have provided the following information.

(a) The frequency of chromosome changes which can be considered as "one hit" events is directly proportional to dose.

(b) The capacity of broken ends of chromosomes to rejoin is retained for some time, depending on the material irradiated. In *Tradescantia* microspores it appears to be about one hour.

(c) The yield of "one hit" events is, within limits, independent of intensity.

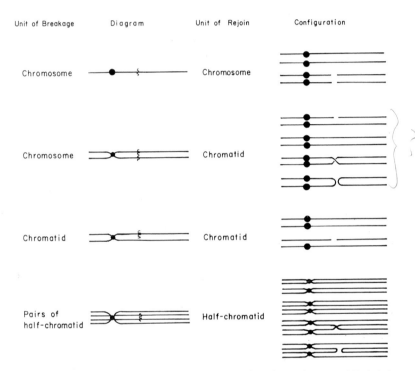

| Unit of Breakage | Diagram | Unit of Rejoin | Configuration |
|---|---|---|---|
| Chromosome | | Chromosome | |
| Chromosome | | Chromatid | |
| Chromatid | | Chromatid | |
| Pairs of half-chromatid | | Half-chromatid | |

Figure 9-1. Schematic Drawing Showing Units of Breakage and Rejoining Following Irradiation.

(d) As a general rule irradiation of nuclei in interphase produces chromosome breaks. Irradiation of early prophase results in chromatid breaks, and of late prophase in rearrangements indicating the 4-stranded condition of the chromosomes (Wilson and Sparrow, 1960; Wilson, *et al.*, 1959). These conditions are illustrated in Figures 9-1, 9-2, 9-3.

(e) Although breaks usually seem to be randomly distributed along chromosomes, there is some evidence of higher sensitivity in heterochromatic regions.

(f) Sensitivity varies with mitotic stage (Figure 9-4). Although there is some controversy over which stages are most sensitive, there seems little doubt that dividing cells are more sensitive than nondividing ones, with early interphase being least susceptible (Sparrow, 1951).

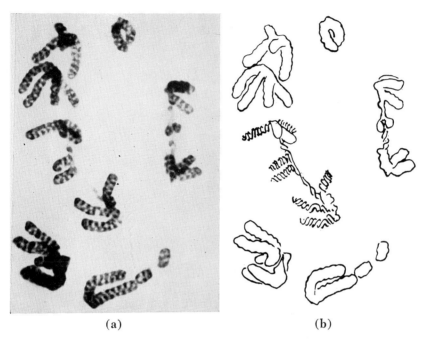

(a)                                    (b)

**Figure 9-2.** (a) Photomicrograph of First Meiotic Anaphase Chromosomes of *Trillium erectum;* (b) Drawing Illustrating the Configuration of a True Two-Side-Arm Bridge. Strands indicated in the bridge are half chromatids. Plant irradiated at diakinesis with 25 r of X Rays. (From Wilson, G. B., Sparrow, A. H., and Pond, V., 1959. "Sub-Chromatid Rearrangements in *Trillium erectum*. I. Origin and Nature of Configurations Induced by Ionizing Radiation," *Am. J. Botany*, **46**, Fig. 2, p. 310.)

## MODIFICATION OF RADIATION EFFECTS

The question of modifying radiation effects, especially in the direction of minimizing them, is, of course, of practical importance, and consequently has received considerable attention. So far, although sensitivity can be modified in both directions by a variety of conditions, there is no real understanding of the mechanism involved. In general, conditions which might be expected to reduce metabolic activity also reduce sensitivity. These include reduced oxygen tension, low temperature, and nonlethal doses of respiratory poisons. There are, however, exceptions in which these normally "protecting" conditions actually increase sensitivity. A number of chemicals are known to increase or decrease peroxide formation, the former generally enhancing and the latter generally decreasing radiation effects. However, no general valid principle can be set forth at the present time.

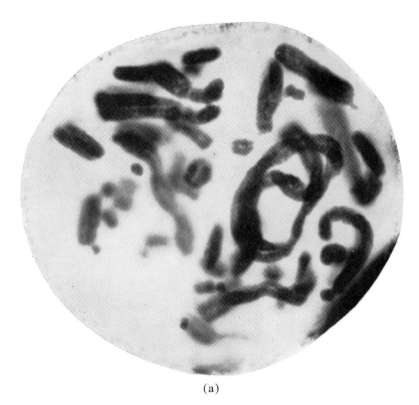

(a)

Figure 9-3. (a) Tetraploid Microspore Metaphase with a High Degree of Fragmentation Resulting from Irradiation with 100 r of X Rays at First Meiotic Metaphase. (b) Drawing of Tetraploid Metaphase Illustrated in (a). The chromosome drawn in black appears to be monocentric and is about four times the length of the longest chromosome in a normal complement. It could include a triplication. The two arrows indicate the approximate

(*Contin.* on opposite page.)

In recent years the testing of radioactive explosive devices has been carried out at high level, resulting in bitter worldwide debate concerning the hazards of radioactivity. It is not a function of this book to debate these issues, but a few pertinent points should be made, especially since much of the argument has little or nothing to do with known facts. Radiation damages biological systems in essentially three ways: (1) It kills cells and thus organisms, (2) it modifies metabolic systems generally to the detriment of the organism concerned, and (3) it induces changes in genetic material usually detrimental to subsequent genera-

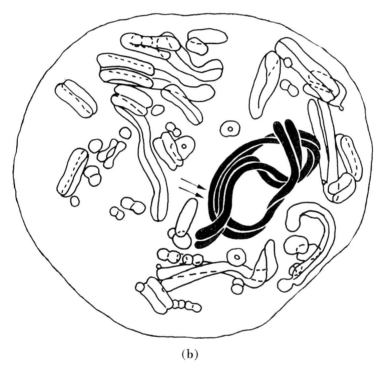

(b)

**Figure 9-3.** (*Contin.*)

position of two small fragments located under the long chromosome. They were omitted for reasons of clarity. (From Wilson, G. B. and Sparrow, A. H., 1960. "Configurations Resulting from Iso-Chromatid and Iso-Subchromatid Unions after Meiotic and Mitotic Prophase Irradiation," *Chromosoma,* **11,** Figs. 10 and 11, p. 240. Courtesy of Dr. A. H. Sparrow, Brookhaven National Laboratory.)

tions. In general, the evidence to date indicates that the more exposure the human race as a whole receives, the more it will be damaged. The questions of how much is too much, and what is a permissible dose, are patently unanswerable in the light of present knowledge. The problem is somewhat like that pertaining to the use of antibiotics—indiscriminate use is indefensible, but where there is a choice between two evils one is expected to choose the lesser. In most cases this is more a matter of ethics than of science.

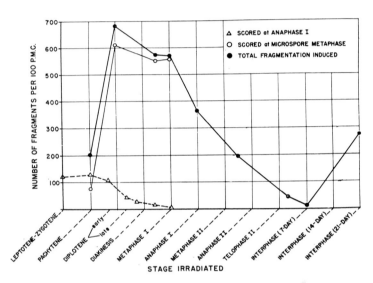

Figure 9-4. Graph Showing the Number of Chromosome Fragments Induced by 50 r of X Rays at Various Stages of Meiosis in *Trillium erectum*. (From Sparrow, A. H., 1951. "Radiation Sensitivity of Cells During Mitotic and Meiotic Cycles with Emphasis on Possible Cytochemical Changes," *Ann. N. Y. Acad. Sci.,* **51**, Fig. 2, p. 1513.)

## BIBLIOGRAPHY

Altenberg, E., 1928. "The Limit of Radiation Frequency Effective in Producing Mutations," *Am. Naturalist,* **62**, 540-545.

Blum, H. F., 1959. "Environmental Radiation and Cancer," *Science,* **130**, 1545-1547.

Errera, M., 1959. "Effects of Radiations on Cells," *in* "The Cell," J. Brachet and A. E. Mirsky (Eds.), Vol. 1, Academic Press, New York, N.Y., pp. 695-740.

Kihlman, B. A., 1956. "Factors Affecting the Production of Chromosome Aberrations by Chemicals," *J. Biophys. Biochem. Cytol.,* **2**, 543-555.

Kihlman, B. A., Merz, T., and Swanson, C. P., 1957. "Experimentally Induced Chromosome Aberrations in Plants. II. The Effect of Cyanide and Other Heavy Metal Complexing Agents on the Production of Chromosome Aberrations by X-rays," *J. Biophys. Biochem. Cytol.,* **3,** 381-390.

Lea, D. E., 1955. "Actions of Radiations on Living Cells," 2nd ed., Cambridge University Press, Cambridge.

Muller, H. J., 1928. "The Problem of Genic Modification," Verhandl. V, Intern. Kongr. Vererbungsl., Berlin, 1927. *Zeitschr. Ind. Abstam. Vererbungsl., Suppl.,* **1,** 234-260.

Muller, H. J., 1950. "Radiation Damage to the Genetic Material," *Am. Scientist,* **38,** 33-59.

Sax, K., 1938. "Induction by X-rays of Chromosome Aberrations in *Tradescantia* Microspores," *Genetics,* **23,** 494-516.

Sax, K., 1940. "An Analysis of X-ray Induced Chromosomal Aberrations in *Tradescantia,*" *Genetics,* **25,** 41-68.

Sax, K., 1950. "The Effect of X rays on Chromosome Structure," *J. Cell Comp. Physiol., Suppl. 1,* **35,** 71-81.

Sax, K., 1957. "The Effect of Ionizing Radiation on Chromosomes," *Quart. Rev. Biol.,* **32,** 15-26.

"Somatic Radiation Dose for the General Population," 1960. Report of the *Ad Hoc* Committee, National Committee on Radiation Protection and Measurements, 1959. *Science,* **131,** 482-486.

Sparrow, A. H., 1951. "Radiation Sensitivity of Cells During Mitotic and Meiotic Cycle with Emphasis on Possible Cytochemical Changes," *Ann. N.Y. Acad. Sci.,* **51,** 1508-1540.

Stadler, L. J., 1928. "Mutations in Barley Induced by X-rays and Radium," *Science,* **68,** 186.

Stone, W. S., Wyss, O., and Hass, F., 1947. "The Production of Mutations in *Staphylococcus aureus* by Irradiation of Substrate," *Proc. Natl. Acad. Sci.,* **33,** 54-66.

Wilson, G. B. and Sparrow, A. H., 1960. "Configurations Resulting from Iso-Chromatid and Iso-Subchromatid Unions after Meiotic and Mitotic Prophase Irradiation," *Chromosoma,* **11,** 229-244.

Wilson, G. B., Sparrow, A. H., and Pond, V., 1959. "Sub-chromatid Rearrangements in *Trillium erectum.* I. Origin and Nature of Configurations Induced by Ionizing Radiation," *Am. J. Botany,* **46,** 309-316.

# 10

# *Replication of Genetic Material in Microorganisms*

Maintenance of genetic continuity in a clonal line of cells depends on the successful accomplishment of two processes: (1) reasonably faithful replication of the genetic information, and (2) rather precise distribution of the products of replication to daughter cells. While it is generally assumed that these processes are carried out in essentially the same fashion by all living things, this may not necessarily be so. If it is true, as it appears to be, that genetic information is encoded in nucleic acid chains in all organisms including viruses, then the presumption that the basic mechanism of replication is universally the same is probably justified. Just what this mechanism may be is not yet known, although a number of hypotheses have been proposed (Delbruck and Stent, 1957). Most of these assume validity for the Watson-Crick model of DNA structure as an entwined duplex of complementary strands (Figure 2-5). Basically there seem to be three possible situations: (1) where the parental duplex directly or indirectly serves as a template for a daughter duplex, (2) where the chains of a duplex are separated so that each daughter complex consists of one old and one new chain, and (3) where the original parental material is distributed through the four chains of the daughter duplexes. Theoretically, the answer to the question of mechanism may emerge from genetic and biochemical analyses of replication of phage DNA. In the case of this type of virus (Figure 10-1), the protein coat is left outside the infected bacterial cell and only the DNA core penetrates, where it undergoes replication and the products then resynthesize the protein body prior to lysis of the infected cell. Correlation of radioactive tag with genetic recombination has been invoked by a number of workers in hopes of determining how replication takes place, but so far no unequivocal evidence for any hypothesis has emerged (Delbruck and Stent, 1957; Levinthal and Thomas, 1957). Presumably

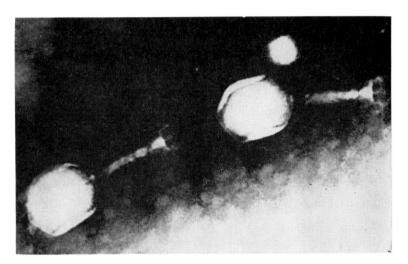

**Figure 10-1.** Electron Micrograph of Intact $T_2$ Bacteriophage or Virus Showing Polyhedral-shaped Head and Tail with Pronged Device at Its Extremity. (From Jacob, F. and Wollman, E. L., 1961. "Viruses and Genes," *Scientific American*. 204, p. 92. Electron micrograph by Drs. S. Brenner and R. W. Horne, University of Cambridge.)

in the case of the phage virus, the problem of replication of genetic material may be synonymous with the problem of replication of the DNA macromolecule. In organisms with more sophisticated chromosomes, the problem includes that of replication of non-nucleic acid moieties as well, so that, at present, one is not justified in equating molecular replication of DNA with chromosome replication. Nonetheless, it does seem rather probable that the basic mechanism of replication of genetic information is the same in all organisms, including viruses.

The mechanism of separation of the products of replication is another matter. In the vast majority of cases where detailed analysis is possible, the mechanism involves orientation of bichromatid chromosomes in a central position with respect to two poles and separation of the sister chromatids to opposite ends of the cell. All this is somehow mediated by an extrachromosomal apparatus, namely, the spindle. The questions of how this mechanism evolved and of how universal it is have received little attention. In the case of viruses, no such mechanism seems to exist or be needed. In organisms with two or more chromosomes some method of synchronization of chromatid separation would be expected, but

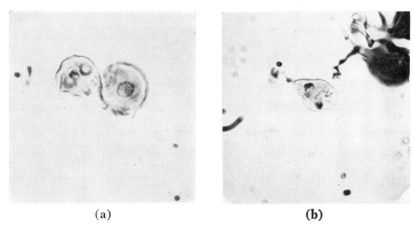

(a)                                    (b)

Figure 10-2. Photomicrographs Showing Mitotic-like Configurations in the Mold, *Blastocladiella emersonii*. (a) Interphase nuclei displaying beaded ring of chromatic material tightly appressed along the surface of the central body or nucleolus; (b) Anaphase-like Configuration Formed by the Separation of Two Chromatic Masses. (From Turian, G. and Cantino, E. C., 1960. "A Study of Mitosis in the Mold, *Blastocladiella*, with a Ribonuclease-aceto-orcein Staining Technique," *Cytologia*, 25, Fig. 1, p. 102, and Fig. 5, p. 104. Courtesy of Dr. Gilbert Turian, Institute of Botany, Geneva, Switzerland.)

whether or not one can use mitosis as observed in the cells of something like a root tip as a universal model is questionable. In the ascomycete fungus, *Gelasinospora,* both mitotic and meiotic divisions involved in formation of ascospores seem comparable in all respects with the equivalent divisions of higher plants (Sung, Alexopoulos, and Wilson, 1954). In the yeasts, which belong to the same general group, the situation is more obscure. There have been continuing disputes as to the identity of the various structures in the yeast cell, with the consequence that descriptions of nuclear division offered by different workers have shown marked disagreement. Subramaniam (1952) maintains that, under aerobic conditions, mitosis is essentially the same as in higher organisms except that the chromosomes are arranged with the long axis parallel to the spindle. Under anaerobic conditions, Subramaniam claims that endo-polyploidy occurs. These claims have been denied by a number of workers, including Winge (1951) and Lindegren and Rafalko (1950), who disagree with Subramaniam's identification of the nucleus.

Turian and Cantino (1960) have described mitotic divisions in the water mold, *Blastocladiella*. In this organism what appears to be the nucleus consists of a vacuole, almost completely filled with a nucleolar-like body and surrounded by a dense ring of chromatin. During division, the chromatin becomes organized into two opposing crescents which then separate to give an anaphase-like configuration with the nucleolar-like body serving the purpose of a spindle (Figure 10-2).

Another class of organisms in which disputes concerning nuclear organization and division have generated more fire than light, is the bacteria. DeLamater (1951) described nuclear division in several bacteria in terms which made the process sound virtually identical with that in other organisms. Bisset (1951) among others hotly contested De-Lamater's conclusions. Again the argument centers around the identification of cell parts rather than around the premise of "typical" division.

The blue-green algae (*Cyanophyta*) have long been considered by phycologists to have no organized nuclei or chromosomes in the usual sense, though chromatin bodies have been described. In 1960, Leak and Wilson described "mitotic-like" divisions in the filamentous *Anabaena variabilis* after staining by the Feulgen technique. According to their description, there is no central nucleus but, instead, a number of vacuoles partially surrounded by Feulgen-positive material. Recently, the absence of a typical nuclear boundary has been confirmed by electron microscopy. During division, the vacuoles break down and the chromatic material is distributed through the cell in the form of thread-like bodies. Ultimately, the chromatic material separates into two anaphase-like groups and the cell cleaves (Figure 10-3). Subsequent to their published observations, occasional metaphase-like groupings have been noted. No spindle has so far been seen, but the techniques used are not suitable for revealing the achromatic apparatus. In contrast, green algae such as *Spirogyra* appear to have typical mitotic divisions (Figure 10-4).

Though many more studies need to be made on microorganisms, it would seem that the organization of genetic material in interphase cells is subject to considerable variation, including complete lack of a double-membraned nuclear boundary. If we exclude the viruses, actual division of the chromatin appears to be somewhat similar in all organisms,

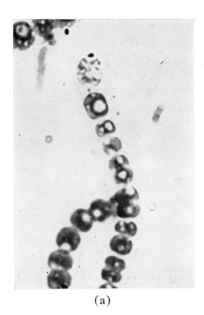

(a)

**Figure 10-3.** Photomicrographs Showing Changes in the Chromatin Pattern During Replication in the Blue-Green Alga, *Anabaena variabilis* Kutz. (a) Typical chromatin pattern in "interphase" cell (second cell from top);

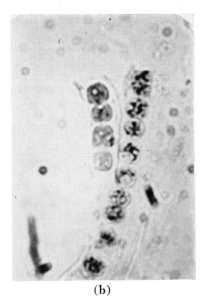

(b)

(b) chromatin pattern characteristic of "prophase" (filament of cells on right);

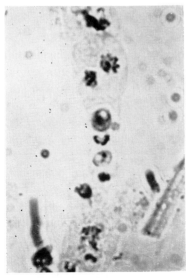

(c)

(c) chromatin pattern in "anaphase" cell (second cell from top). (From Leak, L. V. and Wilson, G. B., 1960. "The Distribution of Chromatin in a Blue Green Alga *Anabaena variabilis* Kutz," *Can. J. Genetics and Cytol.,* **2**, Figs. 2, 4, 5, p. 322. Courtesy of Mr. L. V. Leak, Michigan State University.)

though whether the nature and functioning of the "spindle" is the same in all cases has yet to be determined. Tempting as it may be to parallel "mitotic" stages in a blue-green alga with those in an onion root tip, one should remember that we may be unjustifiably assuming homology of configurations which are really only analogous.

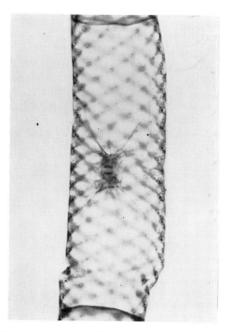

**Figure 10-4.** Photomicrograph Showing Typical Anaphase Configuration During Mitosis in the Alga, *Spirogyra*. Note well-defined spindle apparatus and distinct chromosomes. (Courtesy of General Biological Supply House, Inc., Chicago, Ill.)

## BIBLIOGRAPHY

Bisset, K. A., 1951. "The Genetical Implications of Bacterial Cytology," *Cold Spring Harbor Symposia on Quant. Biol.,* **16,** 381-412.

DeLamater, E. D., 1951. "A New Cytological Basis for Bacterial Genetics," *Cold Spring Harbor Symposia on Quant. Biol.,* **16,** 373-379.

Delbruck, M. and Stent, G. S., 1957. "On the Mechanism of DNA Replication," *in* "The Chemical Basis of Heredity," B. Glass and W. D. McElroy (Eds.), Johns Hopkins Univ. Press, Baltimore, Md., pp. 699-736.

Glass, B., 1957. "A Summary of the Symposium on the Chemical Basis of Heredity," *in* "The Chemical Basis of Heredity," B. Glass and W. D. McElroy (Eds.), Johns Hopkins Univ. Press, Baltimore, Md., pp. 757-834.

Leak, L. V. and Wilson, G. B., 1960. "Distribution of Chromatin in a Blue-Green Alga, *Anabaena variabilis* Kutz," *Can. J. Genetics and Cytol.*, **2**, 320-324.

Levinthal, C. and Thomas, C. A., 1957. "The Molecular Basis of Genetic Recombination in Phage," *in* "The Chemical Basis of Heredity," B. Glass and W. D. McElroy (Eds.), Johns Hopkins Univ. Press, Baltimore, Md., pp. 737-743.

Lindegren, C. and Rafalko, M., 1950. "The Structure of the Nucleus of *Saccharomyces boyanus*," *Expl. Cell. Res.*, **1**, 169-187.

Subramaniam, M. K., 1952. "On the Identification of the Various Structures in the Yeast Cell," *J. Indian Inst. Sci.*, **34**, 11-23.

Sung, H. S., Alexopoulos, C. J., and Wilson, G. B., 1954. "A Cytotaxonomic Study of Three Species of *Gelasinospora*," *Cytologia*, **19**, 255-264.

Turian, G. and Cantino, E., 1960. "A Study of Mitosis in the Mold *Blastocladiella* with a Ribonuclease-Aceto-Orcein Staining Technique," *Cytologia*, **25**, 101-107.

Winge, O., 1951. "A Note on 'Autotetraploidy and the So-called Inbreeding Degeneration of Yeasts,'" *Current Sci.*, **20**, 236.

# *11*

# *Survey of Cytological Techniques*

OUTSTANDING PROGRESS has been made over the last decade in the design and use of instruments for the study of the organization and kinetics of the cell. Future developments in this area would seem to be limited only by the ingenuity of the cytologist in developing new experimental tools or adopting instruments already in use in other fields such as physics and chemistry. Much of the apparatus associated with physical measurements of various kinds and biochemical analyses has been or is in the process of being adopted for studies at the cellular level. In the present chapter those methods which (1) are most widely used, and (2) have given reliable results, will be outlined. The list is by no means exhaustive nor are the descriptions of many of the techniques meant to replace those found in the many excellent reviews available.

## FIXATION

Cytological fixation is the treatment of living cells, usually with chemical agents, to preserve their structural and/or chemical components for subsequent study. The very heterogeneity of living systems generally makes it impossible to devise a fixation system which achieves all-round perfection. At best, one attempts to find fixing agents or combinations of agents capable of preserving certain predetermined features in a reasonably "life-like" state. One very important requirement for any fixation is that whatever alteration it does produce in the cell should be *permanent* and *consistent*.

## Chemical Fixation

In general, chemical fixation of cells and tissues is carried out by immersion in reagents which have been found by experience to give images resembling those of the living cell and, in most cases, known to combine with specific chemical groups of cell constituents. The choice of a suitable fixative, both with respect to the kinds and amounts of chemical reagents, is dictated by the purpose for which the fixative is to be used. For example, the investigator interested primarily in studying chromosome morphology frequently uses acidic fixatives (*Carnoy's*—3 parts absolute ethyl alcohol : 1 part glacial acetic acid; *Bouin's*—5 parts saturated aqueous picric acid : 5 parts 40 per cent formaldehyde (formalin) : 1 part glacial acetic acid), which leave the chromosomes in a highly precipitated form suitable for staining and microscopic study, but do not necessarily preserve the chemical organization of the cell. On the other hand, the investigator concerned with the study of enzyme activity in the cell selects fixatives (acetone, formaldehyde) which produce minimal denaturation and solubilization of proteins and, at the same time, preserve cell structures sufficiently well to permit identification of sites of chemical activity. The development in recent years of methods of freezing and dehydrating tissues which do not involve their immersion in reactive chemical agents, has proved to be of particular value in solving the problem of preservation of chemical groups and enzyme systems in cells.

Individual components of most commonly used fixatives do have known chemical effects and they are used because of these known effects. In general, however, particular combinations of fixing agents are based more on experience than on specific knowledge of effect. It is obviously somewhat difficult to determine whether one has achieved good fixation or not in any given case. Certain information concerning the organization of protoplasm, however, does give a basis for deciding what kinds of chemical agents may be most suitable for a particular study.

It is generally agreed that the essential effect of all fixatives on living protoplasm is the separation of its *solid* phase from its *liquid* phase (Gersh, 1959). During the fixation process, the solid phase may separate out in the form of fibrils, granules, nets, or vacuoles depending on the kind of fixative employed. While it is recognized that fixatives produce changes in the physical and chemical organization of protoplasm, the precise mechanisms operating to produce these changes are, for the most part, poorly understood. According to Wolman (1955), the basis of living protoplasm is protein, which exists mostly in the form of long-chain molecules interconnected by cross linkages (Figure 11-1). Specific chemical groups are associated with the surface of the proteins and the side chains connecting different proteins. These molecular groupings serve to connect protein molecules with each other and with lipid and carbohydrate molecules. The water of protoplasm is either bound to ionized groups of proteins, exists free, or is associated with mobile molecules. Assuming that this concept of the structure of protoplasm is essentially correct, fixation would involve the formation of new cross

**Figure 11-1.** Schematic Representation of the Molecular Organization of Protoplasm in the Native State. The thick, wavy chains represent protein molecules—the fibrous ones being linear, the curved ones globular. The thick, straight chains represent lipid molecules and fatty acid radicals. The dots represent water molecules and crystalloids. Intermolecular linkages are shown as dashed lines; intramolecular linkages as solid lines. (From Wolman, M., 1955. "Problems of Fixation in Cytology, Histology, and Histochemistry," *Intern. Rev. Cytol.,* 4, Fig. 1, p. 89.)

linkages between protein molecules, with the result that new forces of attraction would be established. If the new linkages developed in this way produce excessive clumping of proteins, the result is displacement and distortion of protein structures in the cell and, hence, "poor" fixation (Figure 11-2(b)). On this same basis, a "good" fixative would be one which leads to the formation of many cross linkages between proteins, none of which set up attraction forces of sufficient magnitude to disturb radically the spatial relations already existing between the proteins of the cell (Figure 11-2(a)).

Fixing agents such as formaldehyde, dichromate, and mercuric chloride produce strong cross linkages between protein molecules and are components of such well-known fixatives as *Zenker's, Helly's, Bouin's, Flemming's,* and *Regaud's* (Gray, 1952; Gatenby and Beams, 1950, "Microtomist's Vade-Mecum"). Fixation with formaldehyde is believed to occur in two steps: (1) the combination of formaldehyde with chem-

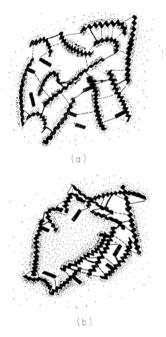

(a)

(b)

Figure 11-2. Schematic Representation of the Molecular Organization of Protoplasm Resulting from Good (above) and Bad (below) Fixation. In good fixation cross linkages between molecules are produced without extreme alteration of the molecular organization. In bad fixation the numerous cross linkages produced result in separation of a coarse coacervate from a liquid phase. (From Wolman, M., 1955. "Problems of Fixation in Cytology, Histology, and Histochemistry," *Intern. Rev. Cytol.,* 4, Figs. 3B and 3C, p. 95.)

ical groupings of proteins to form addition complexes, and (2) the reaction of these addition complexes with free molecular groupings of other proteins to form *methylene* (—CH$_2$—) bridges. Chemical groups which may form addition complexes with formaldehyde are the amino, carboxyl, and indole groups of proteins, to mention only a few. The two-step reaction of formaldehyde with the amino groups of protein may be represented as follows:

(a) $|$—N—H + HCHO $\longrightarrow$ $|$—NH·CH$_2$OH

$\quad\quad$ $|$

$\quad\quad$ H

AMINO $\quad\quad$ FORMALDEHYDE $\quad\quad$ METHYLOL
GROUP

(b) $|$—NH·CH$_2$OH + H—N— $|$ $\longrightarrow$ $|$—NH—CH$_2$—HN— $|$ + H$_2$O

$\quad\quad\quad\quad\quad\quad\quad$ $|$

$\quad\quad\quad\quad\quad\quad\quad$ H

$\quad\quad\quad\quad\quad\quad\quad\quad\quad$ METHYLENE
$\quad\quad\quad\quad\quad\quad\quad\quad\quad$ BRIDGE

The primary fixation effect of chromium salts (e.g., potassium dichromate) is considered to result from formation of chromium linkages between proteins; however, some oxidation of protein may take place during the fixation process. Chromium solutions appear to fix polysaccharides by combining with aliphatic hydroxyl groups and with lipids by oxidation of unsaturated double bonds. Mercuric chloride appears to fix protein structures by combination of the divalent mercuric ion with sulfhydryl, carboxyl, and amino groups of proteins to produce intermolecular mercury linkages.

Alcohol and acetic acid are components of many of the so-called "chromosome" fixatives. Carnoy's fluid (acetic-alcohol) contains only these two substances combined in the proportions of 3:1 and is one of the most reliable and widely used fixatives for the preservation of chromosomes. The mechanism of fixation of protein by acetic acid and alcohol apparently is somewhat different from that of formaldehyde, chromates, and metallic ions. One of the primary effects of acetic acid on tissues is the loss of bound water associated with the ionized groups of proteins. This disappearance of bound water probably brings reactive groups into closer proximity with each other, with the result that new cross linkages are formed. Alcohol produces a similar effect, but appears also to function in rendering proteins insoluble following their precipitation. In dealing with highly hydrated structures such as chromosomes, the use of fixatives that contain substances which not only dehydrate or precipitate nucleoproteins but also render them insoluble, is desirable. For the fixation of cytoplasmic structures, quite the opposite effect is required for cytological study. Fixatives such as formaldehyde, chromium, and osmium tetroxide solutions used in one combination or another generally give poor preservation of chromosome structure but are useful for the preservation of cytoplasmic structures such as the mitochondria. In addition to forming cross linkages between proteins, formaldehyde and chromates also fix lipids when used under appropriate conditions. Treatment of tissues with chromates brings about oxidation of unsaturated lipids, which renders them insoluble. Osmium tetroxide produces a similar effect on unsaturated lipids, the osmium being reduced during the fixation process to black oxides. This blackening of osmium occurs in such structures as the Golgi complex, and has been utilized for many years as a method for revealing this structure in the cytoplasm of certain cells.

### Freezing-Drying

Because of the physical and chemical effects of fixation by immersion in chemical reagents, such treatment is generally not suitable for most cytochemical studies in which the aim is to detect particular substances (e.g., enzymes) and to determine the location of these substances in the

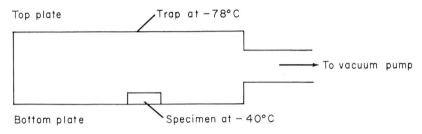

**Figure 11-3.** Diagram Showing the Basic Principles of the Freeze Dryer in Cross-Section. (From Bell, L. G. E., 1952. "The Application of Freezing and Drying Techniques in Cytology," *Intern. Rev. Cytol.,* 1, Fig. 1, p. 46.)

cell. One method which, in most respects, is at least a considerable improvement involves: (1) rapid cooling and freezing of tissues by immersion in a cold bath, and (2) their dehydration by vacuum desiccation at low temperature to prepare them for subsequent embedding, sectioning, and staining.

In the freezing technique, the initial cooling or quenching of the tissue is usually carried out at temperatures in the range of $-160$ to $-190°$ C. This is most easily accomplished by plunging small pieces of tissue, culture cells on coverslips, or smears and imprints on slides into a quenching solution cooled by liquid nitrogen. The solutions most frequently used are isopentane, propane, or a mixture of the two. The most important aspect of the freezing process is the quick cooling of materials through the temperature range $-30$ to $-40°$ C. It is within this range that the rate of ice crystal formation is most rapid. The use of liquid nitrogen permits materials to be cooled rapidly through this critical range to lower temperatures where only finer ice crystal formation occurs.

The drying process subsequent to embedding and sectioning consists of removal of ice from the frozen tissues in a vacuum at temperatures ($-40$ to $-60°$ C) sufficiently low to prevent changes in ice crystal structure. The principal of the freeze dryer is shown in Figure 11-3. It consists essentially of (1) a vacuum or drying chamber in which the specimen is suspended, and (2) a cold bath which serves to keep the drying chamber at a low temperature. Under vacuum, water vapor is removed from the specimen onto the walls of the cold drying tube. Removal of water can be enhanced by placing a chemical desiccant such as phosphorus pentoxide on the bottom of the drying tube. Following removal of water, the specimen is allowed to reach room temperature and prepared for embedding by standard techniques.

### Freezing-Substitution

This method involves placing the specimen after quick freezing in one of a number of reagents (e.g., ethanol, methanol, butanol, acetone) maintained at low temperature ($-20$ to $-60°$ C). These reagents serve to dissolve out the ice crystals in the specimen and to replace them with the reagent. Freezing-substitution is useful for preparing smears and imprints of tissues prior to cytochemical staining, since they can be incubated in staining solutions immediately following solvent substitution at low temperatures without prior drying or embedding.

The rapid cooling of tissues is superior to chemical fixation because (1) postmortem changes are minimal, (2) chemical substances, particularly proteins, are precipitated but not made soluble, (3) solidification of tissues as the result of freezing increases their viscosity and reduces the extent of diffusion of substances, (4) displacement and distortion of cell structures are reduced, and (5) little or no extraction of soluble components occurs.

## STAINING

The stains most often employed in routine cytological studies are solutions of organic aromatic dyes which may be *acid* (anionic) or *basic* (cationic) in character depending on the particular molecular groups they contain. For a compound to function as a dye it must contain (1) an *auxochrome* group which is responsible for the electrolytic dissociation of the compound, and (2) a *chromatophore* group which imparts to the compound the property of color.

Dyes are classified as acidic or basic depending on whether the auxochrome they contain forms a salt with an acid (basic dye) or a base (acid dye). In acid dyes, the auxochrome is generally either a hydroxyl (—OH), carboxyl (—COOH), or sulfonic (—SO₃H) group. The auxochromes of basic dyes are usually an amino (—NH₂) group or one of its derivatives. The chromatophores responsible for the colored properties of dyes are also classified as being either acidic or basic. Examples of acidic chromatophores are the nitro (—NO₂) and quinoid

(O=⟨ ⟩=O) groups. The basic chromatophores are the azo

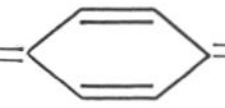

(—N=N—) and indamin (—N=) groups. The yellow acid dye, picric acid, may be used to show the different types of groups present in a dye (Figure 11-4). The color of picric acid is due to the nitro groups (chromatophores), and its dyeing properties are attributed to the hydroxyl group (auxochrome) which is capable of forming salts with a base.

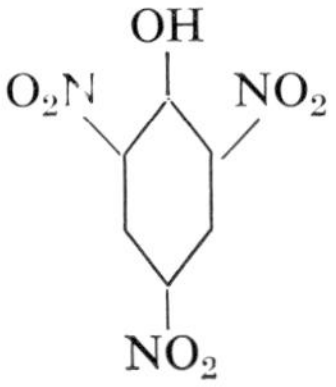

OH

O₂N     NO₂

NO₂

**Figure 11-4.** Diagram of Molecular Structure of the Yellow-Acid Dye, Picric Acid.


## Conventional Staining

A number of factors operate to influence the staining of cell structures. The most important variable is hydrogen ion concentration (pH), although other factors such as tissue fixation, temperature, and ionic strength of the dye are known to play a role (Singer, 1952). The effect of pH on the staining of relatively pure proteins, such as fibrin, with acid and basic dyes is shown in Figure 11-5. In this figure it can be seen that the pH levels where the staining of fibrin with acid and basic dye is maximum are widely separated (pH 3 and pH 8, respectively). Also there is a range of pH where the fibrin stains with neither acid nor basic dyes regardless of the time of staining. The influence of pH on the staining of cell structures is a reflection of the dissociation characteristic of the substances they contain. Proteins and nucleic acids in solution are amphoteric, that is, they can act as acids or bases depending on the pH of the solution. As pointed out in Chapter 2, a protein molecule at its isoelectric point has a net charge of zero due to the balance of positive and negative charges between the dissociated acidic and basic groups of the constituent amino acids. In this state of dissociation, the protein molecule exists as a doubly charged ion or zwitterion. The basic group which contributes most to the positive charge of proteins is the substituted ammonium ($NH_3^+$) group and is present in the amino acids, lysine, histidine, and arginine. The acidic carboxyl group of glutamic and aspartic acid and the acidic hydroxyl group of tyrosine and serine are primarily responsible for giving proteins their negative charge. The influence of pH on the dissociation of free basic and acidic groups

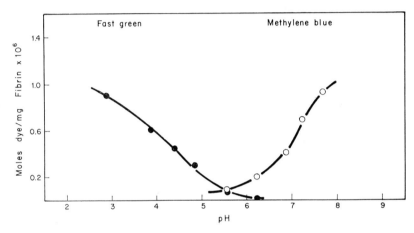

**Figure 11-5.** Variations in Acid (Fast Green) and Basic (Methylene Blue) Dye Uptake by Fixed Films of Fibrin, with Changes in pH of the Staining Solution. Fixation, 10 per cent formaldehyde for 10 hrs; dye concentration, $5 \times 10^{-5}$M; ionic strength, 0.02. (From Singer, M., 1952. "Factors which Control the Staining of Tissue Sections with Acid and Basic Dyes," *Intern. Rev. Cytol.*, 1, Fig. 1, p. 220.)

of the amino acids is shown by the addition of either acid or base to a protein solution at its isoelectric point. At pH's acid to the isoelectric point of proteins, the dissociation of free basic groups of the protein is enhanced to give it a positive charge and to permit its combination with acid dyes. At pH's basic to the isoelectric point, the dissociation of free acid groups is favored to make the proteins negative in charge and capable of reacting with basic dyes.

The net electric charge of nucleic acids is determined primarily by the dissociation of the phosphoric acid group of the sugar moiety and the substituted ammonium group of the pyrimidine and purine base moieties in the molecule. The effect of pH on the dissociation of nucleic acids may be shown as follows:

$$P\text{—OH} \qquad\qquad P\text{—O}^- \qquad\qquad P\text{—O}^-$$

| | | |
|---|---|---|
| P—OH | P—O⁻ | P—O⁻ |
| &#124;&#124;&#124; | &#124;&#124;&#124; | &#124;&#124;&#124; |
| [NA]—NH₃⁺ ⟵ | [NA]—NH₃⁺ ⟶ | [NA]—NH₂ |
| &#124;&#124; | &#124;&#124; | &#124;&#124; |
| C—OH | C—OH | C—OH |
| POSITIVE CHARGE | NUCLEIC ACID (Zwitterion) | NEGATIVE CHARGE |

The isoelectric point of nucleic acids is considered to be pH 2 or less. Because the dissociation of free acidic (i.e., $COO^-$) groups of most proteins is minimal at pH's less than 4.0, it is possible to selectively stain nucleic acids with basic dyes such as Toluidine blue O and Azure B at low pH levels (between pH 2.0 and 4.0).

After fixation, cell structures show a pronounced affinity for both acidic and basic dyes. This is not unexpected when one recalls that the primary action of a fixing agent is on the proteins of the cell and that, in most instances, the proteins are precipitated and made insoluble by the fixative. In addition to the general increase in stainability of cells following fixation, there appears to be a preferential uptake of either acidic or basic dye depending on the method of fixation employed. For example, formaldehyde fixation enhances basic dye uptake whereas mercuric chloride favors acid dye uptake. This selective effect of fixation on dye uptake is mostly the result of combination of the fixing agent with specific groups of proteins, thus making them unavailable for combination with certain groups of the dye. For example, the increase in acid dye uptake following fixation of tissues in salts of metallic ions ($HgCl_2$) or dicromates ($K_2CrO_4$) is probably the result of combination of the mercury or chromium ions with free acidic groups of proteins, especially carboxyl and hydroxyl, and the phosphoric acid of nucleic acids. In this way, more basic groups are made available for dissociation and combination with acid dye. Acid fixatives such as acetic-alcohol (Carnoy's) give excellent preservation of chromosomes by precipitating the nucleoproteins and breaking the linkages between the nucleic acids and proteins in these structures. As a result, the number of acidic groups of chromosomal proteins and nucleic acids is increased to give strong staining with basic dyes.

### Cytochemical Staining

Most of the dyes commonly used to reveal cell structure are nonspecific in the sense that they do not stain selectively any one molecular grouping or substance in the cell. The only exception is the *Feulgen* reaction which is specific for DNA and is routinely employed as a method for staining chromosomes. To demonstrate the presence of substances such as proteins, nucleic acids, carbohydrates, and lipids in a particular cell structure requires the use of specific cytochemical tests employing *chromogenic* agents which are selectively bound to one or more molecular groupings of the substance under study. This specificity can be improved in many cases by differential digestion with enzymes to eliminate interfering substances.

The methods found most reliable for the routine detection of proteins in tissues are (1) the *Millon* reaction for tyrosine, and (2) the *diazonium* reaction for histidine, tyrosine, and tryptophan. Both of these reactions involve the use of a colorless chromogenic agent which, when applied to fixed tissues under appropriate conditions, gives a colored product by combining with a specific group (s) of the protein. When tissues are exposed to Millon's reagent (a solution of mercuric nitrite and nitrate in a mixture of nitric and nitrous acids) a red precipitate is obtained due to the presence of the phenolic $(-\langle\underline{\quad}\rangle-OH)$ group of tyrosine. In the diazonium reaction, the chromogenic reagent is a diazonium hydroxide which reacts with the phenolic group of tyrosine, the indole group of tryptophan, and the imidazole group of histidine to produce a complex which is colored.

The cytochemical determination of specific amino acids is limited by the relatively few techniques available for their identification and the difficulty of applying them to fixed materials. The methods most often used with fixed tissues are (1) the *Sakaguchi* reaction for arginine, and (2) the *mercurial* method for protein sulfhydryl groups. The latter technique involves the treatment of tissues with the red-colored mercurial, Mercury Orange, which combines with —SH groups as follows:

The —SH content of cell components can also be measured quantitatively by photometric analysis of tissues stained by this technique (Bennett and Watts, 1958).

The methods used to demonstrate enzyme activity associated with cellular structures differ from those described above in that the chromogenic agent is not combined with a particular molecular group but instead operates to either *catalyze* a specific enzyme reaction or to *accept* hydrogens (electrons) at a specific point in an enzymatic sequence. The enzymes most extensively studied in terms of their location in cell structures are the esterases (alkaline and acid phosphatase) and oxidases (cytochrome oxidase, succinic dehydrogenase). The cytochemical demonstration of alkaline phosphatase depends on the deposition of calcium phosphate at sites of enzyme action when tissues are incubated with an appropriate organic phosphate ester in the presence of calcium ions at alkaline pH. The localization of oxidases is accomplished by incubating tissues in a solution of a colorless *tetrazolium* salt which, in the presence of a suitable substrate, is reduced to a colored *formazan* by accepting hydrogens from either dehydrogenases or flavoproteins. If succinate is used as the substrate (hydrogen donor) the reaction leading to demonstration of succinic dehydrogenase may be diagrammed as follows:

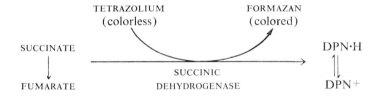

In this reaction, succinate functions as the electron donor. The electrons removed from succinate as the result of its oxidation via succinic dehydrogenase are picked up by the colorless tetrazolium to reduce it to the colored formazan. The tetrazolium reaction is sometimes carried out in the presence of metallic ions which chelate with the formazan as it is produced. This facilitates precipitation of the formazan at sites of enzyme activity.

Quantitative measurement of the amounts of various proteins in cell structures is usually carried out by photometric analysis of tissues stained by appropriate reagents. Methods which have been used successfully for this purpose include (1) the Millon reaction, (2) the alkaline Fast green stain for basic proteins (histones), and (3) the Naphthol yellow S stain for basic groups of lysine, arginine, and histidine.

The localization of polysaccharides in the cell is usually accomplished by the *periodic-acid-Schiff* (PAS) reaction. This method involves the hydrolysis of C—C bonds in carbohydrates by periodic acid ($HIO_4$) to yield dialdehydes (CHO·CHO). The resulting aldehydes are then localized by their combination with *leucobasic fuchsin* (Schiff's reagent) to give a red-colored dye complex.

Lipids are most easily stained with *fat-soluble* dyes such as Sudan black B (phospholipids), sudan red, and oil red (neutral fats). The reduction of osmium tetroxide to black oxides by unsaturated fatty acids is a standard method for the routine demonstration of lipids in the cell. Neutral fats and fatty acids may also be demonstrated by the use of Nile blue sulphate. Phospholipids are identified by the acid hematein method which involves their staining with oxidized acid hematoxylin solution following prolonged exposure to chromates.

The methods used to demonstrate nucleic acids, particularly DNA, are probably the most extensively investigated from the point of view of their validity and mode of action. DNA is best demonstrated by means of the Feulgen reaction. The basic dye, methyl green, is also specific for DNA under specified conditions. The Feulgen reaction depends on the mild acid hydrolysis of tissues to release aldehyde groups of the deoxyribose sugar moiety of DNA which then react with Schiff's reagent. The total reaction occurs in two steps: (1) removal of purines of DNA by acid hydrolysis to permit the deoxyribose sugar rings to open and form reactive aldehyde groups, and (2) reaction of the Schiff's reagent with the aldehydes to give the colored complex.

DNA can be measured quantitatively by photometric analysis of fixed tissues stained by the Feulgen reaction. In this method, the intensity of light transmitted by the Feulgen-stained specimen $(I_s)$ compared with that transmitted by a blank part of the slide $(I_o)$ is measured by means of a photoelectric cell (Figure 11-6). The ratio $I_s/I_o \times 100$ represents the per cent of light transmitted by the Fuelgen-stained specimen. From this information the absorption or extinction coefficient $(E)$ can be calculated. The value of $E$ can then be used to calculate the amount of nuclear DNA in arbitrary units.

In all photometric studies involving the quantitative measurement of cell substances by virtue of their light absorption (Figure 11-7) it is essential to show that the amount of light absorbed by the substance is proportional to the number of absorbing molecules present per unit thickness. This linear relationship between the amount of light absorbed and the number of absorbing molecules is usually expressed as *Beer-Lambert's* law. In the case of the Feulgen reaction, the Beer-Lambert law appears to hold, indicating that the amount of light absorbed by the stain is a reasonably accurate measurement of the amount of DNA.

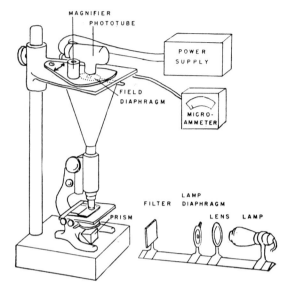

**Figure 11-6.** Diagram Showing the Essential Components of the Cyto-photometer for Absorption Measurements in the Visible Spectrum. (From Swift, H., 1950. "The Desoxyribose Nucleic Acid Content of Animal Nuclei," *Physiol. Zool.*, **23**, Fig. 1, p. 171.)

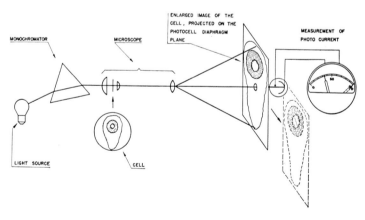

**Figure 11-7.** Diagram Showing the Principle of Photoelectric Micro-spectrophotometry. (From Caspersson, T. O., 1950. "Cell Growth and Cell Function," W. W. Norton & Co., Inc., New York, N. Y., Fig. 4, p. 21.)

## MICROSCOPY

The ability to resolve neighboring objects as being distinct and separate depends on the degree of contrast between the objects and the *resolving power* of the viewing device. In the case of the unaided human eye, the limit of resolution is considered to be only about 0.1 mm (100$\mu$) under optimal viewing conditions. This means that if two adjacent objects are separated by a distance *less* than 0.1 mm they will appear as one object to the eye. The limitation imposed by cell size on direct observation with the eye requires that cells and their component parts be studied with the aid of an instrument such as the microscope, which operates not only to magnify but also to give increased resolution (Figure 11-8).

The component of the optical system of any microscope which is responsible for the initial magnification of the specimen is the *objective lens* (Figure 11-8). This lens also determines the resolving power of the microscope, which is a function of (1) the light-gathering power or *numerical aperture* (*N.A.*) of the objective lens, and (2) the *wavelength* of radiation used to illuminate the specimen. The resolving power, in terms of the size of object which may be seen, is determined from the Abbé formula as follows:

$$R = \frac{0.61\,\lambda}{N.A.}$$

where $\lambda$ is the wavelength of the illumination and *N.A.* is the numerical aperture of the objective lens. The value, 0.61, is a constant representing the minimum difference in contrast that is detectable. Consideration of the above formula shows that with objectives of equivalent numerical aperture, the resolving power of a microscope is *inversely proportional* to the wavelength of light used. That is, the resolving power increases with decrease in wavelength of the illumination. For a microscope using an oil-immersion objective of *N.A.* = 1.2, the Abbé formula gives a limit of resolution of about 0.27$\mu$ for visible light of mean wavelength 5400 Å, and about 0.13$\mu$ for ultraviolet radiation of wavelength 2600 Å. On a similar basis, the same microscope using infrared radiation of 8000 Å wavelength would have a resolving power of only about 0.4$\mu$.

Microscopy includes many different kinds of instruments and techniques. However, all microscopes, regardless of their design, are *magnifying devices* which produce an *enlarged image* of the specimen under study. This means that any information derived by use of the microscope must come ultimately from examination of the enlarged image it forms. Image formation is determined largely by the particular wavelength of radiation used to illuminate the specimen and the physical properties of the specimen. When the image is formed by visible light as in the ordinary light microscope, it can be examined directly with the eye or re-

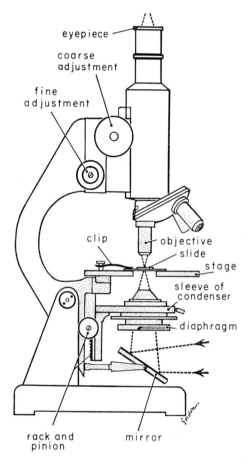

eyepiece

coarse adjustment

fine adjustment

clip

objective

slide

stage

sleeve of condenser

diaphragm

rack and pinion

mirror

**Figure 11-8.** Drawing of a Compound Microscope with its Principle Parts Labeled. (From Ham, A. W., 1957. "Histology," 3rd ed., J. B. Lippincott Co., Philadelphia, Pa., Fig. 14, p. 19.)

corded on a photographic film. Images formed by shorter wavelength radiations, such as the ultraviolet, to which the eye is not sensitive must be examined by means of a recording device such as a photoelectric cell or photographic plate.

The physical properties of the specimen most commonly exploited in microscopy to form the image are: (1) absorption, (2) refractive index and thickness, (3) mass differences, (4) polarization, and (5) fluorescence. The ordinary light microscope is used almost exclusively for the examination of fixed and stained materials where perception of the image is based upon the *differential absorption* of light by the different stained parts of the specimen. As a result, the light making up the image shows variations in intensity or color to give contrast between the different parts of the image. When cell structures show *selective absorption* of light of specific wavelengths such as the ultraviolet, they are examined with the ultraviolet microscope. Living cells, which are highly transparent and absorb virtually no light, must be examined with the phase-contrast microscope, which converts *phase changes* induced by differences in refractive index and thickness of different parts of the cell into *light intensity changes.* Differences in the *mass* of substances containing atoms of carbon, oxygen, and nitrogen in different parts of the cell will cause scattering of an electron beam and are responsible for image formation in the electron microscope. Because some cell structures are *anisotropic* they will alter the natural path of polarized light passing through them and can be examined with the polarization microscope. The presence in cells of substances which *fluoresce* or emit visible light when illuminated with shorter wavelength radiations makes it possible to examine cells with the fluorescence microscope.

## Optical and Electron Microscopy

In the electron microscope and the light microscope, the arrangement and function of the different parts are essentially the same. To emphasize this similarity in basic design, the two microscopes will be described together in this section.

The essential parts of the conventional light microscope are: (1) a light source, (2) a condensing lens system to collect and focus light on the specimen, (3) an objective lens to form and magnify the image of the specimen, and (4) an eyepiece lens to enlarge further the image formed by the objective and to project this image to the retina of the eye or a photographic film (Figures 11-8 and 11-9).

The electron microscope is unique in that it is the only instrument currently available which permits the examination of structures with dimensions as small as 1 m$\mu$ (10 Å). This is quite remarkable when one considers that the intramolecular spacing of atoms is of the order of 1 to 5 Å. The high resolving power of the electron microscope is due simply to the fact that electrons of exceedingly short wavelengths are used to illuminate the specimen. The wavelength of an electron beam is a function of the *acceleration voltage* to which it is subjected and is expressed as

$$\lambda = \sqrt{\frac{150}{V}}$$

where $\lambda$ is the wavelength and $V$ is the voltage employed to accelerate the electrons. It follows from the above equation that electrons accelerated through a potential of 60,000 volts would have a wavelength of only about 0.05 Å. This is a wavelength that is about 100,000 times shorter than the mean wavelength of visible light (5000 Å).

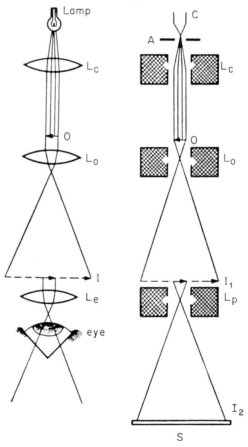

**Figure 11-9.** Simplified Diagram of the Optical System of the Light (left) and Electron (right) Microscope. (From Coslett, V. E., 1955. "Electron Microscopy," *in* Oster, G. and Pollister, A. W. (Eds.), "Physical Techniques in Biological Research," 1, Academic Press, New York, N. Y., Fig. 3, p. 467.)

The major difference between the electron microscope and the ordinary light microscope is the physical design of the two instruments. Because electrons will travel appreciable distances only in a vacuum, the entire microscope unit of the electron microscope is enclosed in a vacuum-tight column. The similarity in arrangement and function of the optical systems of the two microscopes can be seen from examination of Figure 11-9. In the electron microscope, the illuminating source is a cathode filament ($C$) which emits a narrow beam of electrons. This electron beam is collected and focused upon the specimen by an electromagnetic condenser lens ($L_c$). After passing through the specimen, the electrons are collected by the electromagnetic objective lens ($L_o$) which forms an enlarged image of the specimen. An electromagnetic projector or "eyepiece" lens ($L_p$) further magnifies the image of the specimen and projects it on to a fluorescent viewing screen ($S$).

The electron image is focused by varying the magnetic field of the objective lens ($L_o$). Magnification of the image can be increased or decreased by varying the current in the projector lens ($L_p$). Since the objective and projector lenses of the electron microscope contribute more or less equally to the magnification of the image, variation of the magnetic field of the objective lens permits a range of from 1000 to 60,000× to be obtained. In the light microscope, magnification is varied by changing the objective ($L_o$) and/or eyepiece lens ($L_e$). The maximum magnification of an oil-immersion objective is about 100×, while the magnification contributed by the eyepiece generally never exceeds 15×. In practice, the highest magnification possible with reasonable resolution, with the ordinary light microscope, is about 1500×.

## Phase-Contrast Microscopy

Most living cells are essentially *transparent* to *visible light*. This means that light passing through such objects must suffer almost no loss of intensity as the result of absorption by cell components. Because the eye is sensitive only to differences in intensity and/or color, the living cell will show almost no contrast when viewed with the conventional optical microscope. Light transmitted through the living cell, however, does encounter regions of *different refractive index* and *thickness* which alter its *velocity* and *direction*. In Figure 11-10 are represented two adjacent regions of the cell, **A** and **B**, of different thickness, $t_1$ and $t_2$, and of different refractive index, $n_1$ and $n_2$. This variation in thickness and refractive index produces a *difference* in the *optical path* (product of refractive index and thickness) of light transmitted by the two regions, i.e., it takes longer for light to pass through region **B** of higher refractive index ($n_2$) than through region **A** of lower refractive index ($n_1$). As a result, the light transmitted by **B** is *retarded in velocity* with respect to that transmitted by **A** and emerges *out of phase* relative to that emerging from region **A** of lower refractive index. When the difference in refractive index is small, the magnitude of the phase change induced is also small and is measured in wavelengths ($\lambda$). In Figure 11-10, the light ray transmitted by region **B** is shown retarded ¼ wavelength $\left(\dfrac{\lambda}{4}\right)$ behind that transmitted by region **A**. The phase-contrast microscope transforms such phase changes into corresponding variations of brightness or intensity. This serves to enhance the contrast between

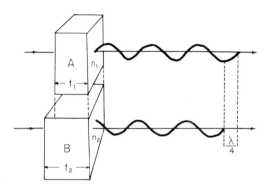

**Figure 11-10.** Schematic Representation of the Retardation in Velocity of Light on Passing Through Two Adjacent Cell Parts (**A** and **B**) which differ from each other in thickness ($t$) and refractive index ($n$).

the cell, its contents, and surroundings, thus permitting its study in the living state. The principle of the phase-contrast microscope is outlined below.

Because most cell structures exhibit irregularities in detail or outline, they are probably best treated as optically *inhomogeneous* objects. Parallel light striking such an object is *deviated* from its original path on passing through and past the edges of an object. This deviated light is retarded or altered in phase (about ¼ wavelength) with respect to light transmitted directly by the object and its surroundings (*undeviated light*) and is spread over the entire surface of the objective lens (Figure 11-11). The light transmitted undeviated by the object and its surroundings passes, for the most part, through the more central part of the objective. In the ordinary light microscope the undeviated light is brought to focus at the rear focal plane of the objective where it diverges and spreads over the entire field of view; the deviated light tends to focus at the plane of the eyepiece lens (Figure 11-12). The image of the object is formed as a result of *interference* between the deviated and undeviated light coming from the object. The image of its surroundings is formed by the undeviated light transmitted by this component only. Separation of the deviated and undeviated light occurs in the optical microscope at the rear focal plane of the objective.

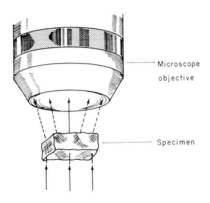

**Figure 11-11.** Diagram Showing the Diffraction of Light on Passing Through and Around the Edges of an Inhomogeneous Object. Light deviated from its original path by the object is spread over the entire surface of the objective lens, while the light transmitted undeviated by the object passes through the more central part of this same lens.

The optical system of the phase-contrast microscope differs from that of the ordinary optical microscope only in the addition of (1) a substage *annular diaphragm* to illuminate the object with a narrow cone of light, and (2) a *diffraction plate* mounted in the objective (Figure 11-13). The diffraction plate is located at the rear focal plane of the objective where the deviated and undeviated light coming from the object is separated. The relative phase of the deviated and undeviated light is changed by introducing a layer of phase-retarding material on that part of the diffraction plate covered by either one of these rays. As already pointed out, the deviated light originating at the object is retarded or altered in phase (about ¼ wavelength) with respect to the light transmitted undeviated by the object. By further retarding this deviated light by another ¼ wavelength at the diffraction plate, it will have a total retardation of ½ wavelength and will be *completely out of phase* with that of the undeviated light (Figure 11-13). The deviated and undeviated light

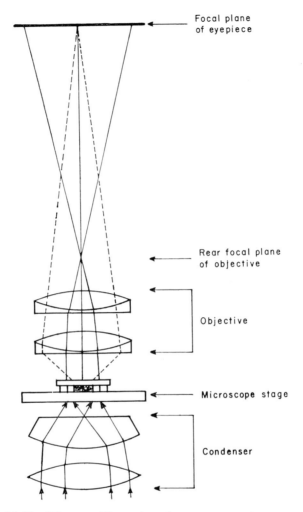

Figure 11-12. Diagram Illustrating the Optical Path of Deviated and Undeviated Light Through the Ordinary Light Microscope.

transmitted by the object will tend to *cancel* each other out (destructive interference) and make the object darker than its surroundings (Figure 11-13). This is *dark* or *positive* phase-contrast (Figure 11-14 (a)).

*Bright* or *negative* phase-contrast, in which the object appears brighter than its surroundings, is obtained by retarding the undeviated light by ¼ wavelength at the diffraction plate (conjugate area). Since the deviated light has already been retarded by ¼ wavelength at the object, the

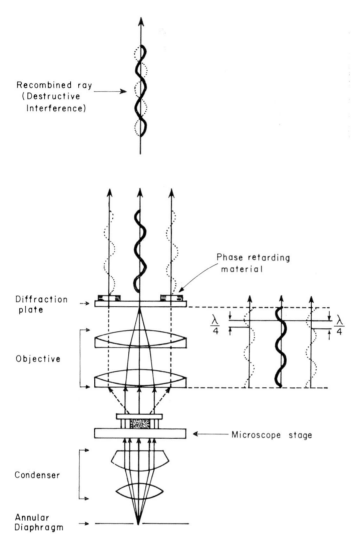

**Figure 11-13.** Diagram Showing the Principle of Phase Microscopy.

deviated and undeviated light will emerge from the diffraction plate *in phase* and recombine to give increased brightness (constructive interference) of the object (Figure 11-14 (b)).

Phase-contrast microscopy can be used to measure the refractive index and solid concentration of cell structures by utilizing the method of *immersion refractometry*. This method involves the immersion of cells

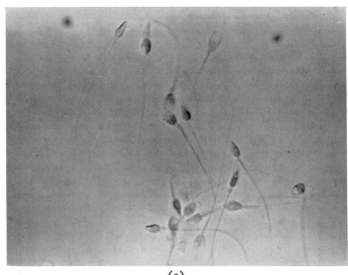

(a)

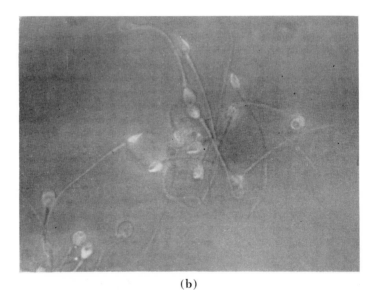

(b)

**Figure 11-14.** Dark (a) and Bright (b) Phase-Contrast Micrographs of Living, Unstained Sperm Cells. (From Richards, O. W., 1946. "Biological Phase Microscopy," *Cold Spring Harbor Symp. Quant. Biol.*, 11, Figs. 20 and 21. Courtesy of Dr. O. W. Richards, American Optical Company, Research Department, Southbridge, Mass.)

in an isotonic solution, the refractive index of which can be varied in small increments.

The phase change ($\emptyset$) or optical path difference introduced by an object is expressed as

$$\emptyset = (n_o - n_m)t$$

where $n_o$ and $n_m$ are the refractive indices of the object and the mounting medium, respectively, and $t$ is the thickness of the object. Consideration of this equation shows that if the refractive index of the mounting medium is made equal to that of the object, the phase change will be zero and the object will be invisible or have minimum contrast when viewed with the phase-contrast microscope. When the refractive index of the mounting medium is greater or less than that of the object, the object will appear in dark or bright contrast, respectively. By varying the refractive index, a value will be found which matches that of the cell structure under study. Since the refractive index of the cell structure is the same as that of the mounting medium at the matching point, the structure will produce virtually no phase change and will show little or no contrast with respect to its surroundings.

Variation of the refractive index of the mounting medium by small orders of magnitude is done most accurately with protein solutions, which for every 1 per cent increase in concentration change their refractive index by a specific amount. This value is called the *specific refraction increment* ($a$) and is calculated to be about 0.00180 for most proteins. Since protein accounts for most of the solid content of protoplasm, the specific refraction increment of protoplasm is considered to be the same as that of protein or 0.00180. The refractive index of a protoplasmic structure ($n$) is directly related to its concentration of solids (mostly proteins). This relationship is expressed by the formula

$$n = n_s + a\,C$$

where $n_s$ is the refractive index of the solvent, $a$ the specific refraction increment, and $C$ the concentration of solids in grams per 100 ml of solution. In the case of living cells, $n_s$ is taken as the refractive index of water or a very dilute salt solution, and is calculated to be about 1.334. The refractive index of the cell structure ($n$) is determined by immersion refractometry and the value $a$ is taken as being equal to that of protein or 0.00180. The unknown $C$ is calculated by the formula

$$C = \frac{n - n_o}{a}$$

Immersion refractometry has been used to measure the changes in refractive index and concentration of solids in cell structures during such activities as cell division and fungal spore development. The method is also useful for the study of X-ray and drug effects on living cells. The variations in cytoplasmic refractive index and solid concentration during different stages of meiosis in the male grasshopper is shown in Figure 11-15.

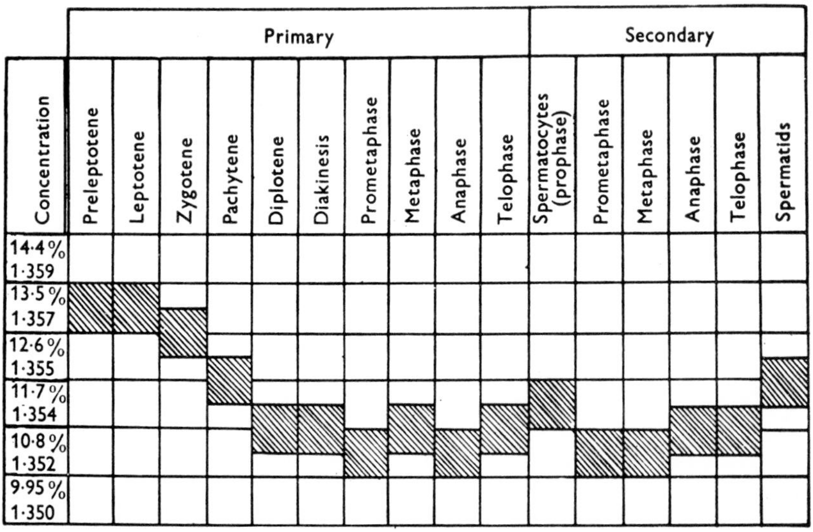

| Concentration | Primary | | | | | | | | | | Secondary | | | | | |
|---|---|---|---|---|---|---|---|---|---|---|---|---|---|---|---|---|
| | Preleptotene | Leptotene | Zygotene | Pachytene | Diplotene | Diakinesis | Prometaphase | Metaphase | Anaphase | Telophase | Spermatocytes (prophase) | Prometaphase | Metaphase | Anaphase | Telophase | Spermatids |
| 14·4% 1·359 | | | | | | | | | | | | | | | | |
| 13·5% 1·357 | ▨ | ▨ | ▨ | | | | | | | | | | | | | |
| 12·6% 1·355 | | | ▨ | ▨ | | | | | | | | | | | | ▨ |
| 11·7% 1·354 | | | | ▨ | | | | | | | ▨ | | | | ▨ | ▨ |
| 10·8% 1·352 | | | | | ▨ | ▨ | ▨ | ▨ | ▨ | ▨ | | ▨ | ▨ | ▨ | | |
| 9·95% 1·350 | | | | | | | | | | | | | | | | |

**Figure 11-15.** Histogram Showing the Changes in Solid Concentration (Per Cent) and Refractive Index in the Ground Cytoplasm of Primary and Secondary Spermatocytes of the Grasshopper, *Chortippus,* During Spermatogenesis. (From Barer, R. and Joseph, S., 1957. "Phase-Contrast and Interference Microscopy in the Study of Cell Structure," *Symp. Soc. Exptl. Biol.,* **10**, Fig. 3, p. 172.)

While use of the phase-contrast microscope makes it possible to detect phase changes by converting them to visible intensity changes, the instrument is not designed to permit precise measurement of these phase changes. As pointed out, a diffraction plate is used in the phase-contrast microscope to separate the direct and diffracted light so that they can be altered in phase relative to each other to give increased or decreased brightness of the object. Because this separation of direct and diffracted light is never complete, it is possible to detect only relatively large changes in phase or optical path by phase microscopy. The phase changes introduced by cell structures are, for the most part, extremely small and usually of the order of fractions of a wavelength. To measure phase changes of this order of magnitude accurately it is necessary to completely separate the directly transmitted light and that deviated by the object such as in the *interference microscope*. The way in which this is accomplished in the interference microscope is shown in Figure 11-16.

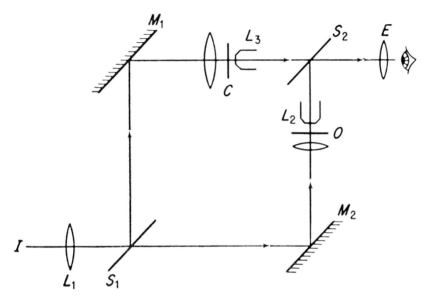

**Figure 11-16.** Schematic Representation of an "Ideal" Interference Microscope System: $S_1$ and $S_2$, semireflecting mirror surfaces; $M_1$ and $M_2$, fully-reflecting mirror surfaces; $L_2$ and $L_3$, microscope lenses; O, object slide; C, comparison or "blank" slide. (From Barer, R., 1959. "Phase, Interference, and Polarizing Microscopy," *in* Mellors, R. C. (Ed.), "Analytical Cytology," 2nd ed., McGraw-Hill Book Co., Inc., New York, N. Y. Fig. 3.22, p. 221.)

The light originating from a common source is split into two beams, one of which is transmitted through the object while the other bypasses the object entirely. In Figure 11-16 a semireflecting mirror ($S_1$) is used as the beam-splitter. One beam is directed onto a mirror ($M_2$) where it is reflected through the microscope and transmitted by the object. The other beam is directed onto another mirror ($M_1$) and is reflected through a lens system. The two beams produce interference when recombined at the semireflecting mirror ($S_2$).

Because the refractive index of a cell structure is related to its solid concentration $(n = n_s + a\,C)$, it follows that measurement of the phase change, $\emptyset$, which is the product of refractive index and thickness, can be used to determine the *dry mass* of cell structures. The concentration of solids is related to phase change $\emptyset$ by the equation

$$\emptyset = a\,Ct$$

Phase change $\emptyset$ is determined by interference microscopy, $C$ by immersion refractometry, and $a$ is taken as equal to protein, or 0.00180. The value of $t$ is determined by the equation

$$t = \frac{\emptyset}{a\,C}$$

The combined use of interference microscopy and immersion refractometry makes it possible to determine the refractive index, solid concentration, dry mass, and thickness of cell structures. The changes in dry mass, solid concentration, and volume during growth and cell division have been studied by this technique (Figure 11-17). The variations in dry mass of sperm nuclei of various species of mammals have also been investigated in a similar way.

### Ultraviolet Microscopy

The use of ultraviolet radiation as a light source has several advantages over that of the visible light ordinarily employed in conventional microscopy. These major advantages are: (1) ability to view unstained, living cells because of the strong absorption of ultraviolet by nucleoproteins of the cell, and (2) to provide a means of measuring quantitatively the amounts and distribution of nucleoprotein in cell structures by their characteristic absorption in the 270 m$\mu$ region of the ultraviolet spectrum.

The ultraviolet microscope differs from the ordinary light microscope only in the use of lenses constructed of transparent *fused quartz* instead of optical glass, which is opaque to the shorter wavelength ultraviolet. The slides and cover glasses used in mounting the specimen for study are also of quartz. Because the eye does not respond to ultraviolet light, focusing of the specimen must be done indirectly by visible light or by means of a fluorescent screen. The image of the specimen is recorded by a photographic plate, photoelectric cell, or television pickup tube.

The ultraviolet microscope has its greatest value in studies dealing with the identification and quantitative measurement of chemical components in cell structures which absorb strongly in the ultraviolet (Figure 11-18). This absorption by cell structures is due to the presence of

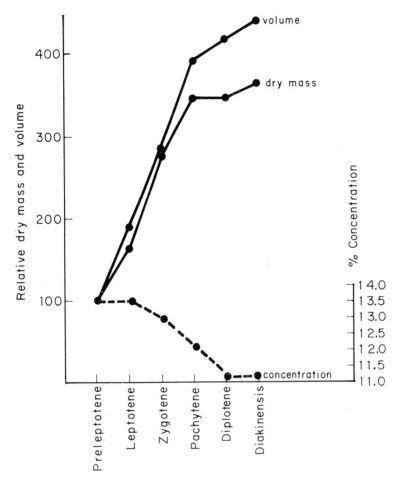

**Figure 11-17.** Graph Showing Variations in Volume, Dry Mass, and Solid Concentration of the Cytoplasm of Primary Spermatocytes During the Early Stages of Meiosis in the Grasshopper. (From Barer, R., 1959. "Phase, Interference, and Polarizing Microscopy," *in* Mellors, R. C. (Ed.), "Analytical Cytology," 2nd ed., McGraw-Hill Book Co., Inc., New York, N. Y., Fig. 3.16, p. 208.)

covalent unsaturated groups such as C=C, C=N, C=O, and N=O in certain organic molecules. Examples of naturally occurring unsaturated covalent groups are the pyrimidine and purine groups of the nucleic acids, DNA and RNA, the bicyclic indole group of tryptophan, the imidazole ring of histidine, and the benzene ring of tyrosine. Because

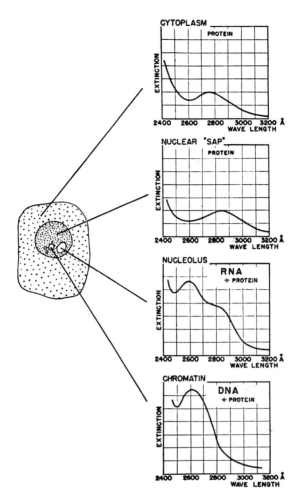

**Figure 11-18.** Ultraviolet Absorption Spectra of Various Cell Components as Measured by Ultraviolet Microspectrophotometry. (From Giese, A. C., 1957. "Cell Physiology," W. B. Saunders Co., Philadelphia, Pa., Fig. 10.5, p. 167. After Caspersson, T. O., 1950. "Cell Growth and Cell Function," W. W. Norton Co., Inc., New York, N. Y., Fig. 32, p. 79.)

the ultraviolet spectra of many organic compounds frequently show only one or two absorption peaks, it is usually not possible to identify a substance entirely by its ultraviolet absorption (Figure 11-19). With the possible exception of tryptophan and tyrosine, which absorb maximally at 280 m$\mu$, most proteins of the cell absorb at wavelengths shorter than 230 m$\mu$. The high specific absorption of nucleic acids in the

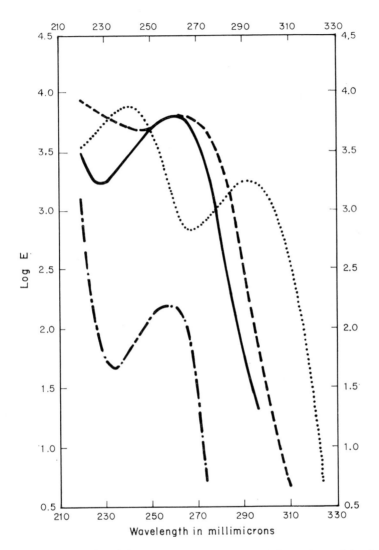

**Figure 11-19.** Ultraviolet Absorption Spectra of Several Nucleic Acid Bases and Protein Amino Acids. Adenine (————), cytosine (— — —), tyrosine (. . . .), and phenylalanine (—·—). (From Blout, E. R., 1953. "Ultraviolet Microscopy and Ultraviolet Microspectroscopy," *in* Lawrence, J. H. and Tobias, C. A. (Eds.), "Advances in Biological and Medical Physics," 3, Academic Press, New York, N. Y., Fig. 1, p. 288.)

260-m$\mu$ region of the ultraviolet spectrum makes possible the identification and measurement of these substances in cell structures such as the chromosomes and cytoplasm (Figure 11-18).

The most serious drawback to use of the ultraviolet microscope is the *lethal effect* of ultraviolet radiation on living cells. The amount of radi-

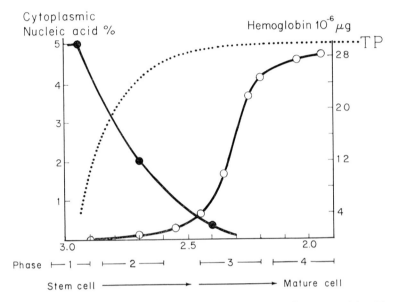

**Figure 11-20.** Graph Showing Changes in Cytoplasmic Composition During Mammalian Red Blood Cell Formation as Measured by Ultraviolet Microspectrophotometry. Synthesis of RNA associated with endocellular growth processes is completed before formation of the mature erythrocyte. The developmental phase where the concentration of cytoplasmic RNA is virtually zero, represents the period during which intensive production of hemoglobin is initiated. Solid circles, per cent cytoplasmic RNA; line through open circles, total amount of hemoglobin in cell; dotted line, total cellular protein. (From Thorell, B., 1947. "The Relation of Nucleic Acids to the Formation and Differentiation of Cellular Proteins," *Cold Spring Harbor Symposia Quant. Biol.,* 12, Fig. 14, p. 253.)

ation necessary to photograph cell structures with ultraviolet light is very close to doses which either kill or seriously damage the living cell. This disadvantage has been overcome somewhat by the use of more sensitive recording devices such as the quartz window television tube. While the advent of television electronics is quite recent in biology it has interesting possibilities for teaching and research.

The ultraviolet microscope can be adapted for use as a spectrophotometer to measure changes in the absorption of nucleic acids and proteins in cell structures. This method has been used to study metabolic changes during cell division, growth, and differentiation (Figure 11-20).

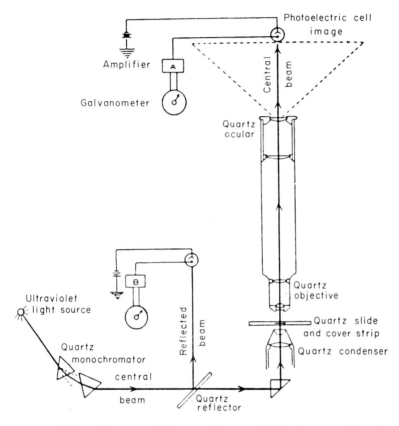

**Figure 11-21.** Schematic Diagram Showing Light Source, Monochromator, Microscope, and Photoelectric Apparatus for Measuring the Absorption of Ultraviolet Light by Cell Structures. (From Gersh, I. and Bodian, D., 1943. "Some Chemical Mechanisms in Chromatolysis," *J. Cell. Comp. Physiol.*, **21**, Fig. 1, p. 257.)

When operated in this manner, the specific absorption of the substance under study is usually recorded by a photoelectric cell mounted above the body tube of the microscope (Figure 11-21). Briefly, the method involves splitting a monochromatic beam of ultraviolet light into two beams, one of which falls directly on a photoelectric cell (the "blank") while the other passes through an ultraviolet microscope to another photoelectric cell. By interposing the sample in the beam passing through the microscope, the reduction in intensity of the light passing through the sample may be determined by comparison of the photoelectric current generated by the two beams. This gives the ratio $I_s/I_o$ directly without moving the sample and reduces the exposure time of the sample to ultra-violet. The per cent transmission ($T$) of the specimen is determined from the ratio $I_s/I_o$, which can then be used to compute the amount of ultraviolet absorbing substance in arbitrary units. This method differs from that used to measure the absorption of Feulgen-stained nuclei in the visible spectrum only in the use of ultraviolet radiation as the light source and a microscope equipped with optics transparent to the shorter ultraviolet wavelengths. While more elaborate ultraviolet microspectro-photometric techniques have been developed, the above will serve to introduce the student to the fundamentals of ultraviolet absorption measurements.

## Polarization Microscopy

The polarizing microscope is similar in principle and construction to the conventional optical microscope. It differs only by the addition of polarizing elements in the optical system to permit illumination of the specimen with plane polarized light instead of ordinary white light. The two chief polarizing elements are the *polarizer* and *analyzer* (Figure 11-22). The polarizer, usually a sheet of Polaroid film, is mounted below the substage condenser and admits linear-polarized light vibrating in a single plane into the optical system of the microscope. The analyzer is rotatable, and is mounted above the objective lens in the body tube of the microscope. When the analyzer is rotated through 360°, the field of view appears *alternately* bright and dark for every 180° turn, that is, for every complete rotation of the analyzer there are two positions at which maximal transmission of light occurs, and two positions at which no transmission occurs. Maximal light transmission by the analyzer re-sults when its axis of transmission is parallel to that of the polarizer (Figure 11-22). No transmission ("extinction") of light occurs when the axis of the analyzer is set at *right angles* to that of the polarizer (Figure 11-22). At extinction, the polarizer and analyzer are spoken of as being in the "crossed" position. By placing an object between crossed polarizer and analyzer any effect the object has on the natural path of the polarized light will become immediately apparent.

Many cell structures are *anisotropic,* that is, they transmit ordinary or plane-polarized light at different velocities depending on the direction in which it passes through the structure. For this reason, such structures are said to be *birefrigent* or *double refracting.* When ordinary white light is passed through a polarizing element, such as a sheet of Polaroid film,

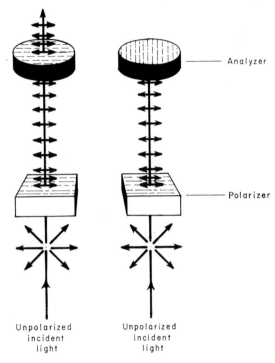

Figure 11-22. Schematic Diagram Showing the Alignment of Polarizer and Analyzer When in the Uncrossed (left) and Crossed Positions (right) in the Polarization Microscope.

it emerges as plane-polarized light oscillating in a single plane perpendicular to the direction in which the light is traveling (Figure 11-23). Plane-polarized light produced in this manner, on passing through an anisotropic object, is split into two components which oscillate in mutually perpendicular planes (Figure 11-24). On emerging from the object, the two polarized components are recombined, but as their relative velocities through the object are different, they will be out of phase, i.e., one ray will be retarded relative to the other. In Figure 11-24, the ray (S) is shown oscillating at right angles to the ray (**F**) and retarded ¼ wavelength behind this ray. Because of this difference in transmission, a birefrigent object is regarded as having *two axes* of *transmission* of polarized light. The axis along which the slow or retarded ray (**S**) travels has a maximal refractive index (slow axis) while the axis along which the fast or nonretarded ray (**F**) travels has a minimal refractive index (fast axis).

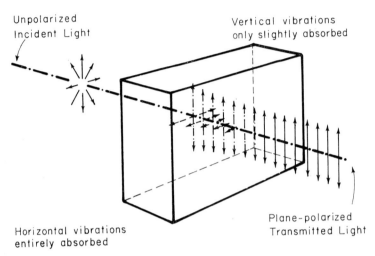

**Figure 11-23.** Schematic Diagram Showing the Production of Plane-polarized Light by Passage of Ordinary White Light Through a Sheet of Polaroid Film. The medium contains oriented electronic resonators which transmit only those components of the incident light vibrating in a perpendicular plane. (From Bennett, H. S., 1950. "The Microscopical Investigation of Biological Materials with Polarized Light," *in* Jones, R. M. (Ed.), "McClung's Handbook of Microscopical Technique," 3rd ed., Paul B. Hoeber, Inc., Harper & Brothers, New York, N. Y., Fig. 102, p. 614.)

When placed on the stage of the polarizing microscope and rotated between crossed polarizer and analyzer, a birefrigent object shows varying degrees of brightness and darkness depending on the position of its axis with respect to those of the analyzer (Figure 11-25). This is the usual test for birefrigence of an object. Brightness of the object is at a maximum when its axes make a ±45° angle with those of the polarizer and analyzer (Figure 11-25). Because the axes of the object are not in line with those of the analyzer, neither of the two polarized components resolved by the object and oscillating in mutually perpendicular planes are exactly "crossed" or at right angles with the axes of the analyzer. Both polarized components of the recombined ray coming from the object are partially transmitted by the analyzer, with the result that the object appears maximally bright. If $n_1$ and $n_2$ are the refractive indices associated with the fast and slow ray, respectively, the quantity $n_2 - n_1$ is the birefrigence. For strongly birefrigent crystals such as calcite, the birefrigence may be as high as 0.01. The birefrigence of biological materials is considerably less than this value, being about 0.0025 for living muscle fibers.

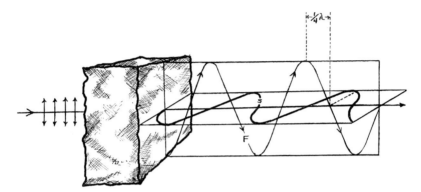

**Figure 11-24.** Schematic Drawing Showing the Splitting of a Beam of Plane-polarized Light by an Anisotropic Body into Two Components Which Oscillate in Mutually Perpendicular Planes. Note that the slow component (**S**) is retarded $\lambda/4$ in velocity relative to the fast component (**F**).

To determine the sign of birefrigence (i.e., positive or negative) of an object it is necessary to know its slow and fast axes of transmission. This is determined by use of a compensator, which is simply a birefrigent material whose slow and fast axes of transmission are known. With the object rotated to its position of maximum brightness ($\pm45°$ angle with respect to analyzer) between crossed polarizer and analyzer, the compensator is inserted below the analyzer in the body tube and rotated. A position is reached where there occurs an enhancement or re-enforcement of brightness of the object. At this setting, the slow ray of the compensator (the direction of which is known) is oscillating in the same plane as the slow ray of the object. The enhancement of brightness results from the summation of the individual retardations of the object and compensator, i.e., the slow ray of the object is further retarded by

the compensator to give increased brightness. The principle is essentially
the same as for bright phase-contrast microscopy. The phase change, $\emptyset$,
is the product of birefrigence and thickness, $t$, and is expressed as

$$\emptyset = (n_2 - n_1)t$$

With the object in the position of increased brightness, one of its axes
(major or minor) will be in line with the slow axis of the compensator

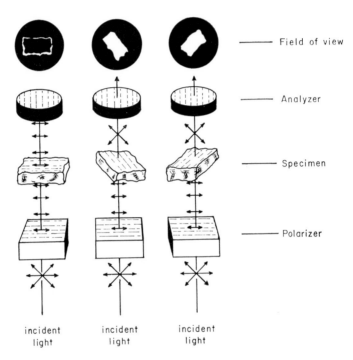

Field of view

Analyzer

Specimen

Polarizer

incident      incident      incident
light          light          light

**Figure 11-25.** Schematic Drawing Showing Variations in Darkness and
Brightness of an Anisotropic Object When Placed Between Crossed Polarizer
and Analyzer and Rotated $\pm 45°$.

and is designated accordingly as the slow axis. The fast axis of the
object, therefore, lies at 90° to that of the slow axis. The sign of birefrigence is designated positive or negative depending on whether the
slow axis of the object is parallel or perpendicular to some previously
selected dimension or direction of the object. It is generally convenient
to take the *long axis* of cylindrical structures (e.g., muscle and collagen
fibers, chromosomes) as the axis of reference, or *radial direction* as in

disc-shaped structures such as the chloroplast. The slow axis of transmission of a collagen fiber is found to be parallel to the long axis of the fiber and, hence, is regarded as showing positive birefrigence with respect to its long axis. Likewise, the fibers of the mitotic spindle exhibit positive birefrigence with respect to their long axes (see Chapter 6, Figure 6-2). In the case of the chromosome, however, its slow axis of transmission is perpendicular rather than parallel to its long axis, and is said to show negative birefrigence with respect to its length.

The birefrigence of biological materials may be due to either (1) a regularity in pattern of molecular structure which produces *intrinsic* birefrigence, or (2) a preferred orientation of asymmetrical particles which produces *form* birefrigence. Materials which exhibit birefrigence when subjected to mechanical stress are spoken of as displaying *strain* birefrigence. For example, the coiled macromolecules of rubber become uncoiled and oriented when put under stress to produce the strain birefrigence exhibited by this material in the stretched condition. Many crystals show intrinsic birefrigence, which is related directly to the particular arrangement of atoms in the crystal lattice. Form birefrigence contributes appreciably to the total birefrigence shown by many cell structures. Two possible arrangements (Figure 11-26, A and B) which may occur in biological materials and produce form birefrigence are (**A**) elongated particles oriented parallel to a long axis (fiber axis), and (**B**) flat, thin discs which are stacked one upon the other as grana are stacked in the plant chloroplast. To determine whether a particular birefrigent object exhibits intrinsic or form birefrigence one simply immerses it in solutions of different refractive index. If the object shows form birefrigence, a solution of specific refractive index will be found which matches that of the asymmetric particles and extinguishes the birefrigence of the object. Intrinsic birefrigence, on the other hand, is unaffected by variations in the refractive index of the surrounding medium. This method permits one to estimate the degree to which both intrinsic and form birefrigence contribute to the total birefrigence of a particular cell structure.

Polarization microscopy is a very sensitive tool for the study of molecular orientation, but is limited by the fact that it tells the observer little about the properties of molecules other than their orientation. Most of the polarization studies dealing with biologic material have been directed toward study of the structure of the mitotic spindle. This type of approach has probably given the most complete information concerning the structural organization of the spindle and the changes it undergoes during the various stages of the mitotic process.

Polarization microscopy has also been used to investigate the structure of nerve fibers. In this case, the myelin sheath shows marked birefrigence which is negative with respect to the nerve fiber axis. The axon, on the other hand, displays only a weak positive birefrigence relative to the fiber axis. Birefrigence studies have shown that a characteristic feature of striated muscle fibers is their longitudinal differentiation into

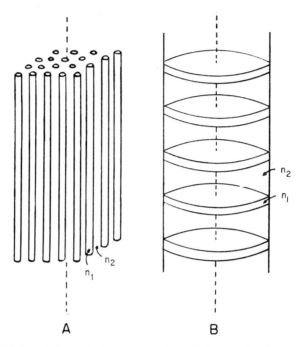

A      B

**Figure 11-26.** Schematic Representation of Composite Structures Made Up of Either Oriented Rods (A), or Flat Discs Stacked One Upon Another (**B**), Which are Most Likely to Exhibit Form Birefrigence. (From Oster, G., 1955. "Birefrigence and Dichroism," *in* Oster, G. and Pollister, A. W. (Eds.), "Physical Techniques in Biological Research," 1, Academic Press, New York, N. Y., Fig. 2, p. 446.)

anisotropic and isotropic regions, and that the birefrigence of the anisotropic region is positive with respect to the direction of the muscle fiber. The specific birefrigence of chloroplasts has been demonstrated to be limited to the grana, suggesting that these structures are composed of parallel lamellae or discs. Later studies of chloroplast structure, using the electron microscope, have confirmed the lamellated structure of grana.

## Fluorescence Microscopy

The fluorescence microscope takes advantage of the fact that certain substances emit visible light when illuminated with ultraviolet, violet, or blue radiation. This property is spoken of as *autofluorescence,* and

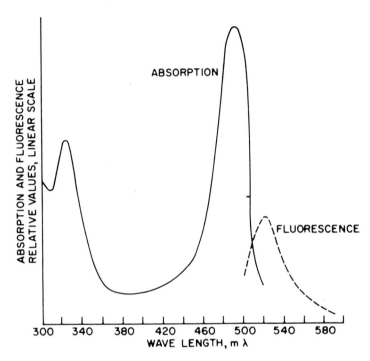

Figure 11-27. Graph Showing Absorption and Fluorescence Spectra of Sodium Fluorescein. (From Mellors, R. C., 1959. "Fluorescent-Antibody Method," *in* Mellors, R. C. (Ed.), "Analytical Cytology," 2nd ed., McGraw-Hill Book Co., Inc., New York, N. Y., Fig. 1.8, p. 24. After Ghosh, I. C. and Sengupta, S. B., 1938. "Studien über Fluorescenzvermögen, Absorptionsspektra und elektrische Leitfähigkeiten an Fluorescein, Rhodamin und Acriflavin in wässerigen Lösungen," *Zeits. Physik. Chemie,* ABT - B, 41, Fig. 3, p. 128.)

is exhibited by such substances as chlorophyll, porphyrin, riboflavin, and vitamin A. Nonfluorescent substances (e.g., proteins, carbohydrates) can be made to show *secondary fluorescence* by combining them with fluorescent dyes called *fluorochromes.* Examples of fluorochromes and the color of light they emit on exposure to shorter wavelength radiation are fluorescein (yellow-green), and rhodamine (orange-red). The absorption and emission spectrum of fluorescein is shown in Figure 11-27. An interesting application of fluorochrome dyes is the fluorescent-antibody technique in which antibody molecules are combined with a fluorochrome. Since the specificity of the antibody for antigen is not destroyed as the result of its combination with the fluorochrome, it is possible to stain appropriately prepared sections of living tissue with fluorescent antibody to determine sites of antigen formation. By illuminating the

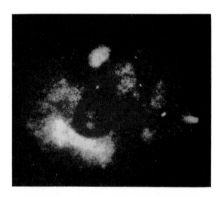

Figure 11-28. Immunofluorescent Photomicrograph of Human Amnion Cell from a Culture Infected Eight Days Previously with Measles Virus. Note perinuclear location of one of two prominent cytoplasmic concentrations of virus antigen. (From Rapp, F., Gordon, I., and Baker, R. F., 1960. "Observations of Measles Virus Infection of Cultured Human Cells. I. A Study of Development and Spread of Virus Antigen by Means of Immunofluorescence," *J. Biophys. Biochem. Cytol.,* **7**, Fig. 2, Plate 17. Courtesy of Dr. Fred Rapp, Philip D. Wilson Research Foundation, New York, N. Y.)

tissue with ultraviolet light, one can observe microscopically the sites where specific antigen is formed by the fluorescence emitted from the antigen-antibody-fluorochrome complex. The antigens of a number of viruses (e.g., poliomyelitis, measles, influenza, mumps, chicken pox) have been localized by this method in tissues of infected animals (Figure 11-28).

With a few minor changes, the conventional optical microscope can be adapted easily for fluorescence microscopy. Most of the fluorescent substances present in biological materials emit visible light when illuminated with the longer-wavelength ultraviolet (about 400 m$\mu$). Since optical glass will transmit ultraviolet light down to about 350 m$\mu$, stand-

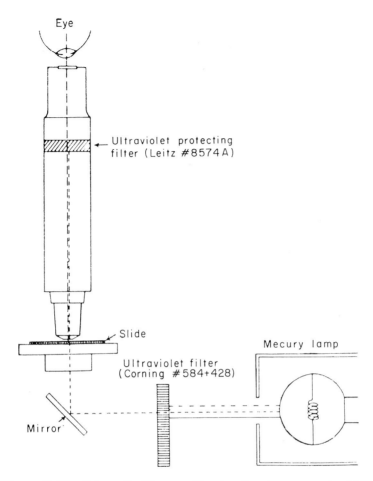

Eye

Ultraviolet protecting
filter (Leitz #8574A)

Slide

Mecury lamp

Ultraviolet filter
(Corning #584+428)

Mirror

**Figure 11-29.** Schematic Diagram Showing the Arrangement of Microscopic Components for the Study of Cells and Tissues by Fluorescent Light.
(From Popper, H. and Szanto, P. B., 1950. "Fluorescence Microscopy," *in*
Jones, R. M. (Ed.), "McClung's Handbook of Microscopical Technique,"
3rd ed., Paul B. Hoeber, Inc., Harper & Brothers. New York, N. Y., Fig.
130, p. 679.)

ard microscope lenses can be used. The method most often employed in
fluorescence microscopy is the *crossed filter* technique (Figure 11-29).
A source filter that transmits only the ultraviolet radiation to be absorbed
by the specimen is positioned in front of the light source (mercury vapor
or carbon arc lamp). A complementary filter is mounted in the eyepiece
or body tube of the microscope for visual observation and photography.

This filter absorbs any ultraviolet radiation not absorbed by the specimen, but transmits the fluorescent light.

The nucleus of the unstained animal cell is usually nonfluorescent, while the cytoplasm shows a weak bluish fluorescence. A relatively strong yellow fluorescence is associated with the mitochondria, which probably is due to the presence of vitamins (e.g., riboflavin) in these structures. The more or less specific colors of fluorescence of substances such as the vitamins and hormones (yellow, green, or blue), the porphyrins (red), and certain minerals (calcium, white fluorescence) has made it possible to follow their distribution in cells undergoing changes in metabolic activity. The autofluorescence of most plant cells is sufficiently strong to permit the recognition of cell structures and tissues in sections. This is especially true of the chloroplasts, which fluoresce a deep red color due to their content of chlorophyll. The staining of microorganisms with fluorochromes has been used to identify strains of bacteria in infected tissues. Certain microorganisms, such as the acid-fast bacteria, are autofluorescent and can be identified in tissues by virtue of this property.

### X-ray Microscopy

X-ray microscopy, specifically applied to the study of biologic materials, includes a number of methods designed to visualize the object through the use of X rays. These methods include (1) contact microradiography, (2) projection microradiography, and (3) X-ray diffraction.

The simplest kind of X-ray microscopy is *direct* contact microradiography. In this method, the specimen is placed in close contact with a fine-grained photographic emulsion and exposed to soft X rays which range in wavelength from 1 to 10 Å (Figure 11-30). A metal diaphragm is generally used to delimit the area of the specimen exposed to the

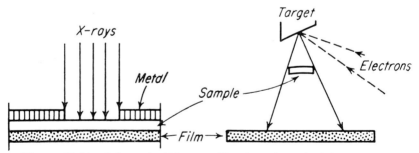

**Figure 11-30.** Schematic Diagram Showing the Principles of Contact (left) and Projection Microradiography (right). (From Engström, A., 1959. "X-ray Microscopy," *in* Mellors, R. C. (Ed.), "Analytical Cytology," 2nd ed., McGraw-Hill Book Co., New York, N. Y., Fig. 5.1, p. 345.)

X rays. Photograhic emulsions are suspensions of silver halide crystals in gelatin. As a result of exposure to light or ionizing radiation (e.g., X rays), the silver bromide crystals are reduced to metallic silver (black) by photographic development. The resultant negative can be examined and rephotographed at higher magnifications by means of the conventional optical microscope (Figure 11-31).

In projection microradiography, the photographic film is moved back from contact with the specimen. This results in *enlargement* of the shadow produced by the X rays passing through the specimen and falling on the photographic emulsion (Figure 11-30). The principle of projection microradiography is utilized in the construction of the compound

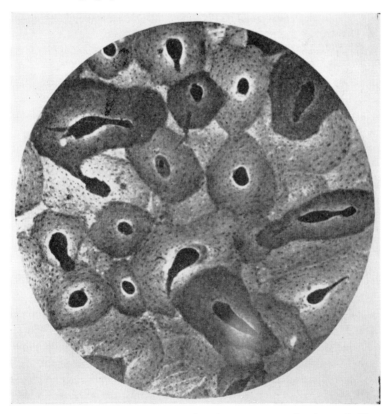

**Figure 11-31.** Contact Radiograph of Transverse Section of Human Bone. (From Kirkpatrick, P. and Pattee, H. H., Jr., 1953. "Approaches to X-Ray Microscopy," *in* Lawrence, J. H. and Tobias, C. A. (Eds.), *Advances in Biol. Med. Physics,* 3, Academic Press Inc., New York, N. Y., Fig. 1, p. 249.)

X-ray microscope which uses a system of two magnetic lenses (Figure 11-32). The X-ray beam diverges on traversing the foil or target and falls on the specimen, which is placed between the target and photographic plate. An enlarged shadow image of the specimen is projected onto the photographic plate as the result of the passage of the X rays through the specimen. In the compound X-ray microscope, reflecting curved mirror surfaces may be used instead of electromagnetic lenses to focus the X-ray beam source. Figure 11-33 shows the principle of X-ray

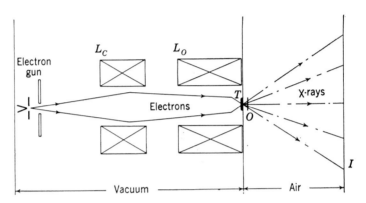

**Figure 11-32.** Schematic Diagram of X-Ray Shadow Projection Microscope Using Electromagnetic Lenses to Focus the Electron Image. $L_c$, condenser lens; $L_o$, objective lens; $T$, metal foil target; $O$, object. (From Cosslett, V. E., 1955. "Electron Microscopy," *in* Oster, G. and Pollister, A. W. (Eds.), "Physical Techniques in Biological Research," **1**, Academic Press, New York, N. Y., Fig. 23, p. 526.)

focusing, using curved mirror surfaces. By taking advantage of the ability of a cylindrical curved surface to concentrate X rays in one plane only, two such mirrors can be combined to give fine focusing. A simplified version of the reflection type compound X-ray microscope is shown in Figure 11-34. The lower part of the drawing shows the usual arrangement for reflection X-ray microscopy. A mirror block serves to focus the enlarged shadow image of the specimen onto the photographic plate. In the upper part of the drawing, the X-ray tube or source is shown moved to the opposite end of the system. The reflection microscope in this arrangement can be used "backwards" for X-ray diffraction. The radiation emitted by the X-ray tube is delimited by means of an aperture to produce a narrow X-ray beam. On passing through the microscope

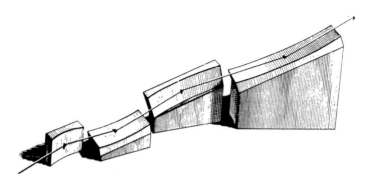

**Figure 11-33.** Schematic diagram showing the principle of X-ray Focusing Using a System of Curved Mirror Surfaces. (From Kirkpatrick, P. and Pattee, H. H. Jr., 1953, "Approaches to X-ray Microscopy," *in* Lawrence, J. H. and Tobias, C. A. (Eds.), "Advances in Biological and Medical Physics," 3, Academic Press, New York, N. Y., Fig. 18, p. 273.)

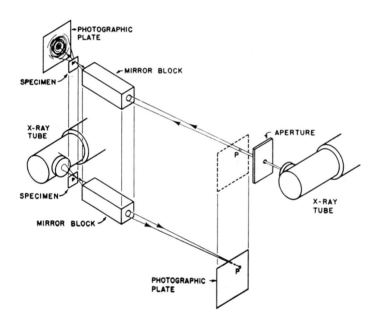

**Figure 11-34.** Schematic Diagram of X-ray Projection Microscope Using a Mirror Block to Focus the Electron Image. (From Kirkpatrick, P. and Pattee, H. H., Jr., 1953. "Approaches to X-ray Microscopy," *in* Lawrence, J. H. and Tobias, C. A. (Eds.), "Advances in Biological and Medical Physics," 3, Academic Press, New York, N. Y., Fig. 23, p. 280.)

backward, the beam is converged on the specimen by the mirror block, and is diffracted to the photographic plate where it registers a pattern characteristic of the specimen.

In X-ray diffraction, a narrow beam of X rays is passed through the object, some of the rays being scattered as the result of diffraction (or

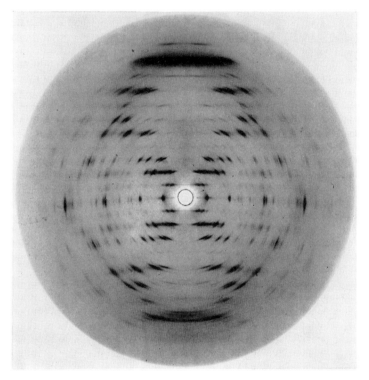

**Figure 11-35.** X-Ray Diffraction Pattern of Micro-crystalline Fibers of Lithium Salt of DNA in the $\beta$ configuration. (Courtesy of Dr. M. H. F. Wilkins, Biophysics Research Unit, King's College, London.)

reflection) by the atoms of the object. The diffracted rays on emerging from the object travel in various directions depending on the angle at which they are diffracted. This pattern of diffraction is recorded by means of a photographic plate placed a short distance (5 to 10 mm) beyond the object. In the case of crystalline materials, the lattice structure of the component crystals tends to concentrate the diffracted X rays in certain definite directions to produce a characteristic diffraction pattern on the photographic plate. By studying the angle and intensity of diffraction produced by the various lattice planes of the crystals, one can gain much information concerning their symmetry.

Many biological materials (e.g., cellulose, keratin, collagen fibers, hemoglobin) are made up of repeating units of similar molecules which tend to show some form of preferred orientation with respect to the main axis of the material. The angle at which the repeating units diffract X rays of known wavelength is a measure of the distance between each repeating unit, that is, the greater the angle of diffraction, the smaller the distance between the repeating units. The preferred orientation of the repeating molecules is revealed by the pattern of interference figures forming the diffraction diagram. The X-ray diffraction method has been a contributing factor in the construction of a statistical model of the DNA molecule. One of the possible diffraction patterns which has been obtained for DNA is shown in Figure 11-35.

## AUTORADIOGRAPHY

Autoradiography involves placing cells or tissues which have been *previously exposed* to a radioactive isotope in contact with a photographic emulsion (Figure 11-36). The ionizing radiations emitted by the incorporated isotope cause a blackening of the emulsion and produce an image of the specimen which can be used to determine the areas containing radioactive material.

In preparing specimens for autoradiography, it is common practice to fix them before the photographic emulsion is applied. The method of fixation depends on the chemical constituents to be studied. For the study of radioisotope incorporation into the nucleoproteins of cell structures such as the chromosomes, Carnoy's acetic-alcohol is generally employed. When it is desirable to retain all of the incorporated radioactive material, tissues may be quick-frozen and dried by vacuum desiccation. In order to follow the incorporation of an isotope into a specific chemical constituent, such as RNA, it is necessary that all DNA be extracted from the tissue. If incorporation of the isotope in DNA is to be investigated, all the RNA must be extracted. The differential extraction of proteins is more difficult, since adequate methods of extraction are not available for the separation of all the different kinds of proteins. Basic proteins (histones) apparently can be extracted sufficiently to permit comparison of isotope incorporation into basic *versus* nonbasic proteins.

There are three methods that are commonly used to make contact between the specimen and the photographic emulsion. The first is the so-called *opposition* method, where the specimen is simply placed in contact with the photographic emulsion in the dark. This method is suitable for making autoradiographs of gross specimens or single cells. Paraffin sections of tissue can be floated on warm water and then picked up on a microscope slide which has previously been coated with a thin emulsion film. The sections remain attached to the slide during photo-

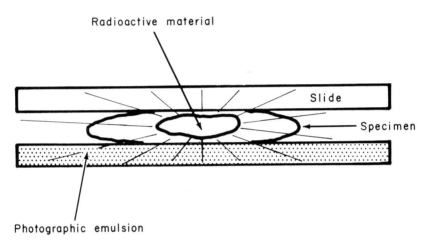

Figure 11-36. Schematic Diagram Showing the Principle of Autoradiography. (From Pelc, S. R., 1958. "Autoradiography as a Cytochemical Method, with Special Reference to $C^{14}$ and $S^{35}$," *in* Danielli, J. F. (Ed.), "General Cytochemical Methods," 1, Academic Press, New York, N. Y., Fig. 1, p. 280.)

graphic processing and subsequent staining and mounting. The second is the *liquid-emulsion* method which involves mounting the specimen on a slide and then coating it with a fluid emulsion that is allowed to harden. Extraction, hydrolysis, or staining of the specimen is generally carried out before application of the emulsion. The third method is the *stripping-film* technique which has been used extensively in this country and abroad. In this method, a thin-film emulsion is stripped from a glass plate and floated, emulsion side down, on the surface of water. The emulsion film is then picked up with a slide on which the specimen (paraffin sections, squashes) has been mounted. The specimen may be stained before or after it has been covered with the stripping film.

The autoradiograph is examined microscopically, using either the phase-contrast or the light microscope. Frequently it is necessary to stain cells in order to determine whether incorporation of the isotope has occurred in a particular type of cell. Staining of the specimen is most conveniently done before application of the emulsion film; however, some fading of the stain may occur during the developing process. The Feulgen stain works well in this respect as it is not appreciably affected in the photographic processing of the autoradiograph.

The autoradiographic technique has made a number of contributions to our knowledge concerning basic cell metabolism. This is especially true in those cases where autoradiography has been used in combination with other cytochemical methods such as microspectrophotometry, enzyme digestion, and specific cytochemical staining (e.g., Feulgen staining). Autoradiographs of oocytes obtained with the use of $C^{14}$-labeled glycine have shown the nucleolus to be a site of active RNA and protein metabolism. This same radioisotope has been used to study rates of turnover of cell populations in the circulating blood of mammals. The use of tritium-labeled thymidine has made it possible to investigate chromosomal DNA metabolism (see Chapter 4, Figure 4-24), cell turnover times, and DNA metabolism in specific bands of dipteran salivary chromosomes during different stages of larval development (Figure 4-23). Tritium-labeled cytidine, a precursor of both DNA and RNA, has been utilized in the study of nucleic acid metabolism in cell structures during regeneration. The changes in nucleic acid and protein metabolism during meiosis in plants have been investigated using orotic acid —$C^{14}$, glycine —$C^{14}$, cytidine —$H^3$, and thymidine —$H^3$. The radioisotope, adenine —$C^{14}$, has also been used to follow changes in nucleic acid metabolism during animal spermatogenesis.

## ISOLATION OF CELL COMPONENTS

The techniques which have probably contributed most to our understanding of cell function are those developed by the biochemist for the separation of the cell into its component parts so that they may be analyzed separately to determine their specific activity or function. The isolation of cell components is accomplished simply by disrupting the cells of a tissue in a suitable medium (homogenization) and then spinning down the resulting suspension or homogenate at different speeds of centrifugation. As a result of differential centrifugation, cells are separated into four general fractions: (1) nuclear, (2) mitochondrial, (3) microsomal, and (4) soluble or supernatant (Figure 11-37 (a) and (b)). A variety of different instruments and media have been proposed for the preparation of homogenates and the suspension of cells during the isolation process. Critical evaluations of the various methods used to isolate cell components may be found in a number of extensive reviews.

(a)           (b)

Figure 11-37. Separation of Cell Components in Rat Liver Homogenate (H) by Continuous Sucrose Gradient: (a) before centrifugation; (b) after centrifugation. (From Anderson, N. G., 1956. "Techniques for the Mass Isolation of Cellular Components," *in* Oster, G. and Pollister, A. W. (Eds.), "Physical Techniques in Biological Research," 3, Academic Press, New York, N. Y., Fig. 16, p. 338. Courtesy of Dr. Norman G. Anderson, Oak Ridge National Laboratory.)

To avoid the loss of nucleoproteins and enzymes from cell structures, particularly nuclei, during the isolation procedure, the method of Behrens has proved useful. In this method, tissues are frozen-dried, suspended in a nonaqueous solvent, and then homogenized by forcing through a colloidal mill. The nuclei are isolated by repeated centrifugation, either in a mixture of known density or in a density gradient of organic substances such as ether and chloroform, which are immiscible with water. While this method is more time-consuming and gives a lower yield of nuclei than more conventional methods, it has the distinct advantage of permitting isolation without excessive loss of water-soluble substances. The main disadvantages of the method are the possible inactivation of certain enzymes as the result of freezing and the loss of lipid-soluble substances because of the use of lipid solvents during homogenization and centrifugation.

The advent of the electron microscope has made it possible to study the fine structure of the various subcellular fractions and to correlate this information with the biochemical activities known to be associated with each of these fractions. A number of important correlations have been made using this kind of approach. For example, the microsomal fraction has been identified with certain membranes and granules of the endoplasmic reticulum (see Chapter 3, Figure 3-26), and the enzymes concerned with electron transport and oxidative phosphorylation have been found associated with the membranes of the mitochrondrion, especially the cristae.

## MICROMANOMETRIC METHODS

While autoradiography, microspectrophotometry, and specific cytochemical staining are the most widely used and sensitive of the micromethods commonly employed by the cytologist for the study of cell function, they are by no means the only ones available for the analysis of metabolic activity in the intact cell. A micromethod which has had only limited use in the past but which is highly quantitative, is the manometric analysis of gas volume changes caused by single cells. The micromanometric methods found most useful because of their high sensitivity are: (1) the *capillary respirometer* method and (2) the *Cartesian diver* method. Both of these techniques permit the measurement of gas volume changes as small as 0.1 $\mu$l per hour.

The capillary respirometer used by Brachet (1949) to measure the oxygen consumption of a single frog egg is shown in Figure 11-38. This instrument consists of a chamber to hold the specimen and a capillary which carries an index drop and is attached to the chamber. The gas volume is measured with a microscope by observation of the changes in level of the index drop. The detail of the Cartesian diver is shown in Figure 11-39. It consists essentially of a container in which there is a gas space enclosed by a liquid on all sides. The volume of the enclosed gas space is altered by changes in the pressure exerted on the surrounding liquid or as the result of the absorption or loss of gas in the diver.

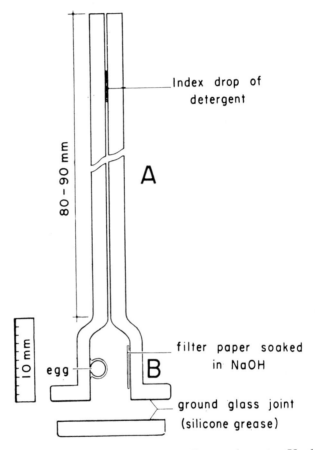

Figure 11-38. Schematic Diagram of Microrespirometer Used for the Measurement of Oxygen Uptake of a Single Frog Egg. (From Brachet, J., 1957. "Biochemical Cytology," Academic Press, New York, N. Y., Fig. 11, p. 23.)

As a result, the diver rises or sinks in the flotation vessel in which it is suspended. The pressure required to bring the diver to rest at a given level is used to calculate the change in gas volume. The Cartesian diver is a constant-volume manometer and works on the same principle as the conventional Warburg manometer apparatus.

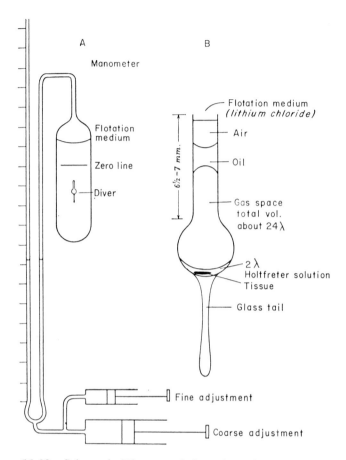

**Figure 11-39.** Schematic Diagram of Cartesian Diver Micromanometer.
(A) Diver vessel with diver suspended in flotation medium (concentrated
lithium chloride solution). The diver vessel is connected to a water manometer, the pressure in which can be adjusted by a coarse and fine syringe
mechanism (bottom). (B) Details of Cartesian diver. The tissue is placed
in 2 λ (1 λ = 1 cu. mm.) of physiological medium at the bottom of the diver
bulb which has a glass tail to maintain the diver in a vertical position. The
neck is partly occupied by a drop of oil, so placed that there is a small bubble
of air between the oil and the flotation medium. A reading is taken by bring-
ing the diver to a temporary standstill at the zero line and noting the pressure
level in the manometer. (From Boell, E. J., Needham, J., and Peters, V.,
1939. "Morphogenesis and Metabolism: Studies with the Cartesian Diver
Ultramicromanometer. 1. Anaerobic Glycolysis of the Regions of the Amphibian Gastrula," *Proc. Roy. Microscop. Soc.* (*London*), **127**, Fig. 1,
p. 326.)

# BIBLIOGRAPHY

Alfert, M. and Geschwind, I. I., 1953. "A Selective Staining Method for the Basic Proteins of Cell Nuclei," *Proc. Natl. Acad. Sci.,* **39**, 991-999.

Allfrey, V., 1959. "The Isolation of Subcellular Components," *in* "The Cell," J. Brachet and A. E. Mirsky (Eds.), Vol. 1, Academic Press, New York, N.Y., pp. 193-290.

Anderson, N. G., 1956. "Techniques for the Mass Isolation of Cellular Components," *in* "Physical Techniques in Biological Research," G. Oster and A. W. Pollister (Eds.), Vol. 3, Academic Press, New York, N.Y., pp. 29-90.

Baker, J. R., 1950. "Cytological Technique," Methuen & Co. Ltd., London.

Baker, J. R., 1951. "Cytological Techniques. A. Preparation of Tissues for Microscopical Examination and Histochemistry," *in* "Cytology and Cell Physiology," G. H. Bourne (Ed.), 2nd ed., Clarendon Press, Oxford, pp. 1-19.

Barer, R., 1951. "Cytological Techniques. C. Microscopy," *in* "Cytology and Cell Physiology," G. H. Bourne (Ed.), 2nd ed., Clarendon Press, Oxford, pp. 39-83.

Barer, R., 1956. "Phase Contrast and Interference Microscopy in Cytology," *in* "Physical Techniques in Biological Research," G. Oster and A. W. Pollister (Eds.), Vol. 3, Academic Press, New York, N.Y., pp. 29-90.

Barer, R., 1959. "Phase, Interference, and Polarizing Microscopy," *in* "Analytical Cytology," R. C. Mellors (Ed.), 2nd ed., Blakiston Division, McGraw-Hill Book Co., New York, N.Y., pp. 169-272.

Barer, R. and Joseph, S., 1954. "Refractometry of Living Cells. I. Basic Principles," *Quart. J. Microscop. Sci.,* **95**, 399-423.

Barer, R. and Dick, D. A. T., 1957. "Interferometry and Refractometry of Cells in Tissue Culture," *Exptl. Cell Res., Suppl.,* **4**, 103-135.

Bell, L. G. E., 1952. "The Application of Freezing and Drying Techniques in Cytology," *Intern. Rev. Cytol.,* **1**, 35-63.

Bell, L. G. E., 1956. "Freezing-Drying," *in* "Physical Techniques in Biological Research," G. Oster and A. W. Pollister (Eds.), Vol. 3, Academic Press, New York, N.Y., pp. 1-27.

Bennett, H. S., 1950. "The Microscopical Investigation of Biological Materials with Polarized Light," *in* "McClung's Handbook of Microscopical Technique," R. M. Jones (Ed.), 3rd ed., Paul B. Hoeber, Inc., New York, N.Y., pp. 591-677.

Bennett, H. S. and Watts, R. M., 1958. "The Cytochemical Demonstration and Measurement of Sulfhydryl Groups by Azo-Aryl Mercaptide Coupling, with Special Reference to Mercury Orange," *in* "General Cytochemical Methods," J. F. Danielli (Ed.), Vol. 1, Academic Press, New York, N.Y., pp. 317-374.

Bennett, A. H., Osterberg, H., Jupnik, H., and Richards, A. O., 1951. "Phase Microscopy," John Wiley & Sons, Inc., New York, N.Y.

Blout, E. R., 1953. "Ultraviolet Microscopy and Ultraviolet Microspectroscopy," *in* "Advances in Biological and Medical Physics," J. H. Lawrence and C. A. Tobias (Eds.), Vol. 3, Academic Press, New York, N.Y., pp. 286-336.

Blum, H. F., 1950. "Action Spectra and Absorption Spectra," *in* "Biophysical Research Methods," F. M. Uber (Ed.), Interscience Publishers, Inc., New York, N.Y., pp. 417-449.

Brachet, J., 1957. "Biochemical Cytology," Academic Press, New York, N.Y.

Caspersson, T. O., 1950. "Cell Growth and Cell Function," W. W. Norton & Co., Inc., New York, N.Y.

Claude, A., 1946. "Fractionation of Mammalian Liver Cells by Differential Centrifugation. II. Experimental Procedures and Results," *J. Exptl. Med.*, 84, 61-89.

Conn, H. J., 1925. "Biological Stains," Commission on Standardization of Biological Stains, Geneva, N.Y.

Conn, H. J., 1950. "Stains and Staining," *in* "McClung's Handbook of Microscopical Technique," R. M. Jones (Ed.), 3rd ed., Paul B. Hoeber, Inc., New York, N.Y., pp. 72-114.

Coons, A. H., 1956. "Histochemistry with Labelled Antibody," *Intern. Rev. Cytol.*, 5, 1-23.

Coons, A. H., 1958. "Fluorescent Antibody Methods," *in* "General Cytochemical Methods," J. F. Danielli (Ed.), Vol. 1, Academic Press, New York, N.Y., pp. 399-422.

Cosslett, V. E., 1955. "Electron Microscopy," *in* "Physical Techniques in Biological Research," G. Oster and A. W. Pollister (Eds.), Vol. 1, Academic Press, New York, N.Y., pp. 461-531.

Danielli, J. F., 1953. "Cytochemistry. A Critical Approach," John Wiley & Sons, Inc., New York, N.Y.

Davies, H. G., 1958. "The Determination of Mass and Concentration by Microscope Interferometry," *in* "General Cytochemical Methods," J. F. Danielli (Ed.), Vol. 1, Academic Press, New York, N.Y., pp. 55-161.

DeDuve, C. and Berthet, J., 1954. "The Use of Differential Centrifugation in the Study of Tissue Enzymes," *Intern. Rev. Cytol.*, 3, 225-277.

Deitsch, A. D., 1955. "Microspectrophotometric Study of the Binding of the Anionic Dye, Naphthol Yellow S, by Tissue Sections and by Purified Proteins," *Lab. Invest.*, 4, 324-351.

Engström, A., 1950. "Use of Soft X-rays in the Assay of Biological Materials," *Progr. in Biophys.*, 1, 104-196.

Engström, A., 1956. "Historadiography," *in* "Physical Techniques in Biological Research," G. Oster and A. W. Pollister (Eds.), Vol. 3, Academic Press, New York, N.Y., pp. 489-544.

Engström, A., 1959. "X-ray Microscopy," *in* "Analytical Cytology," R. C. Mellors (Ed.), 3rd ed., Blakiston Division, McGraw-Hill Book Co., New York, N.Y., pp. 343-379.

Ficq, A., 1959. "Autoradiography," *in* "The Cell," J. Brachet and A. E. Mirsky (Eds.), Vol. 1, Academic Press, New York, N.Y., pp. 67-90.

Fitzgerald, P. J., 1959. "Autoradiography in Cytology," *in* "Analytical Cytology," R. C. Mellors (Ed.), 2nd ed., Blakiston Division, McGraw-Hill Book Co., New York, N.Y., pp. 381-429.

Flax, M. H. and Himes, M. H., 1952. "Microspectrophotometric Analysis of Metachromatic Staining of Nucleic Acids," *Physiol. Zool.*, 25, 297-311.

Freed, J. J., 1955. "Freeze-drying Technique in Cytology and Cytochemistry," *Lab. Invest.,* **4,** 106-122.

Gatenby, J. B. and Beams, H. W., 1950. "The Microtomist's Vade-Mecum," 11th ed., The Blakiston Company, Philadelphia, Pa.

Gersh, I., 1959. "Fixation and Staining," *in* "The Cell," J. Brachet and A. E. Mirsky (Eds.), Vol. 1, Academic Press, New York, N.Y., pp. 21-66.

Gersh, I. and Bodian, D., 1943. "Some Chemical Mechanisms in Chromatolysis," *J. Cellular Comp. Physiol.,* **21,** 253-280.

Glick, D., 1953. "A Critical Survey of Current Approaches in Quantitative Histo- and Cytochemistry," *Intern. Rev. Cytol.,* **2,** 447-474.

Gomori, G., 1952. "Microscopic Histochemistry. Principles and Practice," University of Chicago Press, Chicago, Ill.

Gray, Peter, 1952. "Handbook of Basic Microtechnique," The Blakiston Company, New York, N.Y.

Hancox, N. M., 1957. "Experiments on the Fundamental Effects of Freeze-substitution," *Exptl. Cell Res.,* **13,** 263-275.

Harker, D., 1956. "X-ray Diffraction Applied to Crystalline Proteins," *in* "Advances in Biological and Medical Physics," J. H. Lawrence and C. A. Tobias (Eds.), Vol. 4, Academic Press, New York, N.Y., pp. 1-22.

Holter, H., Linderstrøm-Lang, K., and Zeuthen, E., 1956. "Manometric Techniques for Single Cells," *in* "Physical Techniques in Biological Research," G. Oster and A. W. Pollister (Eds.), Vol. 3, Academic Press, New York, N.Y., pp. 577-625.

Inoué, S. and Dan, K., 1951. "Birefrigence of the Dividing Cell," *J. Morphol.,* **89,** 423-451.

Kirkpatrick, P. and Pattee, H. H., Jr., 1953. "Approaches to X-ray Microscopy," *in* "Advances in Biological and Medical Physics," J. H. Lawrence and C. A. Tobias (Eds.), Vol. 3, Academic Press, New York, N.Y., pp. 247-283.

Kurnick, N. B., 1950. "Methyl Green Pyronin. The Basis of Selective Staining of Nucleic Acids," *J. Gen. Physiol.,* **33,** 243-264.

Leuchtenberger, C., 1958. "Quantitative Determination of DNA in Cells by Feulgen Microspectrophotometry," *in* "General Cytochemical Methods," J. F. Danielli (Ed.), Vol. 1, Academic Press, New York, N.Y., pp. 219-278.

Martin, L. C., 1955. "The Light Microscope," *in* "Physical Techniques in Biological Research," G. Oster and A. W. Pollister (Eds.), Vol. 1, Academic Press, New York, N.Y., pp. 325-375.

Mazia, D., 1956. "Materials for the Biophysical and Biochemical Study of Cell Division," *in* "Advances in Biological and Medical Physics," J. H. Lawrence and C. A. Tobias (Eds.), Vol. 4, Academic Press, New York, N.Y., pp. 69-118.

Mellors, R. C., 1959. "Fluorescent-Antibody Method," *in* "Analytical Cytology," R. C. Mellors (Ed.), 2nd ed., Blakiston Division, McGraw-Hill Book Co., New York, N.Y., pp. 1-67.

Mitchison, J. M. and Swann, M. M., 1953. "Measurements on Sea-urchin Eggs with an Interference Microscope," *Quart. J. Microscop. Sci.,* **94,** 381-389.

Moses, M. J., 1952. "Quantitative Optical Techniques in the Study of Nuclear Chemistry," *Exptl. Cell Res., Suppl.,* 2, 75-102.

Novikoff, A. B., 1959. "The Intracellular Localization of Chemical Constituents," *in* "Analytical Cytology," R. C. Mellors (Ed.), 2nd ed., Blakiston Division, McGraw-Hill Book Co., New York, N.Y., pp. 69-168.

Oster, G., 1955. "Birefrigence and Dichroism," *in* "Physical Techniques in Biological Research," G. Oster and A. W. Pollister (Eds.), Vol. 1, Academic Press, New York, N.Y., pp. 439-460.

Osterberg, H., 1955. "Phase and Interference Microscopy," *in* "Physical Techniques in Biological Research," G. Oster and A. W. Pollister (Eds.), Vol. 1, Academic Press, New York, N.Y., pp. 377-437.

Pearse, A. G. E., 1960. "Histochemistry. Theoretical and Applied," 2nd ed., Little, Brown & Company, Boston, Mass.

Pelc, S. R., 1958. "Autoradiography as a Cytochemical Method, with Special Reference to $C^{14}$ and $S^{35}$," *in* "General Cytochemical Methods," J. F. Danielli (Ed.), Vol. 1, Academic Press, New York, N.Y., pp. 279-316.

Pollister, A. W., 1952. "Microspectrophotometry of Fixed Cells by Visible Light," *Lab. Invest.,* 1, 231-249.

Pollister, A. W. and Ris, H., 1947. "Nucleoprotein Determination in Cytological Preparations," *Cold Spring Harbor Symposia Quant. Biol.,* 12, 147-157.

Pollister, A. W. and Ornstein, L., 1959. "The Photometric Chemical Analysis of Cells," *in* "Analytical Cytology," R. C. Mellors (Ed.), 2nd ed., Blakiston Division, McGraw-Hill Book Co., New York, N.Y., pp. 431-518.

Popper, H. and Szanto, P. B., 1950. "Fluorescence Microscopy," *in* "McClung's Handbook of Microscopical Technique," R. M. Jones (Ed.), 3rd ed., Paul B. Hoeber, Inc., New York, N.Y., pp. 678-686.

Price, G. R. and Schwartz, J., 1956. "Fluorescence Microscopy," *in* "Physical Techniques in Biological Research," G. Oster and A. W. Pollister (Eds.), Vol. 3, Academic Press, New York, N.Y., pp. 91-148.

Richards, O. W., 1950. "When to Use Special Microscopes," *in* "Biophysical Research Methods," F. M. Uber (Ed.), Interscience Publishers, Inc., New York, N.Y., pp. 343-380.

Ruch, F., 1956. "Birefrigence and Dichroism of Cells and Tissues," *in* "Physical Techniques in Biological Research," G. Oster and A. W. Pollister (Eds.), Vol. 3, Academic Press, New York, N.Y., pp. 149-176.

Selby, C. C., 1959. "Electron Microscopy: Techniques and Applications in Cytology," *in* "Analytical Cytology," R. C. Mellors (Ed.), 2nd ed., Blakiston Division, McGraw-Hill Book Co., New York, N.Y., pp. 273-341.

Singer, M., 1952. "Factors Which Control the Staining of Tissue Sections with Acid and Basic Dyes," *Intern. Rev. Cytol.,* 1, 211-256.

Swann, M. M., 1951. "The Birefrigence of the Metaphase Spindle and Asters of the Living Sea Urchin Egg." *J. Exptl. Biol.,* 28, 417-433.

Swann, M. M., 1951. "The Nature and Cause of Birefrigence Changes in the Sea Urchin Egg at Anaphase," *J. Exptl. Biol.,* 28, 434-444.

Swift, H., 1950. "The Desoxyribose Nucleic Acid Content of Animal Nuclei," *Physiol. Zool.,* 23, 169-198.

Swift, H., 1955. "Cytochemical Techniques for Nucleic Acids," *in* "The Nucleic Acids," E. Chargaff and J. N. Davidson (Eds.), Vol. 2, Academic Press, New York, N.Y., pp. 51-92.

Swift, H. and Rasch, E., 1956. "Microphotometry with Visible Light," *in* "Physical Techniques in Biological Research," G. Oster and A. W. Pollister (Eds.), Vol. 3, Academic Press, New York, N.Y., pp. 353-400.

Taylor, J. H., 1956. "Autoradiography at the Cellular Level," *in* "Physical Techniques in Biological Research," G. Oster and A. W. Pollister (Eds.), Vol. 3, Academic Press, New York, N.Y., pp. 545-576.

Thorell, B., 1947. "The Relation of Nucleic Acids to the Formation and Differentiation of Cellular Proteins," *Cold Spring Harbor Symposia Quant. Biol.,* 12, 247-255.

Walker, P. M. P., 1958. "Ultraviolet Microspectrophotometry," *in* "General Cytochemical Methods," J. F. Danielli (Ed.), Vol. 1, Academic Press, New York, N.Y., pp. 164-217.

Whatley, F. R., 1956. "Cytochemical Methods," *in* "Moderne Methoden der Pflanzenanalyse," K. Paech and M. V. Tracy (Eds.), Vol. 1, Springer-Verlag, Berlin, pp. 452-467.

Wyckoff, R. W. G., 1958. "The World of the Electron Microscope," Yale University Press, New Haven, Conn.

Wyckoff, R. W. G., 1959. "Optical Methods in Cytology," *in* "The Cell," J. Brachet and A. E. Mirsky (Eds.), Vol. 1, Academic Press, New York, N.Y., pp. 1-20.

Zworykin, V. K., 1957. "Television Techniques in Biology and Medicine," *in* "Advances in Biological and Medical Physics," J. H. Lawrence and C. A. Tobias (Eds.), Vol. 5, Academic Press, New York, N.Y., pp. 243-283.

# 12

# General Remarks

CYTOLOGY IN THE proper sense is, as intimated in the beginning of this discussion, a broad field, taking its data from a wide range of sciences both biological and physical, and concerning itself with the fundamental principles involved in the behavior of living stuff generally. The techniques of experiment and analysis are largely derived from those of mathematics, chemistry, and physics, and almost every biological problem may be said to have a cytological vector whether or not it is apparent as such. In 1925 the late Professor E. B. Wilson could write a scholarly treatise which was nearly all-embracing, but 30 years later it would be difficult to cover the field equally well in five or six volumes and no one man could be sufficiently at ease in all branches to manage the compilation alone. The modern counterpart of E. B. Wilson's *The Cell* is the multivolumed work by the same name edited by J. Brachet and A. Mirsky and containing the contributions of a host of specialists. No textbook, including this one, can provide more than a glimpse of the field or serve as anything other than an introduction to an area of biological science which is fascinating, frustrating, and extremely fundamental. The basic concept upon which cytology was founded, namely, the notion that the cell is the unit of structure and function, remains the essential basis of cellular biology. The cell has also been firmly established as the unit of inheritance, both chromosomal and cytoplasmic, and may also be looked upon as the unit which makes evolution possible. Likewise it may be considered the unit of disease and, in many respects, the unit by which control over disease may be exercised. Consciously or otherwise, the cytologist works towards the day when he can, as Carl

Swanson puts it, "view the grand pattern of the cell," which is to say espy the basic pattern of cellular organization in relation to operation. If this day is still well in the future, there are many signs that excellent progress is being made. For example, certain generalizations may now be made with considerable confidence which a few years ago would have seemed premature to say the least:

(1) Few cytologists or geneticists would now doubt that cellular operation is dictated to a considerable degree by the interrelationships of DNA, RNA, and protein (Swanson, 1957). Indeed it is probably safe to conclude that specific protein synthesis is normally controlled by DNA organization through the intermediacy of RNA, and that the ribosomes (small granules of Palade, "microsomes") represent the structural site of at least the final steps. The details of this interrelationship and how it is controlled are still, however, open questions of great import.

(2) Electron micrography has taken giant steps toward confirming a long-standing suspicion that all cells are highly organized at the macro-molecular level and even that a basic pattern can be detected despite the enormous variation associated with diverse cellular function. The apparent universality of double membrane systems as shown in the endo-plasmic reticulum, nuclear envelope, Golgi complex, mitochondria, and plastids certainly suggests a master plan and underscores the importance of surface phenomena.

(3) Biochemical and cytochemical analysis together with electron micrography have combined to establish the mitochondrion, or a rea-sonable facsimile thereof, as the cell's major power plant, and have made it at least as well understood structurally and functionally at the chro-mosome.

These generalizations, together with others that might be made con-cerning the function and structure of other organized components of the protoplast, such as nucleoli, lysosomes, and plastids, provide us with a fair notion of the roles of the several parts of a cell. A consideration of these several roles may also serve as a basis for construction of working hypotheses concerning integration. In somewhat over-simplified terms we may quite safely assume that information is supplied by the organized DNA of the chromosomes, and transmitted—presumably through in-volvement of RNA—to the site of protein synthesis, which appears to be the ribosomes. Most of the energy for these operations may be pre-sumed to be associated with the production of high-energy phosphate compounds largely supplied by the operation of mitochondrial-bound enzyme systems. If what is accomplished in a cell and where it is accomplished are beginning to be understood, albeit vaguely, we are still almost completely in the dark concerning both the evolutionary development of the system and the mechanism of control. The cytologist tends to look with some suspicion on the "ameba to man" notion of increasing complexity, since the single-cell organism appears in most instances to be at least as "sophisticated" in function and structure as any individual cell in a multicellular organism.

## The Role of Cytology

If the cell theory in modern dress has any validity, many problems of biological operation may approach satisfactory solution only when more is known of cellular function. Some of the areas in which cytology plays an important and even dominant role are outlined below:

### Genetics

Even a casual scrutiny of a textbook of genetics will disclose something of the debt which modern genetics owes to cytology. The theory, supported by overwhelming evidence, that the chromosome is essentially a linear organization of genetic material brought cytology and genetics together to produce the highly fertile hybrid, cytogenetics. The bridge between generations is a cell or pair of cells and this, in itself, makes cytology of major concern to genetics. The formation of these important cells (spores, gametes, zygotes) constitutes a series of cytological problems mostly, but not exclusively, associated with mitosis and meiosis. The development of the asexual spore or fertilized egg into a mature organism is also, in large measure, a problem at the cytological level involving changes in cell structure and function.

The major problem with which modern genetics is concerned is the question of the mode of operation of genic material. Two aspects of cytology must be considered in any attempt to answer this question: namely, cellular organization at the level revealed by the electron microscope, and the biochemical capacities of cells of various types. In studies of these types, clonal lines of microorganisms and of plant and animal cells in tissue culture appear to represent the most useful material.

### Medicine

The role of cytology in medical practice and research is extensive. Over a hundred years ago Rudolph Virchow contended that the cell should be considered the unit of pathology as well as of structure and function. Subsequent advances in both cytology and medicine have tended to validate Virchow's opinion in this regard. Some of the general contributions of cytology may be outlined as follows:

*Diagnosis:* Many disease syndromes are, at least in part, diagnosed on the basis of cellular change. Such changes include (1) shifts in relative frequencies of different types of cells, as in haemopoetic tissues and peripheral blood; (2) changes in the morphology of particular kinds of cells, or of granular inclusions, as in nerve cells; and (3) appearance of cells and cellular debris in body fluids, used frequently as an aid to diagnosis of special kinds of cancer. More recently, two kinds of diagnostic procedures involving chromosomal material have become important. One is the use of the so-called "sex chromatin" test for diagnosis of the genetic sex of individuals showing various degrees of sexual dysgenesis. In this test, usually carried out on skin biopses or oral smears, the genetic sex is considered female if 50 per cent or more of the somatic nuclei show a single heteropycnotic chromatin mass near the nuclear boundary (Nelson, 1958). The other new procedure correlates change in karyotype with specific syndromes (Ford, 1960). For example, at least 19 cases of Mongolism have all shown an extra chromosome presumably representing a trisomic condition. When such correlations become better established, human cytogenetics bids well to play a rather direct role in certain kinds of diagnosis.

*Cancer:* The problem of neoplastic growth may be considered to be essentially a problem in applied cytophysiology. Cancerous or tumerous growths, regardless of apparent cause or of whether they occur in plants or animals, have one thing in common, namely, replication of cells without organization or tissue function. This means that fundamental studies on the physiochemical mechanisms involved in the normal mitotic cycle are of direct concern, for until we fully understand the conditions under which cellular replication occurs in normal tissue, we are not very likely to obtain any real understanding of the situation in neoplastic growth. Whatever attributes a cancer cell possesses or does not possess, it is certainly able to perform all functions leading to capability of undergoing mitosis.

Most theories of neoplastic induction are based on the general idea of some specific alteration in a normal cell which eliminates its capacity to integrate into a tissue, but which either increases or at least does not impair its capacity to undergo replication. To date, the nature of these proposed alterations is not known, though many causal agents such as viruses, chemicals, radiation, and other physical stimuli have been demonstrated. Two general theories have received most attention, i.e., somatic mutation and virus infection. These two ideas are not necessarily mutually exclusive, since the latter could conceivably give rise to the former. In its broader sense, of course, mutation covers not only gene change and chromosome alteration but also change in any self-perpetuating extranuclear particle. An hypothesis long held by Otto Warburg is that the key particle involved is the mitochondrion, which becomes impaired and leads to a shift from aerobic to anaerobic respiration. This shift is presumed to favor mitosis rather than differentiation, though definitive evidence for this point of view seems to be lacking. The hypotheses mentioned have stressed intracellular change but, so far, no one has excluded the possibility that cancer initiation may be intercellular by virtue of differential destruction of component cells of a tissue, thus leading to disorganization and loss of control. Certainly all the causal agents mentioned are capable of acting in this fashion. The problem of intercellular relationships in an organized tissue, therefore, becomes an area of concern in cancer research.

*Drug Effects:* Another aspect of cytological studies which is of more or less direct concern to medicine involves the modification of cellular morphology and function by drugs and drug-related substances. Within the confines of this book no extensive discussion of this particular problem is possible. However, the point should be made that ingestion of a drug will inevitably lead to some alteration, temporary or permanent, in the metabolism of some component cells of the organism. For example, there is good evidence that certain antibiotics, most notably, chloromycetin, terramycin, and aureomycin interfere with protein synthesis, though the exact mechanism is not clear. Likewise, tranquilizers of the chlorpromazine type have been shown to inhibit the succinic oxidase system in brain and liver mitochondria. Many drugs appear to interfere with carbohydrate metabolism in one way or another, though the exact mode of action in most cases is unknown. Such drugs include cortical steroids such as corticosterone, antimalaria amidines, anesthetics of the dibucaine type, and other compounds commonly used for some therapeutic purpose. Such effects are not necessarily directly related to therapeutic value, though they may often be related to undesirable "side-effects."

## Taxonomy

In recent years the field of biosystematics on both the plant and animal side has been making increasing use of cytological analysis as a major clue to taxonomic relationship. The most commonly used cytological characteristic is comparative chromosome constitution and behavior. Stebbins has noted that the chromosomes, because they are the bearers of hereditary factors, should be considered as somewhat more fundamental than other structures on which relationship is based. Among the most rewarding studies in this regard are detailed comparisons of karyotypes in apparently related groups, analysis of meiosis, especially in putative hybrids, and studies of natural and synthetic polyploids. Studies on the origin of important crop plants such as wheat, cotton, and tobacco have drawn heavily on such cytological and cytogenetical studies, as have the evolutionary relationships of species of *Crepis* worked out over many years by E. B. Babock and his colleagues. Similar studies have been made on animals, especially on insects and other invertebrates, as described by M. J. D. White.

## Embryology

We may define embryology (plant or animal) as the study of processes associated with the early stages in the development of an individual from a functional egg. As we examine any standard textbook on the subject, it becomes clear very quickly that most of the problems of cellular biology are also problems of developmental biology. Embryology must concern itself with a level of organization generally considered to be higher than that which occupies the attention of the cytologist; namely, cellular interrelationship in the development of tissues and organs. Nonetheless, this major question of embryology demands equal and prior concern for the properties of cells themselves. The problem of cellular replication is a vital one to the student of growth and development, since he is faced with the problem of control of this phenomenon in relation to progressive organization. By the same token the embryologist must take full cognizance of the basic structure of cells, including the role, distribution, origin, and fate of particulate fractions. Whatever may be the specific factors involved in differentiation of cells, tissues, and organs in any particular case, we must look for both the structural organization and biochemical capacities which enable a cell to respond in a specific way and to the extracellular conditions which induce the response. It should be noted here that the extracellular conditions which induce change in one kind of cell may well be the intracellular conditions in another type of cell. In many cases the only thing that distinguishes between an embryologist and a cytologist is some slight difference in the point of view from which they attack the same problems.

While there is no doubt that full comprehension of the "grand plan" of the cell would place our understanding of the organic world on a par with that of the inorganic, it would not automatically solve all biological problems. Such knowledge would be a major step in the right direction, but profound questions concerning the integration of cells into tissues,

tissues into organs, organs into organisms, and organisms into ecological complexes would still be there to answer. No biologist can afford to be ignorant of cellular phenomena, but only the cytologist can theoretically consider such knowledge an end in itself, though in fact, even he cannot indulge in this particular form of isolationism.

## BIBLIOGRAPHY

Babcock, E. B., 1947. "The Genus *Crepis,* I and II," *Univ. Calif. Publ. in Botany,* Vols. 21 and 22.

Brachet, J. and Mirsky, A. E., 1960. "The Cell," Vol. 1, Academic Press, New York, N.Y.

Ford, C. E., 1960. "Human Cytogenetics: Its Present Place and Future Possibilities," *Am. J. Human Genetics,* **12,** 104-117.

Nelson, W. D., 1958. "Application of the Sex-chromatin Test to Conditions of Sexual Dysgenesis," *Trans. N.Y. Acad. Sci.,* **20,** 493-499.

Swanson, C. P., 1957. "Cytology and Cytogenetics," Prentice-Hall, Inc., Englewood Cliffs, N.J.

White, M. J. D., 1954. "Animal Cytology and Evolution," 2nd ed., Cambridge University Press, Cambridge.

Wilson, E. B., 1925. "The Cell in Development and Heredity," 3rd ed., The Macmillan Co., New York, N.Y.

# Annotated Reading List

Bisele, John J., 1958. "Mitotic Poisons and The Cancer Problem," Elsevier Press, 214 pp.

This book is an excellent review of the literature on the observed effects of treating tissues, containing cells in the process of division, with various chemicals. The first two chapters attempt to define and classify mitotic poisons and the first part of Chapter 3 provides a comparatively simple but excellent discussion of the biochemical and physiological activities in interphase pertinent to mitosis. Classification of antimitotics is provided both in terms of observed action and type of chemical.

Bourne, G. H. (Ed.), 1951. "Cytology and Cell Physiology," 2nd ed., Oxford University Press, Oxford, 524 pp.

This book, while somewhat outdated, still remains a very valuable and well-documented text. It is recommended to the beginning student not only as a useful reference source of the cytological literature up to 1951, but also because it probably represents one of the first serious attempts to integrate cell morphology and biochemical function. A number of investigators have contributed to the volume, to cover a wide range of topics such as cytological methods, physical and physicochemical studies of cells, the cell surface and cell physiology, nucleus, chromosomes and genes, and the mitochondria and Golgi complex, to mention only a few. Attention is also directed to the final chapter of the book dealing with some aspects of evolutionary cytology.

Brachet, J., 1957. "Biochemical Cytology," Academic Press, New York, N.Y., 516 pp.

This is a rather advanced treatise concerned almost entirely with various aspects of cell chemistry, including the chemistry and physiological function of cell organelles. There is a particularly good discussion (Chapter VI) of the role of the nucleic acids in heredity and protein synthesis, and some rather interesting analyses (Chapter VIII) of the nucleus and cytoplasmic differentiation during animal embryogeny. There are many references to original papers, mostly from 1950 to 1955. The book presupposes considerable knowledge of morphology on the part of the reader since, except for some discussion of fine structure as revealed by electron micrography, this aspect of cytology is almost entirely missing.

Brachet, J. and Mirsky, A. (Eds.), 1959. "The Cell," Vol. 1, Academic Press, New York, N.Y., 816 pp.

This volume is the first to be released of a projected three-volume work made up of contributions from a number of specialists in various fields of cellular biology. The first volume is in two parts. Part 1, containing eight papers, deals with techniques; and Part 2, containing seven papers, deals with a number of general problems including sex determination, differentiation, and effects of radiation. Volume II will deal with cell parts, and Volume III with specialized cells.

Butler, J. A. V., 1959. "Inside the Living Cell," Basic Books, New York, N.Y., 174 pp.

This book is a somewhat popularized account of the general biochemistry of cells, including some comment on the chemistry and role of proteins, nucleic acids, vitamins, and hormones. The later chapters, from Chapter 15 on, depart somewhat from consideration of the cell as such, to discuss the make-up and function of the brain, the process of aging, and the origin of life.

D'Arcy, Thompson, 1942. "Growth and Form," Cambridge University Press, Cambridge, Vol. 1, 2nd ed., 462 pp.

This delightful and scholarly book provides a most fascinating discussion of form in biological systems, and includes in Chapters IV and V a detailed analysis of cellular form both in division and in special cases. Particular attention is paid to the significance of surface tension phenomena and equilibrium forms.

Darlington, C. D., 1937. "Recent Advances in Cytology," 2nd ed., P. Blakiston's Son & Co., Inc., Philadelphia, 671 pp.

This book might be considered a classic in many respects. It is almost entirely concerned with facts and hypotheses of chromosome mechanics, especially in relation to genetics. This book is important for two reasons: (1) It was so controversial that it, as well as the 1st edition, stimulated a tremendous amount of work, particularly in the area of chromosome structure; and (2) it represents the first attempt to provide a unified theory of cytogenetics.

Darlington, C. D., 1956. "Chromosome Botany," Allen and Unwin Ltd., London, 186 pp.

This little book, which is of special interest to plant taxonomists and systematists, provides an introduction to the use of chromosome studies in relation to a number of botanical problems, including taxonomy, plant geography, speciation, and ecology. There is also considerable discussion of the importance of chromosome studies in problems of plant breeding and origin of cultivated plants.

Darlington, C. D. and Wylie, A. P., 1956. "Chromosome Atlas of Flowering Plants," The Macmillan Co., New York, N.Y.

This is the most up-to-date handbook of chromosome numbers in plants, arranged by family, genus, and species. It is interesting to note that while some 17,000 species are listed, this amounts to only about one tenth of the known species.

Davidson, J. N., 1957. "The Biochemistry of the Nucleic Acids," 3rd ed., Methuen & Co. Ltd., London, 248 pp.

In his preface, the author refers to this little monograph as "The Child's Guide to the Nucleic Acids." This is being rather over-modest. The book covers the basic chemistry of the nucleic acids, general methods of detection and analysis, and distribution and function, in a form intelligible to anyone with a knowledge of general biology and elementary organic chemistry.

DeRobertis, E. D. P., Nowinski, W. W., and Saez, F. A., 1954. "General Cytology," 2nd ed., W. B. Saunders Co., Philadelphia, Pa., 456 pp.

As the title indicates, this book is a text in general cytology rather than a monograph on a particular aspect. An effort has been made to cover salient facts and hypotheses of cell structure, chemistry, and function. About 100 pages are devoted to chromosome structure and behavior, with the rest of the book being concerned with submicroscopic structure, cytochemistry, and cell physiology.

Eigsti, O. J. and Dustin, P., Jr., 1956. "Colchicine in Agriculture, Medicine, Biology, and Chemistry," Iowa State College Press, Ames, Iowa, 470 pp.

This monograph concerns one single substance, the alkaloid colchicine, which is used (a) in medicine, as a specific for gout; (b) in plant breeding as a polyploidizing agent, and (c) as an antimitotic in the study of mitosis and as a possible mechanism of anticarcinogenic action.

Furness, F., White, E. W., and Gross, Paul (Eds.), 1960. "Second Conference on the Mechanisms of Cell Division," *Annals N.Y. Acad. Sci.,* **90,** 345-613.

This volume presents 22 technical papers on the central theme of mitosis, together with an introductory article by Dr. Gross. The participants represent not only a very distinguished group, but also almost the entire range of methodologies for attacking this very basic problem.

Harrow, B. and Mazur, A., 1958. "Textbook of Biochemistry," 7th ed., W. B. Saunders Co., Philadelphia, Pa., 557 pp.

This is a standard textbook of biochemistry written primarily for medical students. It was selected as a reference in this particular case largely because it provides a relatively simple discussion of metabolic pathways without presuming a particularly sophisticated chemistry background.

Hayashi, T. (Ed.), 1959. "Subcellular Particles," The Ronald Press, New York, N.Y., 11 papers, 213 pp.

This volume contains a series of reviews coordinating structure of cell organelles with biochemical and physiological function. Included are discussions of changes in the endoplasmic reticulum and mitochondria, the nature and function of the Golgi complex, the detection and function of lysosomes, and a review of the biochemical properties of the isolated nucleus. The reviews dealing with photosynthetic phosphorylation, intermediate reactions in protein synthesis, and polynucleotide synthesis in nucleolus and chromosomes, are timely also and well worth a careful reading by the student.

Hollaender, A. (Ed.), 1954. "High Energy Radiation," Vol. 1 of "Radiation Biology" (Part 1, pp. 1-626; Part 2, pp. 627-1265), McGraw-Hill Book Co., New York, N.Y., 1266 pp.

This volume of a two-volume work is of special interest to the cytologist concerned with cellular effects of ionizing radiation. The first six papers are concerned with the properties and general effects of ionizing radiation itself, and provide the nonphysicist with an excellent introduction to the physics involved. Papers 9 and 10 take up the subject of radiation-induced changes in chromosomes in animals and plants, and Paper 11 is concerned with the general effects of radiation on cells. Other papers discuss genetic effects, pathological changes and cancer induction. The references offer good coverage of pre-1954 literature.

Hughes, A., 1952. "The Mitotic Cycle," Academic Press, New York, N.Y., 232 pp.

This monograph on cellular replication combines rather well the pertinent morphological and physiological literature. There is also a fairly extensive section on chemical and physical modification of mitosis.

Hughes, A., 1959. "A History of Cytology," Abelard-Schuman, London, 158 pp.

This brief history of the development of the science of cytology is recommended reading for any biologist, if only to combat what appears to be an innate tendency to consider any finding or idea over 25 years old to be primitive if not downright wrong. The early history is handled in a much better way than the more recent, presumably because of a normal tendency to assume less objective viewpoints as one approaches one's own times.

Lea, D. E., 1955. "Actions of Radiations on Living Cells," Cambridge University Press, Cambridge, 416 pp.

This book is an extensive, and sometimes rather mathematical, discussion of methods of measuring the effects of radiation on cells in general and on chromosomes in particular. Much of the argument depends on the validity of the target theory, which the author accepts without much question.

Makino, S., 1951. "An Atlas of the Chromosome Numbers in Animals," 2nd ed., Iowa State College Press, Ames, Iowa, 290 pp.

This is a list of most of the known animal chromosome numbers, covering about 3200 species, listed according to family, genus, and species. This number, of course, represents only a very minute fraction of all named animal species.

McElroy, E. D. and Glass, B. (Eds.), 1957. "A Symposium on the Chemical Basis of Heredity," Johns Hopkins University Press, Baltimore, Md., 848 pp.

Although the orientation of this collection of papers is genetical, many, especially those dealing with the distribution, function, and structure of the nucleic acids, are of direct interest to cytologists. Taken as a whole, this volume is an excellent example of the dependence of modern genetics on modern cytology. We may almost speak of this relationship as the "new cytogenetics."

Mellors, R. C. (Ed.), 1959. "Analytical Cytology," 2nd ed., Blakiston Division, McGraw-Hill Book Co., New York, N.Y., 534 pp.

An outstanding text dealing with the theory and practical application of some of the physical and chemical methods presently used for the study of cellular structure and function. The book is made up of seven chapters, each of which has been contributed by a specialist in the area under discussion. The advanced student, in particular, will find that the critical reviews of the fluorescent-antibody method, of the intracellular localization of chemical constituents, of phase, interference, and polarizing microscopy, electron microscopy, X-ray microscopy, autoradiography, and the photometric chemical analysis of cells, will serve as excellent reference sources.

Oncley, J. L. (Ed.), 1959. "Biophysical Science—A Study Program," John Wiley & Sons, Inc., New York, N.Y., 568 pp. (AI, 1-14; SI, 1-27).

This book consists of 61 short papers, almost all of which are directly concerned with cellular phenomena. Among the subjects discussed are the molecular organization of proteins and nucleic acids, properties of macromolecules, radiation effects on macromolecules, energy transformation, and fine structure of cellular components.

Palay, S. L. (Ed.), 1958. "Frontiers of Cytology," Yale University Press, New Haven, Conn., 529 pp.

This book is made up of 17 lectures given by various specialists on a diverse collection of cytological problems. Papers 2 to 10, inclusive, are of particular interest to the student of general cytology since they cover cellular structure, chromosomes, mitotic deviations, nucleic acids, protein histochemistry, and the role of the ribosomes.

Rudnick, Dorothea (Ed.), 1957. "Developmental Cytology," The Ronald Press, New York, N.Y., 9 papers, 215 pp.

This symposium is primarily concerned with structure and function of various kinds of cells, especially in relation to problems of differentiation. All of the papers are of more or less equal interest to the general student of cytology, but attention may be drawn to two papers on chromosome variations within animals and plants and a paper on changes in the fine structure of cell organelles.

Schrader, F., 1953. "Mitosis," 2nd ed., Columbia University Press, New York, N.Y., 170 pp.

The reader will find here an excellent critical review of the numerous mechanically based hypotheses of chromosome movements involved in orientation on a metaphase plate, and poleward movement at anaphase. The impression will be gained that a purely mechanistic approach will not lead to solutions to these problems, but there is also a caution that chemistry divorced from morphological considerations will not serve much better.

*Scientific American:*

A number of articles have appeared in this magazine in recent years which the beginning student in cytology will find both interesting and informative. Those selected by the authors as especially pertinent to the cytological field are as follows:

Allfrey, V. G. and Mirsky, A. E., 1961. "How Cells Make Molecules," Vol. 205, No. 3, pp. 74-82.

Arnold, J. A. and Martell, E. A., 1959. "The Circulation of Radioactive Isotopes," Vol. 201, No. 3, pp. 85-93.

Arnon, D. I., 1960. "The Role of Light in Photosynthesis," Vol. 203, No. 5, pp. 105-118.

Brachet, J., "The Living Cell," 1961. Vol. 205, No. 3, pp. 50-61.

Crow, J. F., 1959. "Ionizing Radiation and Evolution," Vol. 201, No. 3, pp. 138-160.

Fischberg, M. and Blackler, A. W., 1961. "How Cells Specialize," Vol. 205, No. 3, pp. 124-140.

Gay, H., 1960. "Nuclear Control of the Cell," Vol. 202, No. 1, pp. 126-136.

Hoagland, M. B., 1960. "Nucleic Acids and Proteins," Vol. 201, No. 6, pp. 55-61.

Hollaender, A. and Stapleton, G. E., 1959. "Radiation and the Cell," Vol. 201, No. 3, pp. 95-100.

Jacob, F. and Wollman, E. L., 1961. "Viruses and Genes," Vol. 204, No. 6, pp. 92-107.

Lehninger, A. L., 1960. "Energy Transformations in the Cell," Vol. 202, No. 5, pp. 102-114.

Lehninger, A. L., 1961. "How Cells Transform Energy," Vol. 205, No. 3, pp. 63-73.

Mazia, D., 1961. "How Cells Divide," Vol. 205, No. 3, pp. 100-120.

Platzman, R. L., 1959. "What is Ionizing Radiation?", Vol. 201, No. 3, pp. 74-83.

Puck, T. T., 1960. "Radiation and the Human Cell," Vol. 202, No. 4, pp. 142-153.

Rose, A. H., 1960. "Yeasts," Vol. 202, No. 2, pp. 136-146.

Stein, W. H., and Moore, S., 1961. "The Structure of Proteins," Vol. 204, No. 2, pp. 81-92.

Sharp, L. W., 1934. "An Introduction to Cytology," 3rd ed., McGraw-Hill Book Co., New York, N.Y., 567 pp.

In contrast to Brachet's "Biochemical Cytology," this book might well have been entitled "Morphological Cytology," and is the last text in English which takes an over-all look at general cellular morphology. Though somewhat out-of-date in certain respects, it is still a valid source of information on many structural features of the cell, and contains particularly detailed descriptions of the cytology of reproduction in both plants and animals.

Sharp, L. W., 1943. "Fundamentals of Cytology," McGraw-Hill Book Co., New York, N.Y., 270 pp.

This book is a sort of "Readers Digest" version of Sharp's earlier (1934) volume, and deals with much the same material. For neophytes in the field, the first chapter, entitled "The Position of Cytology in Biological Science," is recommended reading.

Sparrow, A. H., Bennington, J. P., and Pond, V., 1958. "Bibliography on the Effects of Ionizing Radiations on Plants," Brookhaven National Laboratory, Upton, L.I., New York (BNL 504, L-103), 222 pp.

References to papers on ionizing radiation effects on plants up to 1955 are given under both author and subject indexes.

Swanson, C. P., 1957. "Cytology and Cytogenetics," Prentice-Hall, Inc., Englewood Cliffs, N.J., 596 pp.

This is an excellent, if somewhat advanced, text dealing largely with chromosome structure, behavior, and mechanics especially as related to problems of genetics, sex determination, and evolution. In most cases, the author has given special attention to opposing views. Chapter 8, on crossing over and chiasma formation, is particularly noteworthy as an unusually clear exposition of the several theories concerned with the mechanics of this problem.

Swanson, C. P., 1960. "The Cell," Prentice-Hall, Inc., Englewood Cliffs, N.J., 114 pp.

This book is one of "The Foundations of Modern Biology" series aimed at presenting the essentials of the subject in a form suitable either for the beginning student or the interested general reader.

Walker, P. M. B. (Ed.), 1960. "New Approaches in Cell Biology," Academic Press, New York, N.Y., 208 pp.

This book is a collection of papers presented by participants in a symposium by the same title at the Fifteenth International Congress of Zoology held at Imperial College, London, 1958. Of particular interest to the beginning student are the discussions dealing with the origin of the nucleus after mitotic cell division, lampbrush chromosomes, morphology of developing systems at the submicroscopic level, and the biochemical approach to cell morphology. At a more specialized level are found discussions of such fields of research as the cytochemistry of proteins and nucleic acids, active transport, nuclear transfer, labeled antibodies, chemotherapy, interference microscopy, and flying-spot microscopy.

White, M. J. D., 1950. "The Chromosomes," 4th ed., John Wiley & Sons, Inc., New York, N.Y., i-ix, 134 pp.

This little volume is an outline of chromosome behavior, mitosis and meiosis, and evolution written by an outstanding authority in the field of insect cytology. A brief but excellent glossary of cytological terms is appended.

White, M. J. D., 1954. "Animal Cytology and Evolution," Cambridge University Press, Cambridge, 454 pp.

This volume is strictly animal, and also, as the author points out, strictly chromosome cytology. The book is a particularly good source of detailed examples of many atypical chromosome arrangements found in natural populations. The reader is especially referred to the three chapters (Chaps. 15, 16, and 17) on the chromosomal basis of sex determination, both for examples of various systems and a lesson in complexity.

Wilson, E. B., 1925. "The Cell in Development and Heredity," 3rd ed., The Macmillan Co., New York, N.Y.

This scholarly book is the classic of cytology and should be part of the education of every cytologist. The 3rd edition represents the end of an era of tremendous activity in cytology, and also the last time a single man could write with authority on the whole field of cell studies. The book itself, and its earlier editions (1896, 1900), did much to bring cytology into genetic thought and to initiate the hybrid science of cytogenetics. The three editions taken together represent a fine record of the development of the science. In reading, one can see history in the making. Many of the ideas, both morphological and physiological, are amazingly modern.

Wilson, G. B., Roth, L. E., and Beams, H. W. (Consultants), 1958. "A Scope Monograph on Cytology: The Cell," The Upjohn Co., Kalamazoo, Michigan, 44 pp.

This highly illustrated monograph was originally prepared as a guide to the model of the cell built for the company for display. In capsule form it outlines some of the modern information on the cell. Particular attention has been given to fine structure as revealed by the electron microscope.

*Index*

# Author Index

Sax, K., 153, 154, 162, 165, 172, 193, 201
Schairer, M. V., 106, 118
Schepartz, B., 24, 160
Schleiden, M. J., 2, 3, 6
Schneider, W. C., 70, 72, 157, 161
Schrader, F., 2, 7, 115, 143, 144, 162, 282
Schultz, J., 116
Schwann, T., 2, 3, 6
Schwartz, J., 267
Scott, J. F., 70
Sedar, A. W., 31, 66, 72
Seifriz, W., 24
Selby, C. C., 30, 32, 64, 72, 267
Serra, J. A., 111, 116
Sharp, L. W., 192, 283
Shaw, G. W., 105, 114
Siebert, G., 157, 158, 162
Siekevitz, P., 35, 47, 55, 57, 71, 72, 73
Simms, H. S., 24
Singer, M., 216, 217, 267
Sinnott, E. W., 95, 116
Sjöstrand, F. S., 53, 54, 72
Slautterback, D. B., 69, 72
Smellie, R. M. S., 157, 158, 162
Smith, S. G., 172, 187, 192
Snoad, B., 135
Sotelo, J. R., 85, 113
Soles, A., 68
Sparrow, A. H., 94, 116, 120, 123, 126, 136, 166, 167, 168, 169, 170, 173, 196, 197, 199, 200, 201, 283
Sparrow, R. C., 94, 116
Srb, A. M., 183, 192
Stadler, L. J., 193, 201
Stebbins, L., 175, 177, 178, 192
Stedman, E., 110, 117
Steinitz, L. N., 192
Stenram, U., 117
Stent, G. S., 203, 207
Stephenson, M. C., 70
Stephenson, M. L., 58, 72
Stein, W. H., 282
Stern, C., 129, 136
Stern, H., 111, 147, 149, 155, 156, 157, 158, 159, 160, 162, 163
Steward, F. C., 13, 24
Stich, H. F., 104, 117
Stone, W. S., 194, 201
Strasburger, E., 3, 4
Strittmatter, P., 72
Subramaniam, M. K., 204, 205, 208
Sung, H. S., 204, 208
Sutton, E., 4

Swann, M. M., 142, 146, 148, 150, 155, 156, 163, 267
Swanson, C. P., 24, 72, 163, 173, 182, 192, 201, 270, 275, 282
Swift, H., 73, 104, 117, 222, 267, 268
Szanto, P. B., 251, 267
Szent-Györgyi, A., 24

Tahmisian, T. N., 37, 73
Taylor, J. H., 104, 105, 107, 109, 115, 117, 139, 140, 156, 158, 163, 268
Thomas, C. A., 203, 208
Thompson, D'Arcy, 9, 24, 49, 278
Thompson, H. P., 71
Thorell, B., 85, 117, 240, 268
Timonen, S., 158, 163
Tobias, C. A., 253, 264, 266, 268
Tracy, M. V., 268
Ts'o, P. O. P., 58
Tsou, T. M., 132, 133, 136, 175
Turian, G., 204, 205, 208
Turpin, J. P. F., 3
Tyler, S. A., 172

Uber, F. M., 265, 267

van Beneden, E., 3, 4
van Leeuwenhoek, A., 3
Van't Hof, J., 132
Velick, S. F., 72
Vendrely, C., 112, 117
Vendrely, R., 112, 117
Vincent, W. S., 87, 117
Virchow, R., 3, 271
von Mohl, H., 3
von Tschermak, E., 5
von Wettstein, D., 41, 42, 44, 45, 46, 73

Wadkins, C. L., 70
Walker, P. M. B., 104, 117, 268, 283
Wang, L., 27
Warburg, O., 262, 273
Warmke, H. E., 189, 192
Watson, M. C., 72
Watson, M. L., 35, 73, 75, 77, 118
Watson, J. D., 18, 19, 24, 105, 117, 118
Wattiaux, R., 68
Watts, R. M., 219, 264
Weakley, D. R., 70
Webster, G. C., 73
Weismann, A., 4, 5
Wellings, R. S., 69
Whaley, W. G., 61, 73, 78, 118, 124, 136, 163

Whatley, F. R., 268
White, E. W., 279
White, M. J. D., 86, 99, 118, 192, 274, 275, 284
Whiting, P. W., 190, 192
Wilbur, K. M., 111
Wilkins, M. H. F., 256
Williams, G. G., 68
Willmer, E. N., 156, 162
Wilson, E. B., 2, 7, 141, 163, 269, 275, 284
Wilson, G. B., 67, 82, 89, 91, 93, 114, 115, 118, 120, 123, 126, 127, 132, 133, 136, 139, 140, 150, 152, 156, 161, 163, 165, 167, 168, 169, 170, 172, 173, 175, 176, 186, 192, 196, 197, 199, 201, 204, 205, 206, 208, 284

Windle, W. F., 9
Winge, O., 205, 208
Wolff, K. F., 3
Wolman, M., 203, 210, 211, 212
Woods, P. S., 106, 107, 109, 117, 118, 139, 163
Wyckoff, R. W. G., 18, 268
Wyss, O., 201

Yates, H. B., 104, 117

Zalokar, M., 109, 118
Zamecnik, P. C., 70, 72
Zebrun, W., 73
Zenker, 212
Zeuthen, E., 266
Zirkle, R., 123
Zworykin, V. K., 268

# Subject Index

295